WHAT
SORT
OF
FUCKERY
IS
THIS
?

WHAT SORT OF FUCKERY IS THIS?

DEVIL'S
PARTY
PRESS

MILTON, DE
1 9 9 6 8

**WHAT
SORT
OF
FUCKERY
IS
THIS
?**

ISBN: 978-0-9996558-8-7

devilspartypress.com

CONTENTS

WHAT
SORT
OF
FUCKERY
IS
THIS
?

What kind of fuckery is this?

Amy Winehouse

The Fuckery
of It All:
An Introduction

Welcome to our sixth anthology. You may be wondering, "What sort of anthology is *What Sort of Fuckery Is This?* What, exactly, is a *fuckery*?"

Since launching Devil's Party Press in 2017, it's been our mission to publish writers over 40 years of age. So let's talk about aging.

Aging is beautiful. With aging comes wisdom, skill, experience, and patience. But aging is also cruel. It is full of death by a thousand cuts large and small. Aging is a damn fuckery.

Let's talk briefly about censorship. For as long as there have been writers, there have been censors. From a purely textbook definition, a censor is any official who examines material that is about to be released, such as books, movies, news, and art, and suppresses any parts that are considered obscene, politically unacceptable, or a threat to security.

So, yeah, those people.

Let me tell you about our writers, our *older* writers.

Our writers have been parents. They have raised children. They have had grandchildren. Some of them have lost those very same children or grandchildren. Some have desperately wanted to be parents but, for one or more reasons, were unable to have children of their own.

They've held good jobs, taken crap jobs to put food on the table, and have been unemployed during the worst possible times.

They've got plenty of money and no money, honey, and just enough cash to not have their world fall apart tomorrow.

They've owned homes and lost homes and shared homes and couch surfed.

They've graduated and flunked out and never gone.

They've had parts removed and parts replaced and had terrible diagnoses and beat death more than a few times and more than they should.

I won't mention all the age-appropriate tests and screenings they've had, but if you don't already know about those, you'll know soon enough.

They've loved and lost. They've been cheated on, separated, divorced, and widowed. They've cried and cried and cried, found love again, remarried, and have been loved more than they even knew by more than a few.

They've carved out identities over the decades, discovering who they are, reinventing who they are, and keeping pace with a world that never slows down.

They've adapted to ever-changing technologies, from albums and reel-to-reel tapes to cassettes and 8-tracks to CDs and digital downloads to name but one example.

They've seen history as it was made, having lived through the assassinations of JFK, Dr. King, Bobby Kennedy, John Lennon and others. They experienced Woodstock and Three Mile Island and the fall of the Berlin Wall.

And they've laughed long and hard with their bellies like children.

The authors we publish are the voices of experience, of triumph, of tragedy, and of life. They're bad-asses, one and all. *What Sort of Fuckery Is This?* is a celebration of their unique badassery. We'd sooner close our fucking doors than censor our wonderfully rebellious wordsmiths.

I hope you enjoy this collection. It's filled with funny, tragic, real, obscenity laced poetry, prose, and memoir from one-helluva group of great fucking writers.

Dianne Pearce
Milton, Delaware

I am the man who yells at his wife, "Bitch, I'll put a cap in your ass!"

BILL AYRES

because you asked me to repeat
what the villain said on TV.
I raise my voice to say I love you,
bellow how good you look
in your new blue blouse,
shout about the chicken enchiladas
you made for my dinner.
Tuesday, you get your new hearing aids.
Wednesday, you will know that I've come home
from the jangle of keys unlocking the door.
You will know where I am in the house
when you hear the creak of the floorboards,
water running in the shower,
the clack of hangers in the closet.
I will speak softly
and my words will be fingertips
massaging the base of your skull.
I'll whisper something in your ear
and hear the music of your laughter.

AUTHOR'S NOTE

When I read a poem or listen to a song, I wonder if truths are being told. Sylvia Plath's "Lady Lazarus" isn't true, not exactly. She didn't really eat men like air–at least they weren't a regular part of her diet. But there is plenty of Plath's real life in her poem.

When I hear John Lennon sing about how he used to beat his woman on The Beatles' song "It's Getting Better," I hope it's not something he actually did, but I wonder.

This poem of mine is a truthful one. My wife and I were binge watching *Breaking Bad*, and she didn't hear something Walt said to Jesse.

She asked, "What did he say?"

I told her.

The questioning and answering had been going on most of the afternoon, but this time I realized what I had said. It wasn't anything I had ever imagined I would be yelling at my wife.

When I told the story to my brother-in-law, he almost fell out of his chair laughing. I soon realized there was a poem waiting to be written.

My poems have come from stranger places than this.

BA

If You're Going Through Hell, Go Through the Back Room

MAUREEN MCVEIGH

I've had better Saturday mornings than the one I spent hungover, helping my mom choose a chemo wig.

Her doctor had recommended a shop in the New Castle Farmers Market. That seemed unusual. When we saw the low concrete building with stalls of knock-off track suits and greasy pizza slices, it seemed impossible. The wig store lived down to expectations. Elvis pompadours and Farrah Fawcett waves hung limply from pegboard walls. We were leaving when the salesman pointed at my mom.

"You cancer," he said, in a blunt accent. An accusation? Diagnosis? My mom nodded. A question. We wished the answer wasn't yes, but her bald head gave it away.

She'd chopped off her hair the night before. Where thick dark swirls usually flowed, sparse gray strands stood. Startled by the change in her appearance, fear wrapped around my heart like kudzu vines. My mom had cancer. I knew this. I'd cried when she'd told me, driven her to doctor's appointments, and snuck a cup of real coffee into the hospital after surgery. Her hair loss, though, was a definitive sign of my mom's mortality. She had always been so vigorous. I couldn't believe cancer dared challenge her. *Good luck with that*, I thought, remembering my teen years.

I felt guilty imagining my mom in her bathroom, going full G.I. Jane on her head. Should I have cut it for her? She wouldn't have asked, might not have acquiesced. I could have insisted until she surrendered–to placate me as much as to help herself. But I hadn't been there. Pretending to still be a carefree twenty-something, I'd gone out drinking and dancing with friends. Meanwhile, my mom tried to protect her shower drain and sense of control.

After she nodded, the salesman opened the curtain behind the register like the Wizard of Oz unexpectedly revealing his secret. He waved for us to follow. Suddenly Cowardly Lions, we doubted we should dive deeper into the dingy shop. Silvery strands dropped onto my mom's shoulders. We knew of no other nearby wig stores. With little choice, we entered the back room.

In contrast to the disorganized costume accessories, though, tidy shelves of white boxes lined the walls. A single chair faced a large mirror. The salesman pointed for my mom to sit. I stood beside her, as if posing for the worst Renaissance painting ever. Gone were the fluorescent blue and pink "fantasy" wigs, like bags of shiny cotton candy. These wigs were for those needing to maintain the everyday, not escape it.

The salesman fit a tight mesh cap to my mom's head and slid on a dark gray wig. It resembled real hair, not a Halloween accessory, but I said, "No." My mom offered no reaction. He removed the wig, tried another.

"No," I said again. "You're trying to match her current hair. It doesn't usually look like that. More like mine, but curlier." She often said I had her thick dark mane, the closest she'd ever come to vanity. Knowing her hair would fall out, she hadn't colored it since starting treatment.

Pulling boxes from another shelf, the salesman got closer to the right one for my mom. We now realized why the oncologist recommended him. Finally, one option was so flattering, I suggested my mom show her hairdresser when she recovered. We still talked about the future even if her breast cancer diagnosis had upended our secure assumptions about it. My parents had always been healthy. The gravity of cancer shocked us.

Her oncologist expected a full recovery, so when surgery went well, we thought the worst was over. Chemotherapy and radiation, though, leveled my mom. Instead of running her own floral design business, cooking for our family, and planning future vacations, she napped on the sofa more often than the cat. Before cancer, she'd been the Energizer Bunny. During, she became Eeyore.

While she suffered, I struggled with how to help. She usually cared for everyone. She'd read me my favorite childhood books so many times, she could still recite *Horton Hatches the Egg*. In high school, I sometimes asked my friends if they'd come over to hang out with me or to talk through their problems with her. I couldn't name a cousin she hadn't set up in the spare room when they needed it for a night. Or a month.

Despite these examples, I didn't know how to support her. I could barely cook, but she had no appetite anyway. I tried to sympathize, but had never even had stitches, much less two surgeries and months of treatments.

As we admired the wig in the mirror, the salesman said, "Your insurance pays for two. You need another?"

My unpretentious mom only wanted one, but we were invited to continue browsing. We marveled at all the celebrities with their own wig lines.

"So this is what Raquel Welch has been up to," I said, pointing to a row of boxes with her signature. My mom grinned. Like a desperate court jester, I flailed around for something to make her smile again. Donning a bright blond bob, I Groucho Marxed my dark eyebrows. She smiled at the ridiculousness of my face under Marilyn Monroe's hair.

"You should get it," she said. I flipped the ends like a triumphant movie star. She suggested I wear it home to shock my dad and brother. Perhaps a goofy wig I didn't need might draw attention from the one she did need. I would have worn a rainbow clown bouffant to do that.

As my mom recovered, I told her funny stories about my friends. I delivered family gossip from parties she felt too ill to attend. We binged watched *The Sopranos*. From perpendicular sofas, we fixated on Tony's Cosa Nostra to forget about our own family's "this thing of ours." I didn't possess the magical mom healing power she had when I was sick, but I could distract and entertain her. It wasn't much, but maybe I inherited more than just her hair.

AUTHOR'S NOTE

This unusual shopping trip occurred more years ago than I care to admit, except to realize how grateful I am that my mom regained her health. I can't speak for her experience, but her illness was a coming-of-age event for me, and that particular day was a stark example of the time. My mom has since become an amazing grandmother to my brother's kids and my own. She now shops exclusively for toys and baby clothes and doesn't need any help with that.

MM

The Last Lootenant
Wins His Fuckin'
Medal

WILLIAM F. CRANDELL

Yuh ast me what a hero is, it's some guy who don't know enough to come in out of a barrage, like Lootenant Brill. Dum luck's the only kind he ever had, but he had plenty of that. Me, I'm from Joizey City, so I could be prejudiced, but my idea is that while most of the poor slobs who didn't grow up in Italian neighborhoods in Joizey are losers, the real dips come from weenie towns in the South so boring they print the newspapers two weeks in advance. The lootenant, he was one of them, a six-foot stack of gristle who got through the Citadel luggin' a football acrost a series of straight lines if somebody pointed him in the right direction.

Yeah, yuh think I'm jist sayin' that cuz enlisted don't like officers, as if that's irrational somehow. But I was there the day the lootenant reported into B Company, an' I was still there the day we sent him away, an' I didn't get any time off for good behavior.

I was first platoon's radioman, so when the supply chopper dumped him with the week-old mail an' the day's C-rations at the company command post, Beany gets me on the horn an' sez come up to the CP cuz our new butter bar–that's what we call a green seckint lootenant–is in with The Old Man. Baby-faced Beany from Boise used to love callin' twenty-seven-year-old Captain Glenn "The Old Man."

Yuh could tell right off that Lootenant Brill shoulda been a hotel porter. He comes outa the Captain's tent jugglin' a duffel bag, his rucksack, a bran'-new di-di bag, one of them vinyl attaché cases the PX sells, an' an M-16 with no scratches on the handguards yet, wearin'–so help me–starched cotton Stateside fatigues with polished metal insignia that were brighter than he was, a shiny pair of silver jump wings on his chest in case the local snipers need somethin' to catch their eyes. His steel pot an' all his field gear are in the duffel bag, but he's got an enameled helmet over his white sidewalls haircut wit' Confed'rut flags an' "Citadel Football" painted all over it, an' he's got a pair of those silver-eyed cop sunglasses on so yuh can't tell if he's got any feelins' or anythin'.

"Private DyLoocha?" he asts me, in a voice like he's reportin' all present an' accounted for outside some barracks built on red clay at Fort Redneck.

Normally I don't salute officers in the field, but seein' I got a prime chump wit' his hands full, I pop one on him an' he drops half his stuff in the mud. "DiLucca, Lootenant," I sez, carefully avoidin' that one word my mouth don't make.

"DiLucca, *sir*," he snaps back.

"Aw, jeez, Lootenant, you don't hafta call me that," I sez to him. "I work for a livin'. Jist call me Duck like ever'buddy else." An' I swear to God he either didn't get the joke or realize I'm bein' rude, jist thought I was too damn dumb to understand him. I grabbed his attaché case, leavin' him wit' the rest, an' sez, "The platoon's right this way."

———

Still, dum luck seemed to be plenty for Lootenant Brill. I mean, a guy swaggers inta a grunt platoon where he's the only one who ain't been outdoors yet an' starts actin' like there's a big parade comin' up an' we better all get our boots shined, an' he's jist astin' for somebody to stick a grenade up his butt the first time Charlie plays games wit' us. In fact, he almost didn't last that long.

Somehow we got lucky an' did a week or two of day patrols an' night ambushes wit'out seein' anybody more sinister than a few kids an' old ladies, but bustin' paddies is hard work. Yuh walk in knee-deep mud out in the sky-wide open, makin' yuh a tin pigeon in the world's slowest shootin' gallery if anybody opens up on yuh, knowin' we always give Charlie the courtesy of startin' things. The only solid ground is the dikes between paddies, so it's the easiest place to walk if it goes where you're goin'. That makes it the best place for the little guys in Dixie Cup hats to set up boobytraps. There must be a manual somewhere that says it's smarter to clomp though mud, but it was written by some doofus whose brain got exposed to more air-conditionin' than daylight.

Anyhow, we're stompin' through one paddy after another while the sun makes mashed potatoes outa our heads, an' we finally come to a measly half-click of dike that's goin' the same way we are. By common courtesy we let Leroy Washington, the black oak who carries our one functional machinegun an' two-hundred rounds of belted ammo, use it as a sidewalk for a while.

An' who splashes right over an' jumps in his face but Brilliantman? "Washington," the lootenant barks out, "are you gonna get your ass off this dike or am I gonna blow it off?"

Prob'ly they don't teach yuh at the Citadel that a little one-inch by one-quarter-inch brown cloth lootenant bar isn't much protection against bullets. Leroy turns his hips ever so slightly, casually bringin' the muzzle of his M-60 around till it's starin' at Lootenant Brill's navel, an sez, "You ain't gonna blow nobody's ass off *nothin'*, man."

That's when my radio starts squawking an' Beany sez the choppers to pick us up jist spotted us.

—

Nobuddy ever wanted so much respect an' got so little. The next mornin' Brilliantman has me borrow the Captain's jeep an' run him up to the PX in Saigon. He tells me to wait in the jeep, like there's nothin' in there I could wanta buy, an' disappears inside.

One hour an' eight or nine Marlboros later, the lootenant boogies out wit' this olive drab baseball cap he's had some mama-san embroider all over–a brown bar an' a black set of parachute wings on the front an' some kinda vines in brown startin' in back an' weavin' around the sides–an' a corncob hillbilly pipe so squeaky clean it looks like he's been blowin' bubbles in it.

"How do you like it, Duck?" he sez to me.

"Like what, Lootenant?" I asts him. Never let on yuh know what they're talkin' about, that's my rule.

"My trademark."

I look around. "Got it on yuh, Lootenant?"

His forehead crunches down over his eyes. "The o.d. hat with the laurel wreath, the corncob pipe," he sez. "The General Mac-Arthur look."

"But you're a sekint lootenant, Lootenant. I mean, General MacArthur was *General MacArthur*."

He didn't get it, so on the way back to our company, I waited till we were on the engineers' ferry over by Can Tho, standin' by the little chain guardrail on the side an' both of us starin' at this nice-lookin' girl in a slope hat on the shore. Jist when there's a breeze I turn real fast an' point at a seagull, an' I bop his silly MacArthur cap inta the river like it was an accident, apologizin' all over the place like I was a lootenant an' he was a stoopid major or somethin'. I mean, he can look ridiculous on his own time, but he was my platoon leader an' that reflected on the guys, right?

But the lootenant's itch for respect didn't go away. One night the two of us are sittin' in the hooch, an' I try hintin' that the guys aren't too crazy about havin' to shine their boots before they dry out.

"Being an officer's not a popularity contest, Duck," he tells me like he's readin' it outa the Bible.

"I didn't know that, Lootenant," I tell him.

He laughs his Poor Dumb Enlisted Men laugh. "If there's one thing I learned at the Citadel," he explains, "it's that an officer can set out either to be liked or respected. Being liked doesn't get the job done."

"So yuh gotta be disliked?" I asts him.

He gives me a look like his shoes jist got too tight. "Maybe so, Duck," he sez. "Maybe so."

I'm tryin' to think of a way to tell him we respected our last platoon leader an' liked him, too, but he cuts me off. "Do you think I don't want to be liked as much as anybody else?" he asts me. "I'm not in Vietnam just to win some medals."

Medals! Holy Mother! Oh, I'da been happy for a fuckin' medal to send my Ma, 'cept I didn't want the Purple Heart, 'cause yuh get it for bein' wounded, or the Medal of Honor, 'cause yuh got a good chance of not attendin' the ceremony in person.

Then the lootenant sniffs, mumbles some bullshit regardin' seein' a man about a horse, an' storms out.

———

I tell all this to Sarge Spinelli, one of the squad leaders in the platoon, mebbe an hour later at the village whorehouse. He tosses his steel pot on the floor an' kicks it. "I don't need any more of this bozo," he tells Beany an' me. "We come off patrols, he wants us to scrub our sandbags, mentions to Crimp and me that idleness is what gets soldiers in trouble, like he's never heard of gunfire. We're out in the paddies and he can't tell a road from a river on the map, thinks the compass already knows what direction you want and just points to it automatically. I tell you, when he was in paratroop school they must have had some sergeant jump out with him and show him which way down was."

Well, I had to agree land navigation wasn't the lootenant's long suit an' we were lucky two of our patrols in AO Skunk ran from south to north because that's the way compasses point.

"Lucky!" Screamin' Jay Baxter coughs. "We're lucky we're not in the DMZ. We'd be invading North Vietnam with thirty or so grunts."

We all grumble an' laugh an' smoke some more, an' finally Screamin' Jay gets this look on his face like he jist invented sex or somethin'. "A transfer. Beany mentioned it this morning."

"Whaddayuh mean?" I ast him.

"Beany gets all the dumb bulletins from Division," the Screamer sez. "Like the ones that order us to wear sandals in the rainy season so our feet can dry out when we're walking to chow. The latest pearl is that the Hundred-and-Worst Airborne needs a hell of a lot of 'seasoned officers with in-country experience' quick pronto. Beany explains that Hamburger Hill wasn't the training exercise *Stars and Stripes* made it sound like, and the word is out that the One-Oh-One needs replacements bad."

"How bad?"

"Any captain or lieutenant who wants to transfer can do it. If he's got one little thing. A set of jump wings."

—

So Screamin' Jay calls some old high school buddy at Two Field Force in Long Binh, an' the guy agrees to slip a Request for Transfer wit' an illegible scrawl at the bottom inta the thin little stack on his desk. Three days later Battalion sends us on a company-size sweep ten clicks, mebbe six miles, inta some province nobody owns. Captain Glenn's got seckint an' third platoons up front, strung out like guitar strings in a straight line so they can "flush out" any Charlies if they find 'em. My hunch is he put us on reserve, marchin' in a bunch in back of him an' Beany, cuz we weren't heading north.

We'd been humpin' paddies for two-three hours with the tide goin' out, so the mud sucked down ev'ry time yuh lifted a foot. The heat made yuh think somebuddy was gonna stick a toothpick inta yuh any minute to see if yuh were done. No roads, no villes, no dikes. Jist wide, flat fields of shitty-smellin' goo wit' little clumps of nippa palm a bit farther apart than they looked.

Yuh get so tired yuh march wit' your eyes shut.

Alluvasudden Captain Glenn's head becomes a little pink cloud an' Beany dances sideways an' I notice I'm lyin' flat as my buttons an' the mud will let me.

A bunch of nippa palm that's jist too far to our left to check out seems to have a movie projector in it, but that flickerin' flash sounds like a jackhammer, an' it's splattering mud all over us. I'm thinkin' some moron built a bunker in there, all the way out here, an' I realize there's a machinegun in it an' it's not ours. One or two guys are in there, hosin' us down like a newly seeded front lawn, an' we're lined up jist right to make it easy.

The bunker's mebbe a hundred yards away–a football field– an' the only cover we got is each other. The CO's dead, Beany's dead, a dozen guys are bloody, some of 'em face down in the mud. One of the medics is patchin' up the third platoon leader's gut, an' I recognize the long, skinny black stiff as Lieutenant Cool.

Nobuddy's in charge. I'm jist tryin' to reach my radio to get some help when I feel a burst of bullets rip it up, so I smoosh down as deep as I can, but I get this smell of ozone. When I open my eyes it dawns on me that one round musta set off a purple smoke grenade on the side of my radio, which is great, as far as it goes, cuz two-thirds of the company is covered wit' lavender fog.

I'm in the other third.

Next thing I know this big lunk goes roarin' past me, blastin' away at the bunker wit' a lousy .45 automatic. Brilliantman, the Last Lootenant, is chargin' this dug-in machinegun nest. The Charlies are so stunned by his stoopidity that they stop shootin' for a few seck-ints–prob'ly laughin their asses off–an' he makes it alive right to where the muzzle is pokin' out before he realizes he's outa bullets.

I see him slap the side of his helmet an' come runnin' back, disappearin' inta the purple haze, an' I almost give him credit for havin' a brain. But faster than I can do that, he chugs right back, with a fresh clip in his pistol an' a sack of hand grenades under his arm, so help me Jesus, like a football.

This time the VC machinegunner don't sit back an' watch, but he's swingin' ev'ry which way while the lootenant runs straight at 'em, missin' the whole goddam bunker each time he fires but makin' a first-rate racket. He flattens out beside their little firin' window an' tosses the sack of grenades through it.

"The pins, Lootenant!" I yell at him, gettin' on my knees I'm so angry. "Yuh didn't pull the fuckin' pins!"

Even Charlie knows how to do that, it turns out, an' right away I see one of our grenades drop back out the window beside the Lootenant, its safety handle flyin' away as it falls.

He grabs it an' chucks it inside. It makes a wonderful explosion wit' the ammo an' all. Then nobuddy's firing' at us anymore.

"That was the stoopidist thing I ever saw," I yell at him when he comes limpin' back. "Sir."

The lootenant give me this embarrassed grin. "I forgot to say, 'Follow me,'" he sez.

—

So they give him a Silver Star jist before his transfer to the One-Oh-One comes through. They ship the company–minus the dead an' wounded–back to Battalion an' give us a couple pallets of beer for a sendoff. We all get pretty blasted an' even so, nobuddy sez very much. Some rear echelon motherfucker comes by an' tells us we got off pretty easy wit' only seven killed an' nine wounded, but one of the guys straightens him out. Horizontal.

Ev'ry time Screamin' Jay or Crimp or Tommy Cudlow or somebuddy goes over to say somethin' to the lootenant, he tells 'em their belt's crooked or their sleeves aren't rolled properly.

Finally a company clerk sticks his head outa the CP an' yells, "Here comes your chopper, Lieutenant!"

Brilliantman swaggers out in front of us, an' we kinda slouch inta formation. "You're not the sorriest bunch of bastards I ever met," he tells us. "Try not to screw up like that again."

He hops the chopper an' he's gone.

—

I hope he made it home.

AUTHOR'S NOTE

Mozart, some say, snatched all that music by standing outside the Pearly Gates and taking down everything he heard. Me, I got the truth by touring Vietnam with a stubby black carbine in hand and my ears.

WFC

Not Getting Flirted With at the Fucking Gym

JOHN SHEIRER

"You're not an unattractive man, at least not in a terribly *unhandsome* way," Staci told Rob, as they chatted near a table lined with appetizers. "You just need to meet someone."

"Well, that's the trick, isn't it?" Rob said.

"Maybe you should join a gym."

"She's right," Staci's husband, Mark, chimed in. "Better to meet someone there than in a seedy bar."

"I'm already in shape," Rob said.

"You wouldn't be joining for the exercise," Mark said.

"Women will flirt with you. That's what we do," Staci added. "I mean, aren't you tired of coming to these dinner parties without a date?"

The words stung. Rob joined a gym the next day and started going five or six times a week. But to his dismay, while there were plenty of exercise machines and free weights, flirtatious women seemed to be nonexistent.

A recent Friday night trip to the gym was a pretty typical example of Rob's plight. He arrived at 7:00 PM and slid his key card over the infrared eye of the access system. A pretty woman working behind the desk smiled and wished Rob a happy workout. *She's so professional and nice*, Rob thought, *but I'm here to get flirted with, not visit with the cute receptionist.* He smiled and headed toward the exercise equipment.

As he passed the treadmills, a curvaceous woman in a white tank top and tights made eye contact and called out to Rob. "I'm so silly," she said. "I just can't seem to figure out how to program this machine. Can you help me, please?"

Rob was on a mission to get flirted with, but he paused to

program the treadmill for her. She smiled the whole time, hovering near him and even placing her hand on his shoulder several times.

"Thank you so much," she said, warmly.

"You're welcome," Rob said, walking away from the tread-mills toward the exercise bikes. *Are these machines really that difficult to figure out?* Rob thought. *It's just a couple of buttons.*

Rob brought a book to read on the exercise bike. He usually spent lots of time glancing sideways to see what other people were reading, so he figured women would probably be curious about his book, *Pigs in Heaven* by Barbara Kingsolver. He hoped that a book like this would reveal his sensitive side. This, combined with the hard-muscled body he was surely developing from working out regularly would, he reasoned, make it difficult for women *not* to flirt with him.

After ten minutes of reading, an attractive older woman took his literary bait.

"*Pigs in Heaven*?" she asked. "Sounds like a book about my first husband, except for the heaven part!"

She laughed and lingered for a few seconds, but by this point, Rob was really absorbed in the tome and wondered what would happen to sweet little Turtle and her accidental adoptive mother. He hardly noticed when the woman shrugged and walked away.

Thirty minutes later, the LED readout on the bike flashed to indicate that he'd completed his programmed workout. *Gosh*, Rob thought, *the time and the pages just fly by when you have a good book*. The number of flirt-potential women around the exercise machines was sparse, so Rob headed downstairs to the weight room.

On the way there, he met an acquaintance of his ex-girl-friend. Rob tried to but couldn't remember her name.

"Hi Rob! It's Joslyn. Remember?"

"Of course," Rob smiled.

Joslyn carried a racquetball racquet. Rob enjoyed racquet-ball, so they talked for a while about the sport.

"I can't find anyone to play with me," Joslyn said, a bit downcast, "so I've just been playing with myself every chance I get." She suddenly brightened. "Hey, would you like to play with me?"

"I'm sorry," Rob replied. "I've played racquetball for a long time, usually with guys, so playing with you probably wouldn't be much fun for either of us."

"Oh, um ... okay. Sure." Joslyn excused herself and hurried off.

The evening's quickly disappearing, Rob thought, *and I haven't been flirted with once the whole time.* He continued to the weight room.

Two women quickly caught his eye. Both were in great shape with thick-muscled backs and arms. Rob pulled a couple of dumbbells from the rack next to the women and started doing biceps curls. Try as he might, Rob couldn't seem to get their attention. He mirrored their routine, moving from station to station, but they were focused only on each other and their workout.

The more they ignored him, the more Rob felt drawn to them. It was a bit of a turn on to watch them spot each other, each taking turns grasping the other's arms or legs or waist to help with the exercise. *They must be sisters or best friends to be so close,* Rob thought. *And I bet they have weight-lifter husbands at home.* Rob reasoned that there wasn't much chance of them flirting with him.

Disappointed, as he'd been on previous nights at the gym, Rob was about ready to leave. *I should probably just cancel my membership. It's pretty obvious that this gym isn't a hotspot for flirting.* But a strange thing suddenly happened that made him stay a bit longer. He was actually getting into his workout. For weeks, he'd been spending time at the gym in hopes of meeting women without so much as a single bite. The exercise machines and weights had been little more than props to give Rob something to do while waiting for the seductions to begin. But Rob started to notice that there might actually be something more to the gym than just sexual tension. He sat down at the butterfly machine to work on his chest muscles for a few minutes before heading home.

"Oh, sorry," Rob heard a woman's voice say. He felt a little bump to his left as he hefted the machine's handle on that side. The machines were situated close to one another. Rob reasoned that she must had accidentally brushed against the machine as he pulled the weights along their path.

"That's okay," Rob replied, as he completed the last four repetitions, feeling his chest expand with each lift.

As Rob rested after his set, he heard the same woman sneeze.

It was a cute, petite little sneeze.

"Bless you," Rob said automatically.

"Thank you," she replied. "It's so nice to hear a man say that. Most men these days just ignore you when you sneeze."

Rob looked directly at her for the first time. She was about his age, maybe a little older, with dark eyes and sandy hair touched with sweat. She was slender and athletic, like she'd been coming to the gym often. She wore a flattering pink top and black tights. She was a real blonde, not dyed–Rob considered himself an observant person who could tell the difference. And she was smiling at … him.

It suddenly dawned on Rob for the first time that night that he might actually be getting flirted with. He didn't quite know what to do. *Should I wait to see what'll happen? Should I think up something witty to say and flirt back?*

Whether she was flirting or not, Rob decided he wasn't interested. Rob said a quick goodnight, grabbed his sweatshirt and book, and headed toward the exit.

It's Friday night. Do I really want to invest my time flirting with someone who can't get a date and is spending her Friday night at the gym?

AUTHOR'S NOTE

So many of my male friends tell stories about meeting romantic partners at the gym. They can't all be lying, can they? Maybe. In the countless visits I've made to various gyms, I don't think I've ever been flirted with by a stranger.

As a writer, I've always enjoyed the "What if?" nature of fiction. This story is based on the question, "What if a guy at the gym turned out to be even more clueless than I am?" That's how the character of Rob, the most clueless dude at the gym, was developed.

These days, I go to the gym with my wife, so I'm blessed to be flirted with by the most attractive woman there.

JS

How the Fuck Are You?

JUDITH SPEIZER CRANDELL

Danny Aaronson
Cleason Charles
Ed McNulty
Jack Plumber
Ted Smith
Rich Szelso
Roger Zimmer

Bless them in the name of the Father, the Son, and the Holy Ghost. Amen.

Roger Zimmer opened the shallow nightstand drawer–pure Cherrywood, his mother always reminded him–and gently removed the rosary she presented him right before he went to Vietnam. He arranged it on an elegant square of green velvet he carefully cut to size when he returned from the war.

Roger looked up at the picture of his squad from 20 years ago and smiled. The way it happened was this. For five months in 1970, the Army had handed Roger Leonard Zimmer his chance to have a small group of men depend on him, while he depended on God and the Virgin Mary and Saint Michael and the President of the United States. And, it seemed to him, they all did a damned fine job.

He dutifully prayed for his men when he was there and all the years after. But his wife of 20 years come December 31st didn't understand. Ever.

"You don't understand, Brenda. You'll never understand. Those were my men, goddammit. You're a woman. You never had to tell men where to march, when to fire. I did, and I was fucking good at it. And they all got home safe and sound and I'll bet they're all happy now, too."

"Because you pray for them?"

"You're damned straight because I pray for them."

Then it came to a head on a breezy Sunday morning in September after Roger decided to remake their bed. Brenda had done her perfunctory job, covering it all with their white chenille bedspread. "I've told you many times. No officer would approve a bed like that, Brenda. You have to make it so taut a quarter could bounce off the sheets."

Brenda screamed. She screamed so loudly that their life–a clean ranch house painted white every other year, sheltering two people who shared breakfasts of warm oatmeal and packed brown bag lunches, and who sent out for Chinese food every Wednesday night–fell apart.

It had all run tight as a drum until then, Roger thought. If only Brenda would leave things neat and tidy. Everything stayed fine as long as she didn't say otherwise. The scream this morning was a new reaction.

"Roger, you don't want anything in your life to change, not your TV set, not my hair style and especially not your war! It happened a long time ago, and you still expect all your men to be marching around an outpost in the jungle." Brenda proceeded to dump armloads of hangers, blouses, jackets, neckties, bras and a muddle of shoes on their half-made bed.

Roger felt hurt. *How can she talk to him about the war this way...shit, look at the clothes,* he thought, *they'll all have to be ironed again.* He carefully sat down on their green Early American armchair with the carved eagle. It was his favorite chair from his mom's house, so he placed it in the bedroom when they first moved in. He could sit there in the morning and be comforted by memories of his dear mother. Meanwhile, Brenda picked among the mess on their bed, separating her stuff from his in quick bursts of anger. *Like a machine gun firing,* he thought.

Then she pushed the cotton, lace, pink of it all into a double heavy-duty black plastic garbage bag which she slung over her shoulder. Roger still sat there thinking about ironing when she noisily started her orange VW bug and drove out of their marriage.

In the half-light of evening, Roger saw this as just the end of a very long argument. She had complained for years about how he cleaned nonexistent fingerprints off the glass coffee table, how he wiped the neck of the toothpaste tube vigorously, how he counted and aligned the napkins in the holder. But the worst of the arguments were about Vietnam.

Brenda said she hated Vietnam, that it ruined their marriage. But it was Brenda, Roger decided. Brenda made a big deal over the picture and the prayers. Brenda walked out after two decades of warm companionship and convenience that sometimes ignited in the marital bed. So what the hell if Roger liked his sex clean, neat and organized?

Roger realized he would miss Brenda, her long braided red hair, her Aunt Sophie's Death-by-Chocolate double fudge cake, and the way his wife sang 60s songs while she waxed the kitchen floor. Now he would have to get used to sleeping alone. But he smiled when he realized the bed would be easier to make.

And he would have the whole house to himself. For years he sucked up the annoying things she repeatedly did despite his discomfort. Like hanging her underwear over the shower bar to dry, especially her pantyhose dangling in his face day after day. He'd been willing to live with that because he cared about her, loved her, in a nice steady line that he could draw from their first blind date to see "The Graduate" to the bubble bath he watched her take on her forty-third birthday. The last time he saw her naked. A mental picture of that, neatly filed in his brain vault of Brenda/Marriage.

—

Exactly three weeks after Brenda left, a phone call that took 20 years to ring interrupted the new rhythm of his single life.

A disembodied voice sang out, "Troop? Hey man, is this Troop Zimmer from the fuckin' old third squad or not?" The now-impatient voice was hard to hear over the background bar noise. Roger could barely breathe as he touched the crucifix on his dog tag chain before responding to the name only six men in the world would use. Which one? Which one of his men was summoning him?

Up until this phone call, Roger thought he preferred the spiritual memory ties, the frozen pictures, the half-heard gunfire that he kept in a special quadrant of his memory vault. But with this real-life connection, Roger realized how wonderful it might feel if all his men called him. It never occurred to him to contact them, just as it never occurred to him to tell Brenda not to go, that he loved her, in his way, and would miss her–in his way.

"Hey man, it's me, Danny." Goddammit, Danny Aaronson was on the phone. The first name in roll call called him first. "I'm here in this godforsaken town you called home when we were in-country. So I looked you up. I had some business with a lady, but now I'm here alone. Course it doesn't sound alone, but you know how it is in a bar." Danny cleared his throat and continued. "Hey, Buddy, it's frickin' Saturday. You're obviously at home. Come on over and I'll spot you a beer and a shot for old time's sake."

—

Roger could barely hold onto the sweaty steering wheel. Danny Aaronson. Maybe Roger's repeating of all their names all these years had worked. He'd be rewarded. God would bring them all back to him. First Danny, then Cleason, Ed–his two girls must be grown by now–Jack and Ted who could pass for brothers, and Richie Szelso, who swore he'd go back to school when he got home. And he did get home, just like all of Roger's men. Well, Roger wouldn't miss Brenda so much if he had all his guys back again . . . and it could happen just by repeating their names every night, year after year after year.

Roger knew the power of the word. His mother Frieda taught him that. Vietnam confirmed it. The counting of the rosary, the reciting of the names. Walking point and roll call and they all left Nam on the Freedom Bird, delivered home whole to the sweetheart in Lansing, the grandmother in Terre Haute, the three-month-old daughter in San Bernardino, the father in Albany and Uncle Sam. A good squad leader, Roger "Troop" Zimmer made sure they all shipped home before he left.

Fuck it all. He remembered his men in detail but he couldn't remember his mother, her hair color or what her eyes behind her large owl-shaped glasses looked like or even whether she smelled of My Sin or cinnamon and cloves from baking. Seventeen years his mother was gone. How could Roger forget his mother? But his men. Roger still knew which kind of c-rations each of them hated the most.

Roger parked his sleek red Triumph TR4 convertible, the

one luxury he allowed himself as a civilian. He could hear the Stones blasting "I Can't Get No Satisfaction" in a muffled blare leaking from the Back Door bar.

He hesitated, then opened the front door of the Back Door, which had a sign thumbtacked on it that asked, "Are you 21?"

"And then some," Roger muttered.

Cigarettes sent unreadable smoke signals into the thick, black air. An auburn-haired looker with shoulders and knees and breasts partially exposed sat perched on a red swivel stool, going round and round as she twirled the pink parasol in her drink, clutched between her thighs. A balding, out-of-the-bottle blond man whose tight madras shirt stretched across his large belly kept trying to rub one of her shoulders, missing as she circled round again. This same man yelled across the loud space, "Hey, Troop!" Then Roger found himself in a sweaty embrace.

"Danny?"

"Could spot me even without the hair, Troop. Good to see you, man. Sit down. Let me buy you that beer and shot." He motioned to the bartender and exchanged signals that bewildered Roger, who never went to bars. But Roger couldn't really focus on that now. Instead he had to focus on this forty-some-year-old man festooned with gold chains, though it wasn't Christmas. How could this be Danny Aaronson, the guy the whores in Cu Chi gave it away to? What became of the handsome, trim Danny of the faded photograph?

"Hell, old man, it's good to see you, Troop. How the fuck are you, man?" As Danny said all this, he pushed the ramrod-straight, at-attention Troop towards an empty red swivel stool that Roger managed to wipe off with his handkerchief before folding his ladder length down to meet it. Roger began lining up goldfish crackers on the bar, tail to mouth, mouth to tail. He couldn't keep his hands quiet.

"Hey, what's with the pin?" Danny asked as Roger then fingered the 25th Division pin with its thin gold-bordered taro leaf and lightning bolt that Roger had attached to his lapel as he left the comfort of his empty house.

"Boy, Troop, haven't seen one of these bastards in years. I know I've changed but hell you look the same. Few gray hairs. Naw, not much different. Sergeant Zimmer. Our choirboy. With the plastic-wrapped Bible. We'd be worryin' 'bout keepin' cigarettes dry and you'd be Saran-Wrappin' your New Testament like a cheese sandwich your mama packed."

"Yes," Roger replied. He turned to Troop. "Do you remember when those choppers–"

Danny cut Roger off. "So I'm divorced, Troop. From Annie. You remember all that horseshit she used to send me, 'Annie Loves Danny' embroidered on a heart pillow. Thing got moldy in Nam, the monsoon, the Delta. Tossed it and saw some sad kid grab it out of the can." Danny lurched into and out of his life story: getting married, girlfriend, getting divorced, girlfriend, house, girlfriend, daughter, selling insurance, eating in the car, girlfriend. But not the war. Roger just sat there fumbling with the goldfish again.

Danny said, "And you? Married? Kids?"

Still nothing about Vietnam, dammit, Roger thought. He could hear Brenda's words repeated again in this awful bar, "The war is over. Why don't you let it be over?" Right. She never understood any of it. Better she was gone.

Finally, Sergeant Zimmer answered Danny. "I'm just separated, work in a bookkeeping department at Our Savior Hospital. But I don't want to talk about those things." Roger had pushed each word out of his mouth, where they had acquired a bitter taste.

"Don't blame you," Danny shrugged. "Tough when you first separate, but there are plenty of girls on the planet. Just look around." He stretched out both arms to encompass the ladies of the Back Door.

Roger felt disconnected from his body and he put his fist down hard on the bar just as the bartender set a frosted mug in front of him. Cold beer sloshed over the edge of the bar. Roger took a few gulps of what was left.

"I … I don't want to talk about picking up women in dives, screwing secretaries, selling insurance or balancing the books. I– I want to talk about us, the war, the guys." His voice began loud then trickled out. Roger felt the front of his pants. The fuckin' beer had spilled on his pants. "I want to talk about the seven brave men of the Third Squad." Roger thought he spoke in a commanding voice, but only heard it as a whisper. However, Danny heard him.

"Seven?" Danny questioned.

Roger felt confused and sweaty and sticky. "Yes, seven. Of course seven." He grabbed several napkins and blotted helplessly at his wet pants.

"No, man, that's not right."

"What do you mean? I'm careful about how I remember the war. Our war. My war."

"Hey, man, there were eight of us for all those months we were with you as our squad leader."

"No, that's wrong," Roger said, his face dripping from this damn crowded, overheated room. He dabbed at his forehead with a napkin but realized too late the napkin was full of blotted-up beer.

"Hell it is," Danny countered.

"But the picture we all had copies of," Roger insisted and began "The Litany of the Names":

Danny Aaronson
Cleason Charles
Ed McNulty
Jack Plumber
Ted Smith
Rich Szelso
Roger Zimmer

"Seven, goddamn you."

"What about Fred Nichols?" Danny asked. "You didn't put his name right after Ed's."

Roger said nothing.

"Hey, shmuck, Fred took the goddamned picture."

Roger fingered his cross, the lapel pin, the dog tag.

"Then wham!" Danny said. "The day after we got all our copies of that picture back from the PX, you put Fred on point and he steps on a mine. The end. Not your fault, man. Poor Fred, son of a bitch. Took the picture. Picture without him and then the whole goddamned everything existed without him."

"No!" Roger said forcefully. "It was us–Third Squad–the war–we loved it–it was our war. I protected you all every–" *No, he would not break down and cry. He was Army all the way. A good soldier. A good squadron leader.*

Danny saw Roger's face crumble and lowered his voice, but

couldn't soften his accusation. "It didn't happen that way, man," he insisted. "You wanna talk about Vietnam, then let's talk about Fred Nichols. Vietnam was a fuckin' mistake and Fred Nichols was a kid who should have lived, should be in a Chicago suburb right now raisin' a family with three girls and a big dog in the yard and his folks happily gettin' old in the next town knowin' their son is alive. He should have lived, Fred Nichols. I loved him, man. So did you. But how can you love a war?"

—

Roger found himself driving toward home, the Back Door and Danny left far behind, a pinpoint, the bar enfolding the man enfolding the lie. Many men had lies about Vietnam, Roger reasoned. He had just heard another one. If it wasn't a lie then it was a twenty-year-old rusted truth and that would be worse, so Roger chose to believe Danny's story was a lie.

At home, Roger tried putting white pillows over his head as a string of words haunted him, "Love a war … should have lived … you put him on point … how can you love a war?" Then as Roger lay alone on his clean bed with the white pillows and taut sheets, it was his tenth-grade gym teacher calling him names, the Blake brothers from catechism class, even his father. Loser. Weakling. Pisshead. Then the image of his father refocused, became Fred.

Roger had made it home from the war and his wife had left him and his mother who loved him more than anyone else was dead and he wasn't sure if her hair was brown. And his father died not loving him. So what if Fred Nichols had made it home from the war like Danny said he should have, who says his parents would be OK and happy and his wife would still be with him? Maybe Roger saved Fred, with his dreams of being a father outside Chicago, from a terrible life. Look at Danny with his failed life and fat belly. Look at Roger huddled alone in his bed crying because for 20 years he had Fred buried beyond memory, beyond guilt.

But if Roger could see Fred there again in front of the men like Danny saw him, right there in front of the rest of the guys taking the picture, and if Roger could once more see Fred's body blown apart, Roger could no longer be happy about Vietnam, about his war. The comfort of the memory Roger constructed and cradled each night would fall prey to a lethal boobytrap.

By morning of the next day, Roger's bed was the empty canvas of a wrestling match with no winners, no losers and no one taken alive. Before Roger Zimmer, the accountant, went off to tally the numbers at Our Savior, he opened the shades and made his bed so that a quarter could bounce off the sheets, downed a bowl of warm oatmeal and raisins, packed a chicken salad sandwich and a washed apple for lunch, and repeated the same seven names that echoed reassuringly for 20 fucking years.

AUTHOR'S NOTE

Years ago, I enrolled in a William Joiner Institute for the Study of War and Social Consequences writers' workshop at the University of Massachusetts to hone my craft. A fiction writer, I was surprised to be slotted into Gloria Emerson's section. A six-foot tall National Book Award-winning nonfiction writer, imposing, eccentric, a *New York Times* reporter, she was the first woman journalist sent to cover the Vietnam War. A world-renowned journalist, Gloria turned out to be an amazing fiction teacher. I had unknowingly signed up for a mind-blowing roller coaster ride packed with a plethora of stories, led by larger-than-life Gloria. I crammed years of learning the craft into our fourteen days.

When Gloria assigned a short story to be written from the opposite gender's point-of-view, I turned my norms inside out and created, "How the Fuck Are You?" I viewed the world through squad leader Roger Zimmer's eyes, a Vietnam vet who worshipped his time in country and the men he brought safely home. For the stretch during which I birthed Roger's story, I inhabited his world from his vantage point. I was Roger. It was an amazing role reversal that taught me much–with Gloria the grand overseer of it all.

This story is dedicated to Gloria … and the troops.

JSC

If you don't care for obscenity, you don't care for the truth; if you don't care for the truth, watch how you vote.

Tim O'Brien
The Things They Carried

Hell No!
We Won't Go!
DAVID W. DUTTON

The cry went up from the crowded, tree-lined mall that stretched down the center of the university campus. Hundreds of angry students packed the space, some spilling onto the stone steps of the adjacent brick buildings. The cry sounded again, repeated itself, and finally became a chant. On the columned portico of the administration building, Felix Armbruster, president of the Students for a Democratic Society, led the chant, a bullhorn pressed to his lips. A voice from the crowd shouted, "SDS forever!"

Amidst the throng, Calvin "Cal" James Findley III stood with his left arm draped over the shoulders of his girlfriend, Melissa. Her arms encircled Cal's waist; Melissa's head rested against the side of his chest. On the opposite side, Cal's new friend, Tony, stood with one hand upon Cal's shoulder. The trio raised their voices in protest of the never-ending Vietnam conflict and the senseless loss of life that had become its legacy. Many of the students had already lost a family member or friend or, at the very least, knew someone who had.

Tony whistled and then laughed as he turned to Cal. "Jim says Armbruster is a farce…only in this for the notoriety. Probably planning on running for office once he graduates."

Cal joined his friend's laughter. "Jim's probably right."

Jim, Tony's roommate, wasn't even a student at the university. He was a skeptic and always suspicious of anything tied to "the establishment." Jim floated from one part-time job to another, often selling "special" cigarettes to boost his meager income.

Tony laughed again. "Jim's right about a lot of things. Bet your old man would have a shitfit if he knew you were out here protesting the war."

"God yes! 'I'm not spending good money for you to be out associating with a bunch of anarchists.'"

"Nice guy."

"Oh, yeah." Cal shook his head sadly. "He's been pissed at me ever since I refused to pledge his old fraternity." Cal had no intention of joining a fraternity or any other organization for that matter.

Like Tony and Jim, Cal didn't even belong to the SDS. As far as he was concerned, such organizations were only for people who were incapable of independent thought.

Cal considered asking Tony how his parents felt but reconsidered. He knew Tony was the product of a broken home, sent off to college to provide time and space for his parents and their dissolving marriage. He was an only child and easily disposable.

Cal leaned down to kiss the top of Melissa's head, her thick, black hair cool to his lips in the cold winter's afternoon. Feeling his kiss, Melissa arched her head back and pressed her soft lips against his cheek. Cal looked down at Melissa and smiled.

Those who knew her considered Melissa an enigma. While she typically appeared happy and carefree, there seemed to be a dark side about which she was unwilling to speak. It was a mystery to Cal, but whenever he pressed the subject, Melissa would simply smile and kiss him.

As the chant finally began to wane, Felix Armbruster's amplified voice filled the void. "It's time we let our government know how we feel! This fiasco has gone on long enough!" A cheer arose from the mass assembled at his feet. "Let Johnson know he's gone too far." Another cheer echoed down the long avenue of trees. The staid, brick buildings paid silent witness to the crowd's discontent.

Suddenly, in the distance, Cal heard the first of the sirens, and realized that the university security and town police would soon arrive. He looked at Tony and indicated the increasing cacophony with a toss of his head of long, blond hair. "Think we ought to split? This could turn nasty real quick."

Tony laughed. "Might be fun to hang and see what happens."

Cal shot him a skeptical look and turned his attention to Melissa. She gazed up at him and smiled. "Whatever you guys want to do."

The sirens grew closer but could not overshadow Arbruster's message. "Stand your ground! Don't give in to them. Sit!"

Moments of confused silence ensued as the sirens' wail increased.

"You heard me! Sit down! You're harder to move if you're sitting."

Slowly, one by one, the crowd began to lower themselves to the ground. As the students assumed this new position, several took the opportunity to disappear between the rows of buildings.

Cal poked Tony in the ribs. "I don't like the looks of this."

Tony feigned a punch at Cal's shoulder. "Aw, don't wimp out on me. Worse they will do is hose us down."

Images of Kent State suddenly filled Cal's head. It had been an incident he would never forget. Since the massacre, Cal found sleep difficult. His dreams were haunted by the countless news stories and the horrid details of the student protesters who'd been shot to death at point-blank range. He wondered if it could that happen here.

He glanced down at Melissa. *Isn't it my job to protect her? Of course, it is! She's a girl. Guys have to protect their girls.*

Cal sensed Tony's movement rather than saw it. He was too busy eyeing Melissa. Suddenly, Melissa laughed and started to follow Tony's lead. As her knees bent, Cal prevented her from sitting.

"We stay," Tony said.

"No! We're outta here." Ignoring the disapproval that stretched across Tony's face, Cal forced his way through the crowd. Melissa's hand held firmly in his.

The first of the patrol cars arrived, their sirens slowly fading. A large firetruck followed; a pumper, its reinforced hoses coiled and ready.

Cal and Melissa finally cleared the throng of students. In confusion, Cal stopped and frantically looked left to right. *Where now? Which way is safest? There, between Scott Lab and Wilson Hall.* He broke into a run. The path would take them to Arch Street, which skirted the east side of the campus. *Once there, we'll be just be another couple out to see what's happening.*

They cleared the shelter of the two buildings, crossed the service area behind them, and ducked through a thick row of privet. Before them lay the narrow verge of grass adjacent to the sidewalk that bordered Arch Street.

Cal paused and pulled Melissa close. *Safe...for now at least.*

"Will Tony be okay?"

"Tony's a big boy. He can take care of himself."

Cal and Melissa walked north along Arch Street until they reached the center of town. There they followed the main drag west as far as the post office and turned north again onto Chancellor Avenue. The side street wound its way north, finally turning east to parallel the railroad tracks. It was along this stretch that the old apartment building housing Jim and Tony's digs was located. They shared a tiny, fourth-floor walk-up tucked under the eaves of the decaying structure. Jim and Tony laughingly referred to the edifice as the LBJ Towers in contrast to its faded stucco and peeling paint.

Inside, the signs of neglect continued. The stairs and center hallways were narrow and dark. The grimy, pale-green walls and dirty, pink woodwork were dismal and drab. Four naked light bulbs fought to illuminate each hallway but did little to dispel the gloom. The overwhelming smell of cooked cabbage was a permanent part of the environment.

Cal and Melissa climbed the three flights of stairs and followed the fourth-floor hallway to the rear of the building. Cal rapped softly on the peeling pink door. There was no response. After knocking several more times, there was the sound of shuffling and the click of a released deadlock.

"Yeah! Who is it?"

Cal looked at Melissa and smiled. Jim was cautious to a fault. "Me and Melissa."

"Shit!" The door swung inward, revealing the cramped apartment. Jim walked away from the couple and resumed his spot at the rickety dining table. "Close the door and don't forget to lock it."

Cal stood aside so Melissa could enter. He followed and pushed the door closed behind him.

"Lock it." Jim didn't give them so much as a glance.

"Tony should be right behind us."

Melissa laughed. "Unless he's in jail."

"You heard me. Lock the fuckin' door."

"Okay, okay."

Melissa walked toward the table and tried to look over Jim's shoulder. "What you working on?"

"A plan. Nothin' that concerns you."

Melissa stepped back and glanced at Cal. "Whatever you say."

Cal unzipped his jacket and tossed it over the back of a chair. "What you got to drink?"

"Bottle of sloe gin under the sink."

Melissa sat across the table from Jim. "A fizz sounds good to me."

Cal crossed to the tiny kitchenette and began fixing Melissa's drink. "Don't you have anything else?"

Jim gazed up from his work and stared at Cal's back. "Beers are in the fridge. You want anything better, go buy it yourself. You can afford it."

Cal ignored the jibe. He opened the refrigerator door, withdrew a green bottle of Rolling Rock, picked up the sloe gin fizz, and crossed to the table. Handing the purple concoction to Melissa, he stared down at Jim's handiwork. "What the hell's that?"

"I told you...a plan. No goddamn concern of yours." Jim paused and stared down at his work. "Not yet, anyway."

Cal turned to Melissa and shrugged as she rolled her eyes in response. Jim was a character, plain and simple. A man with little use for society and its conventions. Jim had his own agenda, which rarely included anyone but Jim.

There was the sudden sound of a key in the lock as the door swung open. A bedraggled and soaking-wet Tony entered the room, slamming the door behind him. "Damn!"

Melissa looked at him and laughed. "They got you good."

"Fuckers!" Tony removed his saturated jacket and hung it on a hook by the door. "Not as bad as some."

Cal smiled. "It's over?"

Tony nodded. "Pretty much. Firehoses did the trick." He walked to the refrigerator and grabbed a beer. "They arrested Armbruster though."

Jim chuckled to himself. "Self-important prick. Serves him right."

Tony glanced over Jim's shoulder and studied the papers spread out before him. "Looks like the plan is coming along."

Jim nodded.

Cal looked from Melissa to Tony. "So, you...uh...know about *the plan*. You privileged or something?"

Tony smiled. "Might say that."

"When do we get brought up to speed?"

Tony placed a hand on Cal's shoulder. "In good time. All in good time."

—

"You're fuckin' kidding me!" Cal looked at his three friends gathered around the kitchen table. No one responded.

Two weeks had passed since the protest. Tony had summoned Cal to the dingy apartment. Without asking, Cal had brought Melissa along as well. Unfortunately for Cal, neither Tony nor Jim seemed happy about Melissa's presence. *Hell, how was I to know this was a no-girls-allowed gathering?*

Jim leveled a cold stare at Cal. "We're in agreement that we need to do something. Something that will really attract attention."

Tony nodded. "If people like us don't make a stand, the government sure as hell isn't gonna get the message."

Cal set down his beer bottle. "But this...this is extreme."

Melissa laughed and clapped her hands together. "I think it's wonderful!"

Jim glared at her. "You're not part of this."

"I'm sitting here, aren't I?"

"Only by accident." Jim glared at Cal and shook his head.

Cal reached out and took Melissa's hand. "Honey...I don't want you involved."

"That's hardly your decision. If this is happening, then I'm going to be a part of it."

Cal squeezed her hand and then looked at Jim and Tony. "I still think it's extreme."

Tony smiled. "That's the intention."

Cal shook his head as if to clear his thoughts. "But...the ROTC building? What if someone gets hurt?"

"No one's going to get hurt." Jim picked up a much-reviewed paper and scanned it. "The ROTC building empties out around 4:30 each afternoon, regular as clockwork. There's no full-time security for the building. Campus security patrols the grounds, checking the ROTC building at 2:00 AM and again at 5:00."

"How can you be sure?"

Jim's patience waned. "I can be sure because I've done my homework. I've scouted out that damned building and the campus fuzz for the last three weeks. The schedule never changes."

Tony nodded. "Jim's right. We've taken turns checking them out."

Cal fell silent. He looked at Melissa, who seemed enthralled by what was happening. *Burning down the ROTC building is the last thing I want to be a part of. How do I get out of this?* It was clear to Cal that Tony and Jim had worked long and hard on the plan. Even Melissa was enthused about the effect the fire would have. Cal sighed inwardly and studied the expressions on his friends' faces. *They're for this. No question about it.*

"Well, pussy," Jim said, sneering at Cal. "You in or out?"

Melissa squeezed Cal's hand. "Of course, he's in!" She looked at Cal and smiled. "Aren't you, babe?"

Cal hesitated for an instant, but Melissa's smile was all it took. He nodded. "Yeah. I'm in."

—

The night was clear and cold. The security patrol had come and gone. The north section of the campus was deserted. The four conspirators, all clothed in black, stood huddled together in the shadow of the arts building. Beyond the shelter of the building was a wide swath of open ground they needed to cross to reach their target. Fortunately, none of pathway lighting reached that far. They would be practically invisible beneath the shadows cast by the tall oak trees.

Their arsenal included two five-gallon cans of gasoline, procured by Jim from one of his many jobs. Tony carried one, Jim the other. Cal held Melissa's gloved hand firmly in his. There had been no talking her out of this self-decreed mission. It was an adventure, and she was…adventurous.

One by one, they scurried across the patch of open ground, seeking refuge behind the low, brick building. Jim set down his gas can, wrapped his right hand in a heavy towel, and drove it through window of the door. The rest was easy. Jim reached in, found the door lock and the deadlock, and undid both without effort. The compromised door swung inward.

All was dark and shadowy within, the furniture and cabinetry serving as ghostly sentinels bearing witness to their crime.

None of the arsonists spoke. Jim had been very specific about that. Silence was essential.

The main room of the building was large and open, filled with worktables and benches. An assortment of offices and storage rooms bordered it on the north side. The doors to these spaces were firmly closed. Jim motioned Melissa toward them. As she began opening the doors, Jim and Tony doused the floors and walls of each room with gasoline. The remaining fuel was dispersed throughout the main room and its furnishings.

When the cans were empty, Jim set his down and motioned the others to the open doorway.

Tony followed suit and exited the building. Melissa was next, and then Cal. Outside, Jim, Tony, and Melissa disappeared into the shadows, each going in a different direction.

Cal stood alone in the open doorway. It was time for him to do his part. The others were depending on him. Cal stooped down. Jim had run a narrow rivulet of gasoline over the door sill and out onto the concrete stoop. The time it would take for the fire to travel its length would enable Cal to clear the scene before the inevitable explosion.

Cal withdrew a lighter and lit the crumpled piece of newspaper he'd been carrying in his pocket. *Well, here goes nothing. No turning back now.* Cal dropped the burning paper and watched to ensure the river of gasoline had ignited. Once the cold, blue flame began to spread, Cal sprinted toward the shelter of evergreens that bordered the ROTC parade ground in a line. Behind him, the flame crept further into the building until it reached the motherlode. With a loud whoosh, the building burst into flame.

—

It was now almost five in the morning. Cal stood looking out the fourth-floor window of the apartment. From there, the view of the fire was frightening. Flame and smoke poured skyward while flashing lights and sirens filled the night. *Shit! Did we really do that? Was this really our handiwork?* He shook his head sadly.

Melissa's laugh pulled Cal from his depressed trance. She,

Tony, and Jim had grown bored of watching the flames and were now seated around the table. They drank, smoked, and reveled in their accomplishment.

Cal turned to look at his friends as Melissa laughed again. "Frankfurters! Frankfurters and marshmallows!" Her words were tinged with too much alcohol.

Tony took a deep swallow of his beer. "Can't have dogs and marshmallows without an open fire."

With that, the trio erupted with raucous laughter.

Jim glowed. "Well, we sure as hell have that!" He extended his right hand and high-fived Tony and Melissa.

"Fuckin' A, man!" Tony's voice had begun to slur.

Cal did not share their enthusiasm and turned back to stare at the distant spectacle. Something was wrong. He didn't know what, but he felt it in his bones. He sighed and rested his forehead against the cold glass. *What's done is done. No turning back now.*

———

Cal dropped the newspaper as if it had burned him. In a sense, it had. It landed on his unmade dormitory bed and stared back at him. Its headline blazed:

Local Firefighter Killed in ROTC Blaze

Killed! Jesus Christ! This was just supposed to be a prank, and now we've taken someone's life! Cal grasped the edge of the desk and collapsed onto its chair. *Jim said no one would be hurt. The building would be empty. It was supposed to be a piece of cake.*

None of them had thought any further than that.

Cal rested his elbows on his knees and held his head in his hands, a desperate caricature of Rodin's thinker. *What to do? What do I do?* The feeling of guilt flooded Cal's body. *I've taken someone's life. Me. I set the fire. There's no denying it.* A muffled sob fled his lips as tears escaped his eyelids and streamed down flushed cheeks.

For several minutes, Cal sat in tortured silence. Then, as a form of punishment, he picked up the newspaper. Tears blurred Cal's vision, but he forced himself to read the opening paragraph.

Local firefighter, 32-year-old Phillip Andrews, was killed in
an early morning fire that consumed the university ROTC
building. Andrews perished when the building's slate roof
collapsed atop him. He leaves behind a wife and two young
children. Funeral services for the fallen firefighter will be ..."

Cal felt the paper slip from his hands. It fell in a heap at his
feet.

*My doing. Sure, the others had loaded the gun, but I
squeeze the trigger. Have they even seen the newspaper?* He had
no way of knowing. Melissa was probably in class. Jim and Tony
did not have a phone. Cal was alone in his grief.

Minutes later, Cal pulled on a jacket and left his dorm room.
He needed to talk with the others, starting with Jim and Tony. The
walk to their crumbling apartment building was short. He knew the
way by heart.

Neither Jim nor Tony owned a car, so the parking area in
front of their building provided no clue as to whether they were
home. Once inside, Cal climbed the stairs through the gloomy structure. He found it strange that nothing had changed. Same dirty paint,
same feeble light bulbs, same cabbage smell. Everything was exactly as it had been before the fire. Almost everything. *My life has
changed. My life will never be the same.*

Cal knocked softly on the apartment door.

"It's open." Tony's voice sounded normal, as if this was
simply any other day.

Cal eased the door open and slipped into the room. Tony sat
on the battered sofa, eyes transfixed on a black-and-white television
set. The box spouted the local news. The fire was the day's top story,
and Phillip Andrews, the fallen hero of the hour.

Without removing his jacket, Cal sighed and sat heavily on
the other end of the sofa. A prisoner of the press, Tony remained
speechless. In shades of gray, the story continued to unfold on the
tiny screen in front of them. When the coverage finally concluded,
Tony sat back and sighed. "Fuck."

Cal nodded. Although he had come seeking emotional support, he didn't feel like talking. The television continued to fill the
void, its screen displaying an inane game show.

Tony stood, stretched, and then walked to the kitchenette.

"Beer?" He popped the top of a cold Rolling Rock.

Cal shook his head.

The strained silence continued. Jim was obviously out or at work or something. It was just the two of them. The isolation didn't help.

Finally, Cal looked up at his friend. "What are we going to do?"

Tony laughed sarcastically. "*Do? What the hell can we do?*" He took a large swallow of the beer. "It's done. Nothing we can do to undo it."

"What did Jim have to say about it?"

Sitting at the kitchen table, Tony set the bottle in front of him. "Don't know. He was gone by the time I got up. Headed off to some sort of job."

"Is he coming back?"

Tony frowned at Cal. "Of course, he's coming back, man. He lives here. Where else would he go?"

Cal shrugged. Knowing Jim, he could be on a bus headed west by now. Jim was loyal only to himself. No one else mattered. Cal sighed and stood.

"Where you going?"

"I'm not sure." Cal headed for the door. "Maybe find Melissa. See what she thinks."

Tony laughed. "Sure, like she's got all the answers."

He's right. Melissa is a follower, not a leader. She'll be looking for support. For her, the whole thing had simply been one big adventure. How's she going to see beyond that?

As the day wound itself out, Cal soon discovered that Melissa was not to be found. Her roommate, Susie, said when she returned from class she found a note from Melissa stating she was going home for a long weekend.

"Her note said she'll be back next Tuesday," Susie said.

Tuesday arrived, but Melissa remained MIA.

"She left me a message that she has the flu and will be home for a few more days," Susie explained to Cal upon seeing him at the school cafeteria.

It all sounded reasonable, but Cal knew better. The fact that Melissa hadn't tried to reach him revealed the real reason behind her absence.

—

The next few days were like a hazy dream for Cal. Nothing seemed real. Cal floated from class to class, to the cafeteria, to the Student Union building, and back to his dormitory. Cal heard nothing from either Jim or Tony for several days until he encountered Tony on his way out of the Student Union. It was obvious that Tony did not want to talk. He did his best to avoid Cal, but Cal grabbed his arm fiercely.

Tony glared at him. "Hey! What's with you?"

Cal stared at Tony for a moment. "Jim back?"

Tony looked down at the ground and shook his head.

"Didn't come back from that job?" Cal persisted.

"Nope." Tony refused to look at his friend.

Cal snorted. "Why am I not surprised?" He released Tony's arm and turned away.

"I hear Melissa's gone, too." His sneer was a jibe, plain and simple.

Without responding, Cal walked away. For the first time in his life, he was truly alone.

—

The funeral was a huge affair that featured an impressive procession through town, the kind reserved for fallen firefighters and police officers. The flag-bedecked casket rode atop a brightly shining firetruck. Bunches of flowers surrounded the gunmetal coffin. A stark, cold, winter sun glinted off polished chrome.

Cal stood with the rest of the crowd and watched the sad parade. Main Street was closed to traffic, and the sidewalks were filled to capacity with pedestrians. The entourage was led by a color guard followed by rank and file of firefighters. The casket followed. Cal assumed the grieving widow and her two children were hidden by the blacked-out windows of the Cadillac limousine which came next. Behind that, a marching bagpiper troupe. The wail of their pipes a soundtrack for the somber occasion.

A gust of cold wind caused Cal to shiver as he stared at the long, gray car creeping past. Nothing stirred behind the black windows. Yet he knew they were there and probably crying. Trying to understand what had happened to their once peaceful lives. Cal shivered again, this time from fear and grief rather than the cold. *My doing. The dead dog lay at my doorstep, a victim of my stupidity and cowardice.* He wanted to run after the limousine, wrench open the rear door, and plead for their mercy. But that wasn't going to happen. They would have no mercy to give, nor, he thought, was he deserving of it.

The crowd watched as the procession climbed the hill and disappeared over its crest. They could still hear the strains of the pipes as they made their way to Phillip Andrews' final resting place. The throng began to disperse; there was little talking. In a matter of minutes, Cal found himself huddled against the cold in the shelter of a storefront, alone once more.

—

The following week crawled along, dragging Cal with it. There was no word from Tony, and, as far as Cal knew, Jim and Melissa were still among the missing. The papers and television were full of the funeral and the investigation into the fire. Of course it was arson. There was no question about that. Traces of accelerant easily confirmed this. But there were really no leads or clues as to the identity of the perpetrators. Members of the Students for a Democratic Society were the prime suspects, and Felix Armbruster had been brought in for questioning. Fortunately for him, Armbruster had an alibi for the night of the fire, having been out of town. If the fire was caused by any SDS member, he knew nothing about it and was unable to shed light on what had happened.

Cal was alone. His life was a shambles, and he had no one in whom to confide. He was unable to shake the cloak of depression from his shoulders. There was simply no way for him to cope with the turn his life had taken. There was no way to undo what had happened, no way to compensate for his actions.

Cal's grades began to show the effect of his mind. Classes became a sometimes thing. Finally, he quit going entirely. What was the point? From Cal's perspective, he had no future...at least no future that he wanted any part of. Drinking became a favorite pastime, but without Melissa, Tony, and Jim, he drank alone. Still, drinking made him feel better. It clouded his mind and dulled his senses. That was the best he could expect right now.

Where can I find the answers to this dilemma? I have to do something, something worthwhile. Probably won't make me feel better about myself, but I could try. The question is…what?

—

Cal sat on a bench in the little park across the street from small, brick building. From his vantage point, he had a clear view of the building and the sidewalk in front of it. He watched as various people came and went about their daily business. In the large, plate glass window, a familiar placard pleaded their cause. But was it his cause? No, that was ridiculous. Of course, it wasn't. Still, it was the first positive move he had made in days.

Pulling his jacket close around him, Cal lit a cigarette and exhaled a plume of white smoke. He studied the poster in the window. He watched men and women come and go. Some were actually in uniform. He took a deep drag on the cigarette and got to his feet. For an instant, he hesitated. *Is this really going to make me feel better? Guess there's only one way to find out.*

Cal took a final drag and then crushed the cigarette beneath his heel. He left the park and stood on the sidewalk across from the building. He looked right and then left. And then right again. No oncoming traffic blocked his path. He stepped off the curb and sprinted across the street. Grabbing the handle of the glass door, he pulled it toward him and entered the building.

Cal didn't even give the poster of Uncle Sam a second glance.

AUTHOR'S NOTE

Why did I write this piece? That's a good question. One of the submission requirements for this anthology was that the title of the work contain a word of profanity. As easy as that might seem, coming up with a profane word that would lead into something meaningful proved to be a real challenge. Sure, I know a multitude of obscenities. I'm 71 years old. I probably know the whole gamut. Still, considering that a story had to follow, the challenge posed a problem. It was a long time before I found the right path.

"Hell no, we won't go!" was a cry heard across most college campuses in the late sixties and early seventies. If you lived it, then you know If you didn't, then be thankful for that gift. It was a period of time filled with confusion, anger, and fear. Few were untouched by it. Many protested. Many went to war and lost their lives.

To say that it wasn't a happy time is an understatement. In fact, it was a dreadfully uncertain time. No one knew what was going to happen next. Despite that uncertainty, those of us who were students did our best to continue our lives with some sense of normalcy. It wasn't easy.

DWD

This book contains a lot of "bad" words.
So if you are easily offended, go fuck yourself.

Oliver Markus

What the Fuck: Monday Morning Strike

CLAIRE MCCABE

Why this morning
they decide to strike?
The programmable pot quits.
   No coffee when I wake.
And the toaster
   burns the bread.
In the dryer
   my jeans lie wet.

The cell phone's dark eye
   obscuring every text.
      What's going on y'all?

Inside my car…
   c.. r.. a.. n.. k   c.. r.. a.. n.. k
I get out and kick the tire,
   grab my bruised foot.

      OK, ok!
      I get it!
      I do, I do
      appreciate you.

I recite that gratitude,
   schlep to the bus stop,
and plot to replace
   the whole fucking lot.

Sonnet for Shitty, Rotten Love
CLAIRE McCABE

I walk into the market where we used to linger.
Tomatoes, once sweet, now appear
as red and accusing
as the rims of my eyes.

Yesterday I saw you shopping with her,
the blanched green of my shock and envy
now confronts me in celery–celery!
standing rigid as a subpoenaed witness.

Once you and I planned our meals in these aisles,
then hurried home to cook, and lick, and suck
the juices on our back stoop, where we played
poor but satisfied lovers.

Now I grasp an eggplant as purple
as my heart gasping for love.

Those Damned Sunday Vices: View from the Third Floor

CLAIRE McCABE

I visit his apartment on Sunday.
He wants me to think the drinking
is under control. I fry eggplant for us.
We need wine with the meal, he says,
and pours red into glasses.

He drinks while I melt butter for onions,
then points to the kitchen window,
Look, he says. *Go on, look.*

I lean over the sill
and peer onto the street.
From three floors up, I see a woman
who sits on a retaining wall, knitting.
She seems out of place in the city
with her long hair and prairie skirt,
the knitting. I shrug my shoulders, so…

She's a prostitute, he says. *Watch.*

I think: it's Sunday afternoon,
who's going to turn tricks, or seek them?

A blue sedan pulls up.
A man rolls down the window and says
something to the woman, who puts
her knitting into a tote bag

and gets into the car.

She'll be back in 10 minutes, he says,
and refills his glass. *It's probably a hand
or a blow job.*

Ten minutes later, when I plate
the eggplant, and he's opened the second
bottle of wine, he says, *Look.*
There's the blue car. The prairie girl
steps out, sits down on the wall,
starts knitting again.

We sit down. He pours more wine.

AUTHOR'S NOTE

What the Fuck: Monday Morning Strike: I often wonder if there is some kind of intelligence behind the inanimate mechanicals that we depend on to get us through each day. What would happen if they really did get sick of serving us? After all, we treat them like objects! I know I'd be pissed and go on strike if I were a neglected toaster.

Sonnet for Shitty, Rotten Love: How does one shake up a traditional sonnet? Add vegetables. I wrote this poem tongue-in-cheek. Really, how serious is heartbreak if you are surrounded by veggies? When I have read this aloud, it is always with melodramatic inflection. A friend pulled me aside and said, "You're not fooling anybody; this is heartbreak." Hmmm, maybe she has a point. You can decide.

Damned Sunday Vices: View from the Third Floor: The idea for this poem started, as many do, with a visual of this "transaction" happening on the street below a friend's apartment. The poem evolved to become much more about how humans deflect from their own shortcomings by pointing out those of others.

CM

One Badass Snowflake
LISA FOX

What came first–the stench, or the squish? It was hard to tell–but it didn't really matter. I'd made my mark. A size nine-and-a-half stamp, smack in the middle of a pile of excrement.

Mom did say it was important to leave an impression.

I scraped the offending goo against the curb, catching the cuff of my too-long black suit pants (Dad's suit pants, actually) between the concrete and my heel. Filth stuck to me like Play-Doh. I stood in the street, one leg up, a human pogo stick shaking off shit with each hop.

I limped my way under a shimmering gold sign that welcomed me to Help Yourself, Inc., dragging my foot as I entered the reception area. I spotted Daisy Maye, Mom's bowling partner and a transplant from the Deep South, behind a 1980s thrift shop desk.

"Why, Chad Moffat, aren't you just a ray of sunshine!" Daisy waddled out from her post, her worn denim dress stretching across an ample bosom, belly, and hips. "Your mama's called here five times, worried sick. Didn't you hear your cell phone ringin'?"

She extended her meaty arms and squeezed me hard. Daisy was a hugger. I grunted with the force of her affection.

Sniffling, Daisy pushed back. Her nose wrinkled as she pursed her painted red lips.

"Chad, honey, what is that smell? It's bad enough to gag a maggot."

"Oh, that," I said. "I had a little mishap on the way in. I guess you can say I stepped in some serious doo-doo to land this interview." I shrugged as I gestured toward my messy shoe.

"Well, I'm gonna fix you up right fine, there, sugar." Daisy grabbed a wad of tissues from her desk and dropped to her knees. Her shock-yellow Muppet perm moved in time with her furious swabbing of my shoe and pant leg. Tufts of tissue formed filthy little balls that littered the floor.

"Much better," she said. I extended a hand and helped Daisy to her feet. She sniffed again. "But, honey, we're not quite there yet."

Retrieving a can of air freshener, Daisy bathed me in the sickly sweet chemical mist of *Summer Breeze*. "You can't be smelling like a sewer for good old Mr. Smugman."

I gagged on the aerosol. "Hold on. I'm actually meeting with Sly Smugman?"

Sly Smugman was a world-famous self-help guru and chief executive officer of Help Yourself, Inc. Why would he interview me himself for an unpaid student internship?

"Mr. Smugman likes to get to know his employees up close and personal-like."

I tugged at my collar, gulping back the butterflies that threatened to escape from my stomach.

"Oh, don't you worry. His bark is worse than his bite! Ya'll will be just fine," Daisy said. She handed me an application and a pen. Its gold embossed letters reminded me that *Every Snowflake Is Unique*.

I sprinted through the first few pages. After fifteen interviews in the past month, I was an expert at all the standard questions.

I am the king of applications. I deserve a trophy for my application-completing skills.

And then came the last three topics.

I tapped the pen against my forehead as I studied the first question.

What is your focus?

Life focus? Vision focus? Academic focus? That's got to be it. But I'm not sure you could call my academics focused. First, I bombed biology, fainting at the sight of a frog in formaldehyde. Mom wrote a letter to the dean, claiming the curriculum discriminated against the squeamish. She threatened a lawsuit if the school denied me a mid-semester switch. Philosophy wasn't a good fit, either. Mom said there were too many questions, not enough answers, and the program was unfair to literal thinkers like me. Which led me to my current major: business administration.

If you could change one thing about yourself, what would

it be?

Well, I would change the fact that I stepped in dog feces today. Right now, it would be nice if I smelled better. It would be good to be taller and have better teeth, maybe look a little more like Ryan Gosling and a little less like Steve Buscemi. (I get that a lot.) What to write? I know! Indecisiveness. Or, is it indecision?

When your last relationship ended, were you the dumper or the dumped?

Huh?

"Hey, Daisy? About these questions?"

Daisy huffed. "That form makes me madder than a wet hen in winter. Mr. Smugman penned those questions himself. You just try as try can."

Right ... dumper or dumped? I worked so hard to forget Chelsea, the last thing I want to do is remember her now. She was the most beautiful barista I'd ever seen, with eyes the color of java. We'd shared some lattes and some laughs, and she'd even let me kiss her once. Each time she served me, she'd draw my name in cute bubble letters on my cup, topped off by a foam-filled heart. I knew it was over the day she wrote "Chump" instead of Chad as she scowled and pushed the coffee across the counter at me, burning my hand. Mom said Chelsea was just waiting for the chance to earn her MRS degree with the first PhD who dipped his biscotti into her cappuccino. Whatever that meant. I guess that makes me the dumped.

Heavy footsteps echoed off the hardwood floor, accompanied by an equally bellowing voice. "Daisy! Where is Chapter Two?"

"Boss man," she whispered.

"Daisy, these books don't write themselves. I need to see Chapter Two, right now!"

She opened her heavily charcoaled, hazel eyes wide, doe-like. "My, my, Mr. Smugman, ya'll should know I'm not the kind of gal to keep a man waiting. The last time I did that, I caught my husband doing the horizontal cha-cha with the housewife next door." Her chuckle was sweet as syrup. "You cool your heels now. I'll have your chapter ready faster than a hot knife through butter."

"You'd better not be slacking, Daisy Maye."

Smugman turned to me then, as if it had just occurred to him that there was another human in the room. Hands deep in his trouser pockets, he rocked back and forth on the balls of his feet like the pendulum of a cuckoo clock, sucking in a gut corseted by the jacket of his white linen suit. His scarlet hair lay slicked back like sliced ham over his ample head. His teeth shone like pearls, aligned perfectly beneath a well-practiced smile. I stood in the shadow of his hulking six-foot-plus frame, unsure of whether I should laugh, cry, or make a run for it.

Smugman dropped a bulky hand on my shoulder. "Let's do this." He led me down the hall to his corner office. Inside was a mahogany desk that extended halfway to the ceiling. A Sly Smugman bobblehead performed sentry duty on the desktop, its massive cranium nodding rhythmically as if saying *yes, yes, yes.*

Smugman's credentials hung on the wall, poster-sized and framed in gold: *Sly Smugman, BS, South Hampton Institute of Thought.*

Smugman retired to his throne. "Take a seat." He gestured toward a chair built for someone half my size. A placard adorned the back of the chair–*Chief Executive Dog.* I looked from the chair, to Smugman, to an aged Basset Hound that lay flopped on a plush golden pillow beside the desk. The tips of his ears grazed the floor.

"Don't worry," Smugman said. "Chief won't mind if you sit there. It's his nap time. He just finished his walk." The hound's large, droopy eyes regarded me with guilt. He lifted his head slightly, sniffed three times, and sneezed loudly.

A whiff of Summer Breeze.

I squeezed my legs together and pushed down, sliding my hips past the armrests of the chair. I sat with a plop. My knees pressed into my chest.

"So, Chad. You're here because you want something from me."

I cleared my throat and wiped my sweating palms on my thighs, leaving a streak. *Mom's going to need to send this suit to the dry cleaner for sure.*

"I am very interested in working for your organization," I said, just as my phone began buzzing against my thigh. The theme from *Psycho* played muffled inside my pocket. A joke from Chelsea. She thought it was hysterical. Mom did not.

Smugman raised his eyebrows. "Need to get that?"

"Can I?" I pushed my hand past the armrest toward my

pocket, stretching out my leg to reach inside. "I'll be just a minute." Mom's photo grinned at me from the screen like a lovesick Cheshire Cat.

"I'm a little busy right now," I mumbled. "I'll call you in a few."

Mom's voice cackled from my earpiece. I poked at the "off" button multiple times for good measure, and turned the phone off.

"Girlfriend?"

"Mom." I grimaced. "She's actually a big fan of yours. She's read all your books."

I gestured toward the titles on Smugman's shelf:

Pride in Participation: You Deserve That Trophy
How to Raise an Entitled Child
Helicopter Parenting at its Best
Anger Non-Management
It's Not Me, it's You. I'd read that one after Chelsea renamed me.

"Mom's a big fan, eh? They always are, Chad, they always are."

Smugman turned from me, flicking an inhumanly large index finger under the chin of the bobblehead. "I'm a handsome devil, aren't I?"

Speechless, I fixed my gaze on the figure and bobbed my head in time with its motion—*yes, yes, yes.*

"Chad, do you know why I need an intern?" Smugman turned in his chair and addressed the bookshelf. "Because these books are lonely. And I am embarking on the greatest self-help book in the history of self-help books."

Smugman thrust his hands heavenward. The bobblehead and I waited for a lightning strike. Instead, thunder rumbled in with a knock, and Daisy bounced into the office. Smugman rolled his eyes. The hound lifted his head and let out a low woof.

"Chapter Two, good as new!" Daisy smiled at me and winked.

Smugman quickly perused the top page and winced, drawing in a deep breath. "Daisy. Do you not know how to spell my name? It's Smugman, not Slugman! Can't you tell the difference between an L and an M?"

Daisy pulled her lips back in a thin red line that Smugman

would have been wise not to cross.

"Well, bless your heart," Daisy said. "Don't ya'll go cryin' over alphabet soup."

Smugman inhaled deeply through his cavernous nostrils. "Just go. And fix it. Now."

Daisy scowled. She pulled back the hem of her skirt in a deep curtsy, turned on her heel, and stormed out.

"Now, where were we?" Smugman asked.

I squirmed in the tiny chair, its metal arm digging into my thigh. "The greatest self-help book in the history of self-help books," I murmured.

"Yes, yes!" Smugman rubbed his hands together as if warming them. "You catch on quickly."

He pushed a contract at me. "Read the first assignment. Aloud."

I cleared my throat. "Internship Assignment Number One: Rest Easy! Demand an overnight stay at a local mattress shop to test the merchandise. Bring your own sheets."

I furrowed my brow. "I don't understand."

Smugman beamed. "Turn the page! Read the second one!"

"Internship Assignment Number Two." My voice cracked like it did when I was thirteen and was forced to sing a solo of *Silent Night* in my middle school Christmas pageant. That day I had hoped the floor would open and swallow me. I was beginning to feel the same way again. "A Modest Proposal. Get down on one knee and pledge your eternal love to the prettiest girl at The Soda III Bar on 14th Street."

"It's magnificent, isn't it! Hands-on field assignments that will feed into my masterpiece. I need to know you have what it takes, Chad. Do you have what it takes?"

Cold sweat seeped into the collar of my dress shirt and leaked down my back like a sticky Popsicle. "I'm not sure I understand the question. Or what this job is …?"

Smugman waved at me dismissively. "Let's review your application. You're twenty-three and in your final year at Morris State College."

I wiggled in the ridiculous dog-chair, attempting to sit upright.

"Morris State College." Smugman rested his elbows on his

desk, his fingertips coming together in a steeple. "Tell me, Chad, does it bother you that you go to a really good school, but no one knows it's a really good school?"

"Well, it's not Yale, but …"

"And you've been an undergraduate for six years. Six years, Chad. Tsk-tsk."

"I matriculate in June," I offered, hoping he would be impressed with my big word.

"Three different majors. Why are you so indecisive?"

"Um … I don't know."

"And you live at home with Mom and Dad? Does Mom do your laundry, Chad?"

"What–"

"Which one of my books is Mom's favorite, Chad?" He peered at me over the mountainous desk separating us. "Tell me, which one?"

I stammered. "*Helicopter Parenting at its Best*? I think." The perspiration dripped like teardrops into to my socks.

"Mom set up this interview for you, Chad?"

I answered with silence.

Smugman hurled questions as if they were baseballs, his office a batting cage with no off switch. He leaned forward, staring into my eyes so hard it hurt my brain.

"And in your last relationship, you were the dumped. You're not a dumper, Chad. Why doesn't this surprise me?"

Smugman glanced at his gold Rolex and sighed. "You're taking up a lot of my time, Chad. Your elevator speech. Give it. Why should I hire you?"

This was it. My moment of truth.

I swallowed hard. "Well, Mr. Smugman, I really need this internship to graduate." I looked down, wringing my hands. "I'll show up on time. I'll do what you ask me to do. I'll–"

"Tell me about your trophies, Chad."

"My trophies?"

"How many trophies did you get as a kid?"

"Um, three? No, four!"

"Merit trophies, or *we try hard* trophies?"

I mumbled. "They were participation trophies."

Smugman slapped his palm on the desk. "I knew it!" He

stood; his shadow eclipsed me.

"You, Chad Moffat, are a loser. A capital L, fucking class-A loser."

My cheeks burned.

Smugman raised his left hand to his forehead, forming a backward L-shape in front of his oversized cranium. "Loser! And you reek something fierce."

Summer Breeze, dog poop, and ripe sweat assaulted my nostrils. A smoldering whip snapped inside my brain. I leapt up to stand.

The chair remained glued to my behind, a metal tail wagging in the delight of my rampage.

"You know what I think? I think you are a nutcase," I hissed. "I think your books are as ridiculous as your gigantic head. I think you have a degree from a crap college. And I wouldn't work for you, even if you paid me."

I wobbled toward the door, the tiny seat still glued to me. My rage bubbled as Smugman sat there, smirking. I grasped the chair's armrests, still digging into my hips, and yanked myself free. I flung the chair hard. It skidded across Smugman's desk and knocked the miniature Sly figure to the floor. The bobble was beheaded. Its noggin landed with a thud next to the old hound, who lay snoring.

"Wait!" Smugman called after me. "Don't go." His deep laugh filled the office. "I like you, Chad. You're one badass snowflake."

What?

"Aren't you even a little curious about the title of my new book?"

My breaths heaved, my cheeks aflame.

"You know, for your field assignments. We went over this. You've got to be a little quicker on the uptake, Chad."

Smugman reached behind his desk, appointing a new bobblehead to sentinel duty. This newborn figurine cradled a golden trophy and flashed rhinestone teeth that rivaled Smugman's own.

"*The Art of Rejection.*" He tapped the head of the bobble; it nodded *yes, yes, yes.* "That's the name of my book, and the focus of your life for the next three months."

I opened my mouth to respond and promptly snapped it shut. Mom always said I looked like a hungry turtle when I gaped at people like that, and she'd kill me if I blew the internship now.

"You've passed the first rejection task here today, with–well, you passed, and the job is yours. I can't wait to see how you handle this first assignment."

Smugman pushed his inhumanly large index finger on a red button on the phone. I wondered if it was some type of self-destruct mechanism.

"Daisy! Get in here. And bring the supplies for Chad."

The door swung open, and in barreled Daisy, a rolled sleeping bag and pillow tucked under her arm. A brown teddy bear dangled from her hand.

"Why, Chad Moffat! You did it! We're gonna be busier than moths in mittens here!" She dropped the bedding at my feet. "Your mama's waitin' outside–she was havin' a dyin' duck fit out there. I just about had to block and tackle to keep her out, what with all that yellin'!"

I looked from Daisy to Smugman, who shook his head. "It's why I keep Daisy around," he said. "She's not much of an assistant, but she's one hell of a bouncer."

"You ain't seen nothin' yet, sugar." She turned and smiled at me before walking out. "I'll hold mama bear off for a few more minutes."

Smugman tapped at his watch as the door closed behind Daisy.

"Mattress store downtown closes at eight. Better get a move on," Smugman said. "Put the sheets and your sleeping bag on the bed first. Then tell them you're staying the night. And don't forget your friend there."

He gestured toward the teddy bear, which I retrieved from the floor.

"Mr. Smugman, I don't understand what a mattress store has anything to do with this internship. Or *The Art of Rejection*."

Smugman chuckled. "Chad, have you ever tried to have a slumber party in a mattress store?"

I shook my head.

"Me either. I can't wait to see what's going to happen tonight."

He extended a beefy hand to me over the Everest of his desk. "I'll expect your write-up by noon tomorrow."

My hand embraced Smugman's in a strong union, sealed

with the sheen of sweat and unseen excrement.

Mom would be proud. I'd left my mark. I'd made an impression.

Chief Executive Dog lifted his head and howled.

AUTHOR'S NOTE

It can be said that interviewing for a job is like a first date–dress to impress, bring your "A" game, show your genuine interest. Sometimes you just click with that person sitting across from you; it's a match made in heaven. Other times you find yourself questioning whether a jump from that third-floor office window would be worth the broken leg or sprained ankle, just to get the hell out of there.

Several factors influenced the writing of "One Badass Snowflake." Crazy, uncomfortable job interviews being the primary. (A few of the interview questions included in the story were taken from the worst job interviews I've ever had. I won't tell you which ones.) I also thought about the many "helicopter parents" I've encountered and what that type of behavior might do to a kid trying to make his mark on the world. And, a few years ago, I saw a story on the local news about a young man who intentionally placed himself in situations that would involve a rejection … just so he would get better at being rejected. That one stuck with me, and I thought it would be a fun idea to bring into a short fiction piece.

Combine these ingredients, mix well, and we are introduced to Chad, one "badass snowflake."

Lastly, the bobblehead is a nod to my husband, who decided to start a side business selling them at flea markets shortly after we were married. *Don't you know that everyone is going to want one of these? Because who doesn't love a bobblehead?* I danced with joy when I gave away, free of charge, the very last one at a garage sale. Yes, yes, yes.

LF

He's My Man, Damn it!

LILIANA WIDOCKS

Hi.

My name is Caroline and I'm beautiful. Yeah, no kidding. I've helped myself with a little bit of surgery, but who doesn't nowadays? We are all Cinderella and they're all Prince Charming. It's true, they seldom choose surgery, but they are good at avoiding mirrors and spend little time at the hair salon. Some of them use moisturizers. They smell ... pretty ... like us. I don't have a problem with that. What I have a problem with is that men age more ... gracefully ... than us. It's not right. It's not right at all.

The Bible tells us that God made Adam first. If that's true, then why don't they look more Methuselah? Why should their wrinkles be more afraid to face the world than mine? Anyway, that's not really my story, I just wanted to point out their fucking luck.

Like many other girls, I longed to marry a millionaire. The blessings (such that they are) and the generosity (such that it is) of the internet has made finding the location of the nearest one in a case of seconds.

I found my very own prince quite easily, in the person of one John E. Adams. John was filthy rich and not very photogenic, but his Porsche certainly was. I applied for a loan, bought the right clothes, then applied for a job in the big city and made it my business to study his daily routine. He was living in an obscenely expensive condo, nothing less than the penthouse suite (or so I've presumed). I didn't know for sure because I never could pass the giant talking gorilla who manned the front door. There was no back entrance. The talking gorilla confirmed that John E. Adams lived there, but he'd tell me nothing more. I obtained a few more details on a rainy Saturday morning by bribing the hungry beast with a three-layer box of gourmet chocolate doughnuts and a cup of the best coffee in town. King Kong made me swear on my own nonexistent grave that I was a dear cousin, whose mother unexpectedly lost touch. He then agreed to point Mr. Adams out to me, just to stop me from crying and feeling so overwhelmed.

I just wanna tell you this: those pictures on internet, his whole "Stay away from me" routine, was a bunch of crap. The guy was fucking handsome. Let others give up! My lucky stars were working for me, even though I'd never won more than ten bucks at the lottery. I knew then that the luck in love was mine to keep. Or to conquer. Everything on this, on this (I will not resort to the "F" expletive again!) planet requires fucking hard work. Damn. I said it again. As a future role model for cute, angelic little girls I must resort to a better brand of soap–the mouth-washing kind.

I began following Mr. Adams every day, from home to the office and back home in the evenings. He was attached. A part-time girlfriend saw to his welfare each Friday and Saturday. Very rare for a Sunday lunch. The rest of the weeknight evenings he socialized with friends, drinking and having much more fun. It was encouraging.

First, I needed to exist. That is to say, I needed him to know I existed, and to gain his interest. I didn't miss a chance. I dropped books and envelopes at his feet, stepped over imaginary cats to fall directly into his arms. I broke heels and probably some common-sense rules as well. Mr. Adams was tight. I invited him three times to share a table and a smile at the nearest coffee shop before he agreed. But even then, he spent most of his time with me blabbing about his perfect blonde girlfriend. I am a brunette. With a temper. Think about it.

Still, I appreciated his loyalty. It would prove a valuable asset at the right time. If you thought I was going to give up–if you would have given up–then you must be either pessimistic or lacking in self-confidence. Buy yourself a pair of glittery pink designer glasses and a feathery hat from Christys' summer collection.

The sixth-century military strategist Sun Zzu was reported to have said, "Keep your friends close and your enemies closer." With this in mind, I befriended his blonde sweetheart. Of course her name was Angel. Of course it was. I told her, in between very real tears, about our affair, the love we shared, and my pregnancy.

"John feels … ashamed … to tell you the truth and leave you abruptly, Angel. He … he doesn't know how to break this to you, and it's causing us such terrible pain."

I can tell you this: that blonde, legal or not, was an ambitious, tough bitch.

"I'm not in this for love. I mean, have you ever taken a really good look at him? I'm in it just for the money. Tell John any nice farewell gift will do."

I believed her. I even recorded her sweet confession, too. I needed a backup. We continued to talk and drink as if we'd been talking about the weather. Soon we were completely drunk and loose. Am I smart or what? Beauty as well as brains.

"I mean, I might have been interested in staying with John," Angel said, while waiting for a taxi to take her home, "but the pregnancy thing is a little too much. Good luck to both of you."

I watched as young, blonde, and straight-to-the-point Angel stumbled into the back of the cab before it sped away. Not bad for a few hours of work. A brainy kind of thing indeed.

—

After a full month of helping John recover from a broken heart, he finally asked me out. The proposition was priceless and certainly worth anything that remained in my bank account.

We made each other happy. It was magic.

Too late, I discovered that he was not John E. Adams, the playboy, but Johnny Adams, the accountant. His millionaire counterpart was merely the owner of the building that bore his name. It certainly explained why he looked so much better in person than in the paparazzi photos I'd seen online.

I married my handsome, sweet Johnny Adams. Today we are doing well. We have beautiful children, a little house on the outskirts of town, and three loyal dogs.

Angel married the other John–the obscenely rich John E. Adams. Today she's the talk of the Hollywood social scene. Seems to me I may have taught her a thing or two on that night we drank ourselves into a more meaningful life better than death.

Perhaps one day I'll write a book about it. Surely, I'm quite skilled on advising on how to land a millionaire. If you don't believe me, ask Angel Adams, the new queen of LA.

AUTHOR'S NOTE

It was (again!) after midnight and that dreadful sleepy-eyes-and-sweet-dreams kind of a prince was still avoiding coming home. He was probably hanging around with some other we-like-better-sex princes. I ran out of ice cream and chocolate. I'm not very good at baking, either, so what I really needed was a housemaid and, looking hopefully into the future, my own easy-to-talk-to millionaire. Instead, I got the idea of this story. Most of the time I get just a headache, so I'm quite pleased with myself.

LW

I Fuck Men Up
LAURA NELSON

"**I told you I don't** want to talk about anything but money and sex," Burt declared to Cora, drawing curious looks from several of the diners who sat around the couple.

"I was only trying to tell you about something funny that happened at work," Cora, flushed. She dropped her head in embarrassment, wishing they'd selected a more isolated table.

"That's not interesting."

Cora looked down at her plate of bacon cheese pasta. She pushed a bite around on her plate with her fork. Finally, she stabbed a couple of noodles and tried to eat. The waitress approached.

"Everything good here? Enjoying your meal?"

Burt nodded.

As the waitress stepped away, Burt turned his entire body to watch.

"Woof. Nice backside on that one."

Cora tried to feign nonchalance by sipping from soda.

"I love going places and looking at women," Burt said, a sly smile forming on his lips. He shook his head of bleached blond shoulder-length hair. "Sex keeps me young. That's why I don't look my age."

Cora merely glared at him as others in the restaurant turned and stared

"What?" Burt asked, meeting Cora's eyes. "I told you if you want to be with me you've got to give me sex."

"Yeah, and you also told me you loved me and you'd be true to me."

Burt shrugged as he looked across the floor at a table of women evidently celebrating something. They laughed boisterously and were surrounded by empty glasses and wine bottles.

"I should go ask one of them if they want sex," he mused out loud.

"Did you actually just say that to me? Who says that to their date?"

"I told you I'm a bad person, honey," Burt said, smiling. "I'm the guy who's jumping out the window when the husband pulls up in the driveway."

"You also said you were trying to make up for that licentious behavior by helping people," Cara said, as she placed her hands lightly over his. Burt slithered his hands out from under Cora's with a smirk.

"Are you done?"

"Yeah. Sure."

They stood, put on their coats, and started toward the exit. Cora glanced at the boisterous women as they passed their table. Burt stopped. Cora continued to walk ahead for several steps before realizing Burt was no longer by her side. She turned around to see Burt talking to a brunette at the table.

"...sex?" Cora heard, as she walked back.

The brunette stared at Burt, looked up and down at his aged, flabby body, and turned away from him as she and her friends burst into laughter. Irate, Burt turned and stomped out the exit. Cora looked back one last time before following. The couple walked to Cora's car in silence.

"The Cora mobile," Burt said, as Cora walked around to open the driver's-side door. "You have a nice car, honey," he commented, fastening his seat belt.

"Thanks."

"Let's go."

"Relax," Cora said, rubbing Burt's arm. "It's Friday night. Neither of us has to be anywhere tomorrow. We have all night."

Burt tensed. Cora started the car and. They drove to her house without speaking.

Once inside Cora's house, Burt sat on the stairs.

"Hey, how about we open up the couch bed, snuggle up, and watch a movie?" Cora suggested.

Burt didn't respond. He watched as Cora picked up the cushions and folded out the bed. They soon sat down and pulled up some blankets Cora had found in the front closet.

"What do you wanna watch?"

Burt shrugged.

"Oh, look. *The Man from Snowy River*. It's one of my favorites."

As they began watching the movie, Cora's two cats climbed on Burt's lap and fell asleep. Suddenly, Burt's phone vibrated. He picked it up, holding the display screen away from Cora. He read the message and pocketed the phone. Cora glanced over at him.

"What was that?"

"It's nothing."

"*Nothing?* What happened to *'My Life is an open book'*?"

"Don't worry about it, honey," Burt said, reaching over and rubbing Cora's back, "It's not like we're exclusive or anything."

Cora jerked upright and stared.

"Stop looking at me like that! You're judging me! You're judging me!" Burt's blue eyes were wide as he stood up and the cats scampered away.

"Wait, can we talk about this?"

"No, you're judging me. I can't be the man you want me to be for you." Burt gathered up his phone and jacket. "You can't even begin to comprehend the shit that I've gone through. This last year was the worst year of my life!"

Burt stomped around the living room to the door.

"Can't we talk?"

Burt left without answering or looking back. Cora threw herself on the sofa bed and cried. About a half hour passed before she was calm enough to get up and walk upstairs to bed, where she cried a little more.

Eventually, her tears stopped.

As the minutes passed and she began to breathe more normally, Cora felt that something had changed. Her soft, warm bed had become hard, cold, and damp. Cora realized with sudden profoundness that she was no longer in her bed but was lying on the ground. She rose but did not recognize her surroundings. No houses, no streetlights. Cora wandered through a shadowy field, bare feet pressing down upon damp grass. She was aware of the sound of dark creatures moving in the distance, just out of her range of vision.

Cora shuddered and wrapped her arms around herself, glancing from side to side as she walked down a narrow path that was gray in the darkness. She considered calling out for help but reasoned the she was no doubt asleep and dreaming. A deep voice sounded from just ahead of her. Startled, Cora jumped.

"Come forward, my child."

Just ahead, Cora saw a silvery light, which she allowed herself to move toward. She stepped through a kind of opening in the path, where she could see the being that had spoken to her.

It was tall and draped in a black clock that covered a misty gray body. The silvery light seemed to radiate from its skin. Cora stopped.

"Come forward," the thing spoke, gesturing with an argentine hand.

Cora complied, embarrassed by her worn tee shirt and bare ass and feet.

"You are a sensuous, middle-aged woman and have no reason to feel ashamed of your body. However, we will make amends for the sake of propriety."

The entity raised its arm. A swirl of warm air surrounded Cora, and she found herself attired in an inviting dark cloak, much the same as the beings. She gratefully pulled it close around her body.

"Thank you."

"Come and sit," the being gestured at its feet.

Cora took a few tentative steps, then slowly lowered herself to the ground, tucking her feet under the cloak.

"You have been hurt by many men. You have spent countless nights seeking retribution."

"Sometimes...yes," Cora said, as she played with the soft material of her cloak. She let her light brown shoulder-blade–length hair fall around her.

"Yes, you have!" the being hissed. "Look inside yourself, you will see it. Leave behind your conscious self which blocks you from seeing what your heart's desire. Look inside yourself."

Cora hesitated, then steadied herself and opened her mind. Feelings long subdued surged forward: Burt, his overt infidelity and distain for her feelings. There were others. Tom, who once thought it fun to hold Cora's her head under water while she bathed; she'd nearly drowned before he released his grip. Felix, who constantly berated Cora for even the most benign reasons. There were others, long suppressed from Cora's memory.

As she revisited her own history, Cora felt her face grow hot and wet with tears. She dropped her head into her hands as she began to sob aloud.

"You see now, how they have wronged you, how powerless they have made you feel."

Cora nodded through anguished sobs.

"I can make you strong; I can teach you how to gain revenge and take power over them."

Cora looked up, rubbing the tears from her eyes. "What do you mean?"

"I mean I can give you power. Power to use over the men who have hurt you."

"Who...what are you? Why are you helping me?"

"Some questions are best not answered. Suffice to say, I exist to bring ... balance ... to unbalanced lives. Your life is badly in need of balance. Would you agree?"

Cora paused and nodded. "What do I have to do?"

"Give yourself to me, and I will fill you with the power."

Cora looked around her at the dark night. She felt strange, as though many more beings were hidden beyond the sterling light in which she sat. *What do I have to lose*? She thought, sighing.

"All right, I'll do it."

The ethereal being nodded its head. "Lay back. Let your body relax. Take several deep breaths."

Cora complied. She was in the middle of her second deep breath when she felt the warmth of an unseen body covering her. The being...merged...with her. Suddenly, Cora's mind was filled with new knowledge: gaining one's trust, learning their vulnerabilities to exploit them. And so much more. A deep satisfaction and contentment diffused through Cora's being.

Gently, the stranger retreated from Cora's body. A moment later, she opened her eyes. The space around her was dark except for the being's lunar light. Cora's head swirled with her new knowledge.

Slowly Cora rose, afraid that if she moved too quickly this new knowledge would be lost. She saw the world through telescopic eyes.

"It's true!" she said, staring at the being in amazement. "Really true!"

The being nodded and smiled. "You are more powerful now

than you could ever have imagined."

"Thank you!"

"Go now, my child. Avenge yourself upon those who have wronged you."

Cora rose and walked down upon a path of sea pebbles. Although the path was dark she never once stumbled.

Abruptly Cora awoke, sitting straight up in her bed. She felt herself sway. *What just happened to me? Such a strange dream.* Cora gazed around at her familiar bedroom and her cats. Both purred softly asleep on her bed. *I need some sleep.* She pulled the covers over herself. Cora reached beneath her bed linens and felt her toes and feet. They were cool and damp. In truth, sleep was long in coming.

———

She waited until Monday to call.

"Oh, Burt, I missed you," Cora cooed. "Can we talk? I want to see you again."

"You'll have to come over here."

"Of course. See you in an hour?"

"Sure."

When Burt opened the front door of his home, Cora entered and hugged him enthusiastically. Burt pressed tightly against her body.

"Mmmmm." Cora purred. She allowed herself to be drawn in close to him. She wanted Burt to feel her moaning in pleasure.

Burt led Cora into the living room. Cora set her purse down and waited for Burt to sit so she could melt into him and pull his arms around her. She rested her head on his shoulder.

"I really missed you."

"Yeah?"

She turned around and faced him, pushing and rubbing her chest against him.

"I really liked having sex with you last week. It made me realize how lonely I've been, home alone with just my cats for company."

Burt embraced Cora. They kissed, Burt shoving his tongue deep into Cora's throat. Appalled, she almost pulled back, but made herself follow-through. Cora needed him to believe this was real.

The kiss finished, Cora stood up and motioned to the bedroom with her head. Burt jumped up and followed her eagerly. Once in the room, they undressed and jumped in bed. Burt rolled on top of Cora. She ran both hands across his naked body to show just how into it she was.

"Oh God," he whispered, "I wish I could get rock hard and ..."

"You okay?" Cora asked, feigning sincerity.

"You know I can't do this. You have to help me."

Burt slid to the side.

"Here, let me feed you," he said, as he frantically began stroking himself. "It takes a little while, but it gets there. And when it does, it's eight inches."

Cora adjusted to a more comfortable position on the bed. Burt kneeled and waddled over to her, gathering himself so he could stuff his member into her mouth. Appalled again, Cora went along with it, but Burt's limp, lifeless penis was difficult to get hold of.

She made an effort, but there was no response. Under the ruse of trying, Cora's thoughts turned to the being that had empowered her. The knowledge of what she needed to do flooded her mind like scenes from a movie she'd watched dozens of times.

Cora continued to suck, but instead of bringing him to an erect climax, she realized her true power as she began to drink Burt's very essence. His penis was merely the conduit. Burt moaned, ecstatic at first as though he were coming, but abruptly the note changed to a cry of fear.

"What're you doing? What're you doing? Stop it!"

Burt tried to pull extricate himself from Cora's mouth, but it was too late. She had hold of him now. Cora felt Burt's lifeforce swirl within his body. Unexpectedly, she felt the presence of the being. It again merged with her body, then expanded to cover Burt's.

"Let me show you," it hissed, telepathically.

As Cora let the being take over, she saw moments of Burt's life through his eyes:

Crashing with his friend Carl while down on his luck, and then sleeping with Carl's two underage daughters.

Standing in the kitchen of a home he once shared with his second wife, shouting at her as she cringed and cried and pleaded with him.

Taunting a soon-to-be ex-girlfriend.

Callously blowing off a one-night stand.

Rationalizing to a girlfriend another one-night stand, this one with a man he'd met at a gay bar. "I was horny; he took advantage of me. I'd never done anything like it before. But you know what? He gave me better head than you ever did."

Once proud of his offences, Cora could feel that Burt now experienced the pain he had caused those who had cared for him. No longer indifferent, Burt suffered their pain tenfold as their anguish became his, overwhelming his senses. His entire body writhed in pain with the knowledge of what it felt like to be totally alone, discarded like worn-out clothing, having his feelings ignored and mocked. Mercilessly, the scenes of sorrow and pain Burt had callously dealt out to others kept coming.

Burt was powerless to relive these memories. How many times had he jumped out of a bedroom window as a husband walked through the front door? How many marriages and relationships had he destroyed, seeking only to please himself while wives, girlfriends, and children waited for him at home?

A voice unlike any he'd ever heard before took over, resounding in his mind.

"You will never feel fulfilled again. You will seek, your body will ache with desire, but you will never again come to fulfillment. Never again will you rise or be a complete man. You will forever be haunted by the memories you have relived this evening. You will finish life as a limp old man, the last drops of your virility gone…evaporated."

Cora stood back and watched as the being finished its work. The lesson of how to use her new power was complete. The swirling mist remained for long moments before abruptly departing. Burt fell back on the bed, writhing in agony. He turned his head, saw Cora, and stretched out his arms, beseeching.

Revolted, Cora backed away. She found her clothes and quickly dressed. She turned, searching for her shoes.

"Have a nice life," Cora said, as she slammed the bedroom door behind her.

Quickly she sat by the door and slid her feet into her shoes.

Cora retrieved her coat and purse from the couch and hurried outside. She felt no regret. This was retribution. It was personal. *I fuck men up*, Cora thought.

Driving home, Cora's thoughts turned to Thomas–a psycho ex-boyfriend who had abused her mentally and physically. She recalled that Thomas often enjoyed surprises. *I've got a surprise waiting for you.* Cora smiled and continued into the night.

AUTHOR'S NOTE

I started this story as a means of therapy to help me deal with some real abusive events in my life. Many of the scenes in here are real (although perhaps slightly altered for clarity). The dream sequence literally evolved from a dream I had.

In real life we're rarely given a chance to make our abusers feel what we felt when we were being abused. I'm not advocating that others start harming their abusers. In my estimation, we should never welcome darkness into our lives. The title of the story should give you some idea of what lies ahead. Keep in mind that it's a story, a fantasy about retribution.

LN

Confidence is being able to say "Fuck you, I'm the shit" without opening your mouth, say it with your walk, with your smile, say it with your entire being.

Tati-Ana Mercedes

A Fucking Catastrophe

V.L. BRUNSKILL

Howling is not heard merely in the ossicles, those tiny vibrating bones of the middle ear; it is embedded in the cerebrum, burned into nerve endings, and singed upon the palms of the helpless to pulse in memory for a lifetime.

The sound of murder is eternal. Even the ripping out of eardrums could not remove it.

Believing in escape was harder after this.

—

I awoke curled on the floor. Fresh from the casket dream, I yawned. Relaxing in the soft white light of the pristine coffin filled with pink roses and purple lilacs. Not at all nightmarish, the idea of being dead relaxed me. Inside the coffin, the air was stagnant, unemotional, still. The dream gave me a much-needed break from the chaos.

Digging the sleep from my eyes, I sniffed, hoping to catch a whiff of the aromatic flowers that lined the coffin of my dreams. Smelling nothing, I opened my eyes, stretching before hurrying to my brother's room. His bed was empty.

"Robbie," I screamed down the hall, half stumbling, half sliding on the wood floor. I found him in the den, comfortably sprawled on the shag rug, oblivious to my panic. He watched Saturday morning cartoons from under unruly bangs and the thick bandage that covered his stitches. Mom was frying eggs and bacon. Spotting me, she smiled, "You slept late. Almost eleven. Dad's in the garage. Get dressed sleepy head. You got chores."

Before breakfast, I knelt next to Robbie to examine his oozy forehead. "Get off me!" he pushed me away.

"Come on. I just want to make sure it's okay."

Robbie slid a finger halfway up his nose, trying to gross me out.

"Disgusting." I stuck out my tongue. Convinced he would not bleed to death; I let him be.

Robbie sat in a masterful stillness he'd perfected after the move to Medford. Prey knows that movement gets you noticed and opens you to the deadly consequences of visibility. Robbie wore a cloak of immobility after every Dad-inflicted injury.

"I'll weed by myself, Mom; Robbie should rest," I informed my mother, determined that Dad would lose a Saturday worker for his bad behavior.

Saturday was weed-pulling day, and the cobblestones were our priority. Dad built the walkway with stolen cobbles from a Long Island Railroad building site. No matter the weather or play possibilities, we pulled weeds on Saturdays until the thin seams between the cobbles were bare. "A smidge of green will make you scream," I reminded Robbie whenever we cleared the sandy cracks.

On weekdays when Dad worked in the city, we played after school, the predictability of his six-PM arrival gifting us with three hours of free time before we returned to tip-toed silence and fear.

For a long while, I feared the uncertainty of weekends, for the way they amplified Dad's malice. Without the safety of school, the forty-eight hours between Friday and Monday became a waiting game. We waited for pain and death, trapped by the randomness of our father's rage.

"The weeds can wait," Mom rubbed my shoulders, "you don't have to shovel it in honey."

"Just want it outta the way." I ate the last slice of crisp bacon before rinsing my dish. Glancing into the den, I worried about Robbie's confused expression and whether the pink center of the bandage meant he was bleeding again. He looked back with far-away eyes. I said nothing, unwilling to interrupt whatever kept his mind from focusing on the pain.

The sound of the electric saw masked my exit. My purple bike with the banana seat leaned against the garage door, reminding me that friends Lisa, Laurie, Susan, Greg, and Patty would race the neighborhood while I tended to the cobblestones.

Picking dirt from under my short fingernails, I sat on the cobbles and watched the road for signs of my friends. The whir of the saw ceased, its stillness stiffening my slouched spine. Dad came from the garage with a hand over his eyes, protecting them from the sun. He squinted at me, a sliver of softness entering his ice-blue eyes. It was a softness I came to despise. I wanted him to hate me as much as I hated him, and with the same antipathy he held for my brother and mother.

Being left out of the physical beatings felt like a betrayal. Besides a few belt beatings (for interfering in my brother's 'punishments') I remained untouched.

Daddy wiped his hands on the stiff fabric of his army-green workpants and the usual grimace returned. "Hey, Dad." I chirped, trying to sound happy.

"Yeah," Dad blurted, "You missed a few at the front." His thick, calloused finger pointed to the place where the stones met the front lawn. He was about to say something else when he spotted a cat crouched amid the green of his lawn.

"Another fucking cat, pissing on my property. Get in the house," he ordered, streaming invective as he headed to the garage.

I watched from inside the screen door as he passed, carrying a canvas sack. Flying up the hall, I panicked. My father had done horrible things to animals before.

I jaunted to the driveway facing window in Robbie's room.

From there, I observed Dad's determined tread across the driveway. The chubby calico, transfixed by the aroma of an insect or some other feline delicacy, did not look up at first. It appeared innocent, hungry, adoptable.

The feline finally looked up. It flicked its tail, appearing used to human interaction. Before it could completely rev its purr box, Dad grabbed the animal by the ruff of its neck. It dangled as if waiting to be raised into a cuddle. Instead, my father dropped the furry intruder in the canvas sack.

Even with the window closed, I heard the cat hiss as it twisted inside, trying to escape. It was the same panicked desperation that sounded in my dreams. I remember thinking we had a lot in common; the cat and me.

I watched, frozen in fear of what he might do to the howling creature with the two-tone fur. Only when Dad disappeared into the side yard did I run for help.

"Mom, Mom," I shrieked. She sat with her slippered feet

over the arm of the brown colonial-print couch. Robbie rested on the floor in front of her; his eyes fixed on the television. Accustomed to having to adjust the volume for raucous interruptions, Robbie crawled instinctively towards the screen. He turned the volume knob past the faded number five. Spider-Man sprayed webs across tall buildings. Robbie sat back, flicking his wrist back to emulate his favorite superhero.

I positioned myself between my mother and brother to report my father's activities. Spitting the words, "Dad caught a cat in the front yard. It's in a bag. You have to stop him. He's gonna hurt it. Like the others."

Mom craned her neck to see around me, giggling at the hi-jinx playing out in the cartoon. Waving me away, she said, "I'm sure he's just getting it out of the yard so that it won't pee in the sand-box."

Mom denied my father's real intention to keep Robbie from knowing Daddy had killed before. In Deer Park, where we owned two German Shepherds that barked whenever a cat passed our yard, my father had prowled the neighborhood one afternoon, plucking unsuspecting felines from private lawns and asphalt lots until he amassed ten cats in a canvas sack. He'd drowned them in the Carlls River that afternoon, bragging about it over Shake and Bake pork chops that night. "Got ten today. Should have heard those pussies hiss."

I wanted to believe Mom, despite all the times she had been wrong in the past. My heart still racing, I passed my brother, ruffling his thick of hair before opening the heavy sliding glass door. I stepped into the aluminum, screened-in patio my father had built one month after we arrived in Medford. Outside, a dozen mowers tidied neighbor's yards. My buzzing worry joined the cacophony of greenskeepers as I approached the back of the enclosure.

My hands in prayer-ready position, I peered at the back treeline, following my father's monstrous boot prints. The hol-lowed-out prints stopped beside a pile of Tonka trucks abandoned after a day of play. There, with his back to me, Dad stood, the cat still squirming in the bag he held in a raised fist.

Without realizing, I wept at the prospect of what he would do next. He was in the patch of pruned pine trees closest to our swing set. In front of him stood the rusty barrel he'd deposited in the yard three months prior. He'd threatened to turn it into a table base, but as weeks became months, the drum remained unused. Rainwater filled it to the brim, forcing Dad to empty it weekly for fear of opportunistic mosquitos. Tilting the heavy drum until its contents soaked the sandy earth, he cursed the insects that dare lay eggs in his barrel.

Dad stood still, holding the bag away from his body. It was the same way he'd held a paper sack of throw-up when I suffered from motion sickness on a family road trip. The cat's hiss morphed into a scream that sounded so human I turned to see if Robbie was okay. My heart leapt hopeful when the bag swayed in Dad's hand, opening for a moment. A white paw poked through the gap. Dad slapped the clawing cat's paw back in, holding the top of the sack tighter.

My father appeared to contemplate the same question I whispered under my breath, "What will he do?"

Dad looked at me, then back at the barrel. Like the dragging of a knife across a movie victim's throat, he lowered the bag into the waist-high barrel. Every hair on my arms rose up. My breathing stopped. The melt began. Immobilized, in a tactile moment between life and death, my diamond-sized tears morphed into a cascade. "Oh no, no Daddy, no."

I covered my mouth, too afraid to rescue the animal. My breath staggered when I realized I had bellowed. The sound fanned the horror of Dad's cruel immersion. Undaunted by my scream, my father waded in the overflow that sloshed from the barrel. The weight of the animal pushed water over the edges, changing his work boots from tan to mustard. I dropped my praying hands to my stomach. My ulcer burned into anxious action.

I doubled over, unable to look away. Hope held my eyes steady. It was the same hope that surfaced every time my father performed an unfathomable act. Hope had no business in the cat's drowning death, but I prayed regardless. "Please God, let it get out. Let it live."

Distracted by the worry of having left the sliding glass door open, I looked back to find it closed. I turned back to the gruesomeness, assured that the sound of murder would not reach Robbie's ears. The water in the barrel undulated less and less. My father lifted the dripping bag, poking at the canvas to see if the intruder was dead.

The sound that rose at his jab was the unearthly song of a million demons.

I gagged. The final caterwaul of the half-drowned animal made its way to Mom and Robbie, who had just switched off the television. Robbie crawled to turn the television back on. The syncopated beat of the Bat-Man theme song joined the gurgling end of the animal's being.

Mom slid open the door, stepped to the coolness of the cement, and closed the door behind her. I crouched on my knees at the back-screen wall. Mom looked toward the barrel where Dad put the deadly finishing touches on the torturous act. Mom pulled me into her arms. Her eyes streamed, but she did not say a word, for the water in the barrel was still, and the animal's soul silent.

Dad looked at the screen porch where we watched, wearing a callous grin. Pulling the wet bag from the barrel, he stepped back to avoid further soaking of his boots. The sound of mowers and squirrels chirping over a stolen acorn filled the void. Dad held the bag at arm's length, still grinning as he carried the body from our view.

My mother did not find a single scream or reprimand to speak over the scene. She saved her voice for the boy in the den. The cat's fate was sad. But it was not the source of her tears. It was the future of her children that washed her cheeks and stole her voice.

I tore from my mother's arms to the front window in my room. The useless hag called hope ran with me. Dad opened the bag, dumping its limp contents into the same trashcan he had hauled to the curb that morning.

Glimpsing a tiny tuft of butterscotch and white fur as he dropped the dead animal, I watched him slam the lid, triumphant. Listening to the ticking of my windup, smiley alarm clock, I stared at the can hoping for movement. I prayed for the same sort of resurrection I'd learned about in Sunday school. When my knees, scratched from the porch cement, joined the needles stabbing my stomach, I abandoned the vigil. Splayed out on the ruffled white comforter of my twin bed, I wore myself out sobbing.

I heard the long swoosh of the sliding glass door, stepping into the den, where Robbie sat, still in pajamas, staring at the television. I scurried to my feet, flying down the hall in time to stand between Dad's temper and my brother. Mom entered from the porch;

her eyes rimmed red.

Dad looked at my drawn shoulders and devastation as if I were an annoying crumb he might wipe from his shirt. The puffiness of my cheeks belied the defiance of my carriage. He turned to Robbie, the merriment of his accomplishment fading with the whistle of the TV.

"Turn that down, you idiot. What are you people, fuckin' deaf?"

Robbie crawled quickly, turning it off. I stared into the bloodshot whites of Dad's milky eyes and answered. "I wish he *was* deaf, Daddy."

Dad pursed his bottom lip, annoyed at my insolence. Lifting a disapproving eyebrow, he declared, "I'm taking a shower. My socks are soaked." Bending to release his water-logged feet he asked, "Does a man get lunch around here?"

Mom was pulling cold cuts from the fridge before Dad had removed the second boot.

Later that day, when Dad drove to the hardware store for barbed wire to dissuade other animals from entering his woods, I crept to the trash can. Placing my hand on the sun-warmed metal cover, I considered checking the cadaver to be sure it was dead. I decided against it. It was easy to picture myself dead, or my father, but the cat was too much. I imagined its eyes popped like a cartoon clock, claws extended in fright. Rather than look at the dead cat, I recited The Lord's Prayer over the closed lid.

A neighbor approached in her convertible. I bent, pretending to tie my shoe. I completed the prayer as the crimson taillights disappeared around the bend. "Dear Lord, please watch over the cat my father killed, and kill Dad as soon as possible."

AUTHOR'S NOTE

"A Fucking Catastrophe" is excerpted from my book *The Killing Closet: A Memoir about Surviving a Father's Rage and Discovering her Gender Truth*. The book explores how we are all prisoners of our own killing closets at some time in our lives.

My father's killing closet was gender.

Mine was abuse.

Whether fear, turmoil, secrets, or emotion send us into hiding, my story demonstrates that we're all born with everything we need to live a life of love and hope. In our darkest hours, when scratchy situations seem impossible to solve, the door to the killing closet may feel stuck, immovable.

However, locks will fail, and beasts be slain if we open our hearts to possibility. With faith, all that binds us becomes memory, allowing the light of freedom to step in.

VLB

Dear Beguiling Fifth of Vodka, or, Oh Shit, What Really Happened the Night I Claimed I Got So Sick Because I Ate a Hotdog at My Girlfriend's Graduation Party Given by Her Parents

ALICE MORRIS

on high school graduation night, invited to a teen party–off
my girlfriend and I go with our large bottle of water-clear Vodka–
    purchased
by my older sister–her words–*just mix it with orange juice and
    you'll be fine–*
have a good time, and I, the Baptist girl, forbidden drink

think the fifth must be the perfect amount for two. My girlfriend and
    I mix
the brew, pour tall glasses full–have one–then two, and then–
this Alice turns into the world's biggest fool, slapping friends, telling
    them
*shit on you–*apparently, quite the comedic act because–everyone
    laughs

and then I'm back in the basement's laundry blubbering to someone
about my boyfriend being in 'Nam–and next the party is ending–but
in walks the alluring bad–ass Catholic–stud–guy called–Pony, and I
    proceed
to tell Pony I have a wild-crazy crush on him–find myself blissfully
    on top

on the sofa both of us moaning–until my wicked girlfriend finds me, pries me

away, shoves me into a car–her sick friend now, barely conscious,
dumped–

outside parent's door, black-moaning all the next day, missing the
lake, not able

to be out laughing on that–sunny boat–*this Alice* clinging to her
newfound vow

Hot Damn, if Only
That Painter Had Not
Gotten Out of Bed
ALICE MORRIS

that morning he'd accidently set the stately old home
on fire, home he told me he'd worked on for two years–
restoring/ scraping/ using a heat gun to remove

the most stubborn paint
today, he says, *the job would have been complete*
but now

ferocious flames devour the roof, eat down walls
shoot through vents
as firemen walk into the black smoke beast

return moments later
hyperventilating
collapsing on the field across the street

firemen hosing cold water over their heads
molten-faced firemen saying *they'd never felt such heat–*
and when the fire marshal arrives

I see how the home's black skeletal remains
provide a striking contrast
to the painter's white shirt, pants, shoes and hat–

the thirty-foot-long ladder the painter had stood on
now abandoned among charred
antiques strewn across a lush green lawn

Damn, the Problem With the Word French-Fries

ALICE MORRIS

is that it sounds
just like–
Just-Us
to people who want to hear it that way
that way these people can have slaves–on purpose
and not allow Blacks to walk on the boardwalk in Rehoboth Beach
not so long ago–on purpose
and deliberately exploit and abuse women and children
and get off without any real fines and jail time because of some Just-
   Us–Male
ordained laws
while all around we hear about *French-fries for all*
even as children, hand upon heart, pledge *to catchup and French-
   fries for all*
even as another hand is stuck into the fryer because some Just-Us
does not like the color of another's accent
or nose, and I've noticed the dictionary does not include Just-Us
as one of the meanings of the word French-fries, I've noticed
the dictionary does not say that the word French-fries is derived
from the Latin roots–*just* and *us*
regardless
so many act like Just-Us is
the definition of the word French-fries
knowing there is no intention of having catchup and French-fries for
   all
knowing that some among the Just-Us horde catchup and French-
   fries
drive up the prices
buy up acreage, cut down forests, use low-paid labor
in chemically toxic tomato and potato fields

workers growing sick, and weak with worry about how to feed
    families with barely enough catchup and French-fries to get by
yet somewhere on this earth orchards are blooming

AUTHOR'S NOTE

Dear Beguiling Fifth of Vodka: The events of this night have
been on my mind for about 50 years. I wanted to get over my
"shame" enough to write about my barely memorable, and possibly
life-changing evening. As I worked on this poem, over time, I began
to see that the title needed to play a key role–it needed to include
what I was leaving out of the poem–the background, and the lie leading up to what actually happened. Finally, seeing the call for this
anthology, I added the cuss in the title and knew the poem was complete.

Hot Damn, if Only That Painter Had Not Gotten Out of Bed:
It took many years for this poem to transition from its original story
form. Off and on the piece would have me return to drop paragraphs/
phrases/words, like the piece was trying to tell me it was really a
poem and it would wait as long as it took for me to figure that out.
Then the notion of putting a curse in the title, something I would
have not considered doing on my own, and there was the final surprise this poem had to offer me.

Damn, the Problem With the Word French-Fries: This piece
was inspired by a couple contemporary poems that we studied at the
2018 Delaware Division of the Arts Seaside Writers' Retreat (San-
dra Beasley, poetry workshop leader). These poems purposely did
not state what the emotional core was about, but it was there, hidden
within images and requiring a bit more thought to discover. One of
the poems kept saying everything was orchards, even objects. I
knew I wanted to write a poem that had a similar "absurd" quality,
a poem that required that extra effort, that extra moment to grasp.

AM

Don't let yourself die without knowing
the wonder of fucking with love.

Gabriel García Márquez

Don't Be
a Bitch

DAVID STURM

I HEAR YOU. Yes, dammit, I can hear what you're saying. I am not deaf. I am not even hard of hearing. So, give us a break. Message received. I am not a simpleton. My question to you is this: Can you hear *me*? Yeah, this guy is asking. What I want to say is simple. Do you care to hear it? Can you listen?

Okay, here it is. The unfairness of what's going on in our relationship is a product of a mindset that you seem addicted to. Yeah, it's unfair. Totally.

I think it has something to do with Lucy. This woman, I don't know, who is she? Is this the woman in your private email? You are not saying. I am trying hard not to ascribe extracurricular meaning to this.

But maybe I am wrong. Can you tell me with certainty that Lucy is not an intimate partner in your life? Say yes, she is, and I will understand. Well, you have to admit that even though I understand it, I remain bitter about it. I mean, we were married, after all. That doesn't count for nothing. Hell, no. I know you. You know me. We've shared a lot. Heck, there's even some mystery in our relationship. That deserves a small wink.

I am going to heave a sigh here and clear my admittedly upset brain.

Maybe it's not Lucy. It could be one of your gym pals. You told me once about that girl on your volleyball team in college. Oh yeah, I remember you telling me about that. In fact, it was a moment you shared with me that made me realize you trusted me. I have never broken that trust. Your secret will always be safe with me.

I guess you might also remember that trip we took to see that couple. You were totally onboard with that, if you don't remember. He was a forest service guy and his wife was named Helen. They had two daughters. Remember? The two little girls had been sent away for our visit. Did that seem strange to you? As usual, you were not paying attention. This was one couple seducing another. Did you not see us as the seducees? Well, when the time came you were certainly enthusiastic. So was I. The forest service guy, I know, turned out to be a total prick. The next morning is best forgotten. That poor woman was trying so hard. Man, it was a long ride home. You even "borrowed" one of my cigarettes.

Here's another topic I want to bring up. No criticism, I just want to set the record straight. Certain ties with your family are not going to go away. Your father—I know you hate for me to bring him up—but your father and I are like this. Yeah, like this. He's a total madman. You already know this story, but in deer season he came through. I had fallen out of my tree limb perch and the perm-support had caught my leg. I was hanging upside down on a tree. Your dad came along and saw me all hanging there (I had to wear a brace for six months). Your dad was with his buddies. He drew his hand down his face, looking at me hanging there, and said to all, "Bless your heart." I don't see him often, but I like to think he's been on my side ever since.

Here's what I'm getting at. Destiny! Yeah, corny as that sounds, it is our fate. Together. The two of us. We have a joint destiny. One road, one path. We have had obstacles along the way. Of that I am sure. But we have conquered them.

I know you wanted kids, but that's a separate issue. Let's just set that aside for now.

Meanwhile, I guess I should address this Mulvany issue. I thought grad school would be a life challenge that would inspire you to great things (and the rewards that come with it). But then I met your prof Mulvany. My god, that guy was pounding martinis and "holding forth." And there you were, in total thrall. I have to say, I was disturbed. Why did you respect this—I hate to say the word, but here it is—charlatan.

Certainly you can see this the way I do. I know you have your own frame of reference, but let's be clear that certain facts are undeniable. You and me. That's a fact.

Meanwhile, let me address the gorilla in the room. Eck. What kind of a name is that? Let's face it, it sounds like … well, I can't think what it sounds like. But it's a joke.

Any you love this guy? A math professor? Whose last name

is Eck?

He sounds pretty Ecky. Bad joke, I know. But I regard him as my rival for your affections and I think I can win you over. Mr. Eck, I can show you, is bad news.

It's admirable you are striking out on your own and winning friends. But, lover, you and I have a history that cannot be denied. Our history is unconventional, it is true. But you and I took a blood oath. Well, that may be overstating it. It wasn't *the* oath, it was *an* oath.

Why am I writing all this crap? I don't need to be forgiven. I don't need an excuse. I don't need to be redeemed.

Honey, just ... don't be a bitch.

I just want you back. Without you, I suffer. Can ya dig it?

How bad is my suffering? You have every right to know.

I woke up yesterday and it was the first thing I thought of. And it was the last thing I thought of when I went to bed.

AUTHOR'S NOTE

Simply put, this story is based on someone I used to know back in the 1970s.

DS

Don't fuck with me, fellas.
This ain't my first time at the rodeo.

Joan Crawford

Screwed by a Lake Trout Called Sir Jack

SARAH LEAMY

A man at the gas station approached me as an easy catch. I'd been staring at the lures and deciding what to do with myself that evening. February is such a dead time.

I said, "I ain't got no gear."

He said he'd take care of that, and he patted his pockets.

We set out for the ice lake up north in the boundary waters. He gave me a blanket and gave me his word. I asked were we going to Craycray Lake? He nodded and drove on silently, flicking ash out the open window.

"I'm Bixby," he said.

He was a short man, thick of thigh, broad of forehead, with wide eyes and shiny skin. I was thinking about how I'd not had a fisherman before, just a cowboy or three. I was thinking how lake trout are the cheetahs of freshwater, prowling predators hunting shallow underwater horseshoes. You just have to know where to be. They'll find you.

As he drove, I thought about myths and archetypes and that damn trout, Sir Jack, the one my dad had talked of all those years at the cabin up north. Dad had told me I'd catch it one day, if I could just hang on. Be patient. Let him come to me. I can't remember all the best things he'd said, my dad. I still missed him. He'd died one winter when the ice was too thin to hold a big man in his prime, that's what my mom had told me as she'd packed up the house hurriedly and moved us to Chicago in an early morning fog.

Bixby and I drove the familiar country lanes in silence. I shrugged deeper into the smoky blanket and stared at the national forest all around us, a tunnel of trees taking me into the cold night.

Well, we came to the lake finally, me and the man in the rusted red Chevy.

Bixby said, "There's a bed out there in the ice shack," and then I knew what he had on his mind. Same as me, though I'd imagined I'd be with someone like Sir Jack perhaps. The snow was outrageous. The wind didn't help. We struggled a while, hanging on for dear life it seemed.

When he died, Bixby–that is–with my knife in his back, I had to go on. Sir Jack waited for me. The pale blue ice cracked underfoot. Craycray Lake was like a casket, but not for Bixby, and so, grabbing his beard, I dragged him back to solid land. I'm a big bugger, fishing or farming stock Mom had once claimed with a disappointed shrug. Ah mothers, never happy enough are they?

I slipped and slid all the way back out toward the empty shack. I was tired after all that activity and craved a good night's sleep, but instead I found Sir Jack right there in the middle of an ice hole, glistening, olive green, emeralds and jade, and with eyes, well, one eye at a time, watching me approach. He was half my size but not bad, he'd filled out over the years, seventy pounds if not more by now.

Blinded by the moon in my eyes, I fell to my knees. He knighted me, righted me, and whispered, "Where you been, girl? You look different. Not the child I saw once too many times. You've been gone a long time. It's been decades, but I'm patient. Are you going to stay this time?"

I said, "If you want me to, I reckon my fugly old man would want me to."

The trout clouted me. "Don't be rude; he isn't so old. I should know. Look."

And he pushed me under the ice to meet the family: Trout never hunt alone.

Dad swam past, a little thinner than I remembered, but he had the same blue eyes as me.

Sir Jack mouthed, "So do you want to stay?"

I said, "If you want me to, then yes, I guess."

He kissed me and my lungs burst into a bubble that reached for the sky, a gunmetal grey still shimmering overhead, and I sank.

AUTHOR'S NOTE

When it comes to writing, every author's process is different. Case in point: I just write. There's no plan. No theme or process as such. I just write whatever's in my head.

SL

All my wisdom and knowledge is nothing compared to what a young horny man and an eager pretty woman would do after feasting on a bottle of wine and fresh sardines baked on open fire. Therefore, fuck, fuck again, and fuck more before you like everyone else fuck up your life.

Vinko Vrbanic

My Old Cock Blues
WILLIAM BUTLER

Flat, alluvial stain.
Water. Air. Mud.
my Mississippi Delta
and my Mississippi blues.
Standing outside PeeWee's juke joint,
clapboards popping and bouncing,
holding my old cock
pissing at passing freight trains,
the engineer's tooting at the crossing here,
and at my flagrant disregard.
The last woman
I danced with inside
in that hot, damp, heavily trodden
wooden floored juke,
said,
"yo cock older'n my cooch!"
Big woman.
She fell on top of me.
Now,
all I can do here
is hold my old cock
while I'm pissing,
and wag it at the midnight trains.

When Cornholing Wasn't a Game

WILLIAM BUTLER

Like Rip Van Winkle
I slept through the tangle of correctness
and found
upon my wakening
that reviled term from my youth
had been accepted,
transformed into an innocent game,
one of bean bag toss.
What? When?
And answered by my grandson, age 8,
It's just a kid's game!
Such wisdom and disdain in one so young.

A Tattooed Asshole

WILLIAM BUTLER

1966, Ft. Benning, Ga.
The cook, a ten times busted, 20-year
Regular Army grizzled vet,
armpit deep in a cauldron of iced tea,
stirring sugar,
turned to face us
raw, naive, KP'ites,
scoffed at our innocent conversation
about tattoo's,
suddenly
lowered his britches,
bent further over his work,
spread his nether cheeks,
displaying mouse tracks around his puckered anus,
and a mouse tail very clearly tattooed
protruding from therein.
0900 hours.
Then it was mop,
buff and wash.
Lunch served at 1130 hours.

AUTHOR'S NOTE

Each poem I write I hear first. Whether while I work or while writing, I hear each, then flesh each out. These preceding three poems are actual pieces in a long life spent in and about the Mississippi Delta with its ripe fruit of literary giants.

"Juke" joints are common in certain areas with music, odd characters, and sullen stories. And I get the blues more often now than ever before.

The corn hole game I find uniquely weird and commonly played by excited young and younger.

The sergeant with the tattoo I met in 1966 while serving Uncle Sam. He meant no harm.

WB

"Cock Tale,
Dick Dialogue,
Penis Patter"
FELIX PIRE

"Here, have a seat."

"Nice place."

"Well, it's a studio. You kinda only have … you can sit on the bed."

A millisecond later Lisa lunges for me. Before I know it, we're making out. She's ripping off my clothes. She's naked. Great rack.

[CUT TO:]

"How does this feel? Is this okay or should I do something else?"

"It's good. What about you? Shouldn't you be starting to … grow?"

"You know, you gotta give me a minute, or at least suck the sugar stick or somethin'."

"Don't get defensive, Bobby."

"Sorry. That's probably why I'm not hard. Gimme a minute to, um, get into it. This is how I am usually."

"You sure?"

"No, no, yeah. I love this. You gotta be patient with me. Engage it in some conversation. Talk to it."

"Talk. To your penis."

"I dunno, a little penis patter, little cock talk. I'm out here on an island. I've never…you know, [WHISPERS] fondled a girl. Look Mr. Pipi has never even seen a live clitoris–I'm not even sure how to pronounce it–*clit-er-us* … in the light before."

"Let's not get clinical."

"You're right. That'll kill it. What do you call *her*?

"Ms. Pounani."

"Yes, well, Mr. Pipi finds Ms. Pounani attractive. It's just that I'm a guy that's used to driving stick, learning automatic. Tell me what you want. You know, wiggle this, rub on that, and–"

"Pull my hair."

[BEAT, CONSIDERS. LOVE THE IDEA.]

"Okay, sure. Yeah!"

Nice. She's a sicko. Havin' a blast!

Mr. Pipi is soon *tickling* Ms. Pounani, causing her to drool. And he's *in*! Pipi's pumping Pounani! Yes! He's in the Venus Flytrap enjoying himself immensely. At least for a moment.

"Hey Bobby, it's me. So ... um ... it's roomier in here than I'm used to! I mean, this is so easy, slipping and slidin' around here. I think I'll just take a little break!"

And right there, Mr. Pipi decides to deflate without finishing the act. Now I'm bummed, because I'm like, well, we got this far! And what about Lisa? She hasn't orgasmed? I'm committed to that. And Lisa, bless her heart, is showing the enthusiasm of an Olympic gymnast out for the gold!

[STOPS SUDDENLY.]

"I'm sorry, Lisa. It won't work."

"Of course it'll work! Listen, Bobby. We'll make it work."

I sit up in bed and sigh.

A moment later, Lisa springs up. "Bobby, I've got it!"

"What?"

"A penis plan."

"You're gonna *force* an erection out of me?"

"Yeah, it's easy."

"Lisa, contrary to what you might think, I kind of don't wanna look at pictures of naked men or gay porn or anything when I'm with you."

"You're such a man. Always thinking with your penis's eye."

"Okay, then what do *you* suggest we do?"

"Well, we … trick your dick."

"Trick my dick?"

"Yeah. A dick trick."

"How?"

"Well, you *do* wake up with boner every morning, don't ya?"

"Always."

"Well, when you get your morning hard-on, just… stick it in."

"Brilllliant!" I say.

Lisa's green eyes smile at me, and we make out, and cuddle asleep.

—

In the morning, Mr. Pipi awakes with his usual rigid salute to the world, and I do it. I stick it in. Lisa's right about the engorged pupils. She's gorge-*ous*. That morning my penis is harder than Chinese arithmetic.

—

A girl comes up to me now, gives me that same, "I want you" look that Lisa had, and Mr. Pipi knows the options. Like a good soldier, I just do what he says.

"Bobby, instead of swinging onto another vine, take a risk, grab a hold of Jane, sex her up, and let 'er trick your dick. Swing, man! Swing like Spider-Man!"

[LOOKS UP. CATCHES A VINE. MIMES SWINGING OFFSTAGE ON VINES.]

I'm Bobby. I'm forty-seven now. Coming out is easy for me. At sixteen I ask my penis, the honorable Mr. Pipi, what it wants, and it points. I swing through boys like vines, like Tarzan on fast-forward through a CGI urban gay jungle. Periodically, Mr. Pipi, talks to me.

[WINKING AN EYE SHUT, CREATING TESTICLE

SHAPES WITH HIS ARMS, GRUFF VOICE.]

"Bobby, it's Pipi. Look, you've seen every kind of phallus, penis, schlong, dick, prick, tally-whacker, My Man Thomas, Jack in the Box, Old Mr. Hornington, wang and ding-dong from here to Hong Kong that there is to see. You've sexed up all kinds of well-hung, donkey-rigged, needle-dicked, cut, uncut, upward shaped, downward slanted schlock cocks. And yet, you've not decided on one particular selection."

[BOBBY DANCES AND SINGS "EVERYBODY DANCE NOW!"]

—

See the crazy redhead? That's Lisa. She works with me. I'm 28. We're so hot. This is a mixed club we're in. I'm in my element. Boys, girls, and some things in between. Lisa is dancing on the bar with the go-go dancer! I can't believe they let her up there! She's crazy! Yeah! Grind 'em baby!

[DANCES OVER TO LISA, WAVES HER DOWN.]

"Hi! What's up?" I yell over the music.
[READING HER LIPS:] "Your pupils are getting bigger," Lisa says.
"What does that mean? We're not on X. At least *I'm* not."
"Edward Hess discovered that the pupil of the human eye expands when it's interested in what it sees."
"No kidding."
[LISA CONTINUES DANCING:] "You know, I'd totally have sex with you if you weren't gay."
"You would?"
"Totally."
"Well, why don't you meet me over at my pad tomorrow night? I'll roll a J, see what happens."
"Okay," she says.
[TO LISA:] "Okay."
[TO AUDIENCE:] Okay. I mean, there'd been so many vines. So many wee-wees, wankers, willys, wieners, tube steaks

and tail tackle in my life that I'd gotten to this point where, like, you know, I'm *out*.

Women today don't <u>need</u> a man! They wanna get laid. A muscle-bound gay guy will do. So sex with horny women when you're twenty-something, and sex when you're sixteen with your "marriage-bound" high school sweetheart are two different things. "Oh my God," I said. "Yes"! Gay, straight, bi? I'm like Tom Cruise: nobody knows.

I recount my offer to my so-called friends, the naysaying psychological piranhas. They attack mercilessly.

Look, Bobby, you hate that you're queer.

You're acting out fantasies that you feel will satisfy your machista ego.

Girl, there's a benefit pool party this weekend at Geffen's. Porn stars galore. Hawaiian theme. Let them lai you and get off the fence! [KNOCKS ON WOOD.]

———

There's a knock on the door of my studio apartment.

[MIMES OPENING A DOOR.]

"Come in, Lisa. Make yourself at home."

AUTHOR'S NOTE

"Cock Tale, Dick Dialogue, Penis Patter" came about when a friend of mine, director Debra DeLiso, approached me about a play she was creating, a male response to *The Vagina Monologues* entitled *Cock Tales*. She asked monologuists she knew to write fresh material about the penis. I wrote two monologues: one about an overweight guy who'd lost so much weight that his penis had gotten larger (which is something I researched, and is an actual phenomenon), and another (a little closer to home) about a young gay guy who is propositioned by a girl to have sex and takes her up on it.

This latter storyline, which you have just read, happened to me. The story is a comedic/fantasy version of how it all went down.

In the early 2000s I oftentimes swung into Debra's show, which jumped around local small theaters and clubs in Los Angeles, and performed this monologue to waves of raucous laughter!

FP

Shitty Mushrooms
PHILIPPA HAWLEY

"Housekeeping," Monique calls, as she taps on the door. She gets no reply.

There's a funny smell up here, she thinks. *Let's see, Monday, Tuesday, Wednesday, Thursday*, Monique counts under her breath. *That's four days with a Do Not Disturb sign on the door of Room 16. I'd better phone Len at the front desk. Duty manager they call him, duty loiterer more like. He's about as useful as a bag of dust. Typical, the bugger's not answering. I'll go down and catch him.*

Monique lets out an offensive burp as she parks her trolley on the landing at The Blue Star Hotel in South London.

Shit, those leftover shitake mushrooms I got from the dining room last night were fucking garlicky. Guess it serves me right, being a scrounger. Jesus, my breath stinks, and my guts are rumbling.

She takes a sip from a bottle of water intended for the minibars, then gives the landing a spray of air freshener before parking her trolley in one corner.

Gloria, our glorious domestic supervisor, won't be pleased if she finds out I nick bottled water most days. I must tell her about this threadbare carpet on the stairs though. It's a bloody trip hazard. Gloria's much too posh to venture upstairs in her high heels these days. I reckon she's after Len's job.

Monique's worn-out sandals click-clack as she carefully makes her way down to reception. One of the straps is about to give way and she hopes it will hold on until the next payday.

If they paid me more to do this bloody cleaning job I wouldn't have to nick food or take water and the toiletries from the rooms. I could get some decent shoes. God he's there, Len the doddering old lech, with his nose stuck in the computer as always. She almost says it aloud but manages to control her gob. *Bet he's looking at porn. Hope his wandering hands are behaving today. Don't know how he keeps his job when nearly all the maids have reported him to the owner. He must be past retirement age.*

Monique sees the guests' keys neatly hanging on their hooks. Nineteen little keys aligned with their fobs dangling down from a wooden shelf. Only one is missing.

"Sorry to disturb you," Monique says, "but I'm worried about Room 16."

"Monique … isn't it?" Len queries, peering at her badge. "What seems to be the problem, my dear? Do I need to call maintenance?"

"I don't think so; it's just that I can't get in."

"If the lock's broken I will phone maintenance."

"The 'Do Not Disturb' sign hasn't moved for at least four days," Monique explains. "Should we check on the guest?"

"Our guests are allowed their privacy. The key to Room 16 is not on its hook, so our guest will simply be inside resting. Don't you worry your pretty little head."

"I thought I heard the television," Monique continues, 'but no-one answered when I knocked."

Len frowns. "Okay, just let me check the booking. I seem to remember a statuesque blonde signing in to that room at the weekend and thinking it odd she had such little luggage for a ten-day stay."

Bet you did, nosey old perv.

"Yes, here it is. Miss Sheena Shitakovala; that's right, American accent, gave a New York address and paid up front for ten days."

"*Shitakovala*?" Monique exclaims. "Some name!"

"You can't really forget one like that, can you?" Len chortles. "It's all coming back to me now. Rather glam, kept her dark glasses on. I couldn't help but notice the long hair and the red lipstick, to say nothing of the ample bosom."

Trust him to have noticed Miss Shitty-tits accoutrements, Monique thinks. *At least I've caught his interest now. Something's not right here and it's not just my gut.*

Monique feels Lens' eyes looking her up and down as she waits for a decision, groaning inside. *Creep. You always know how to make me feel really uncomfortable.* Monique experiences a sudden need to straighten her green tabard.

"Give me a minute and I'll come up with you," Len says.

"I'll just see if the young lady's been ticked off on the breakfast room list or the restaurant. No, no sign of her there. Ah, but here's a strange message from Mr. Sherman, our respected owner, attached to her file."

I know who the flipping owner is, Monique thinks. *Respected? He's the one who cuts corners everywhere and pays peanuts. I can't think how he fills these rooms.*

"Mr. Sherman says Miss Shitakovala is a personal friend and will be here in London doing some important work. Says she must be given anything she requests."

"She hasn't requested anything, has she?" Monique says.

She checks her watch impatiently. Her shift is nearly over and she still has to vacuum the landing and pack away the trolley before Gloria arrives. *And by God, I really do need to use the washroom.*

Monique feels Lens hand slide across her back as he tries to steer her out of reception. She swiftly stands to one side and allows him to lead the way. *I wonder if I should have contacted Gloria first, rather than Len.*

Soon, Monique and Len stand outside of Room 16. Len hesitates. "Odd smell up here," he notes. Len slowly opens the door with his master key and calls out, "Hello, anybody there?"

Monique follows Len into the dingy room. The curtains are half closed, and a crackling sound escapes the flickering television. Monique sees Len sniff and inspect a bunch of wilting tulips, their stems drooping over the sides of a glass vase on a desk near the door.

"Ugh, stagnant water. Smells like mushrooms," he says. "There's no one here. I'll check the bathroom. Where's the blessed light switch?"

"I'll open the curtains," Monique says, glancing around the room. "Can't see any luggage. Oh, my God," Monique gasps out loud, suddenly aware of the human shape beneath the white duvet and a tangled flare of blond hair across the pillow. "Is she ... is she dead?"

Len faints, his head hitting the thinly carpeted floor with a dull thud.

"For fuck's sake!" Monique splutters, then takes a deep breath.

Right girlie, she tells herself. S*top, think, be calm and don't* *touch anything. This could be a crime scene. Whom shall I phone first? Gloria, the police, an ambulance, or Mr Sherman?*

Monique, having read hundreds of crime fiction novels, considers herself an expert on such matters. She experiences a surge of energy. She rolls Len into the recovery position. She listens over the shape in the bed for breath sounds but there are none. She isn't up to checking for a pulse, so she decides to phone Gloria.

"Stay put. Look after Len." Gloria says. "I'll be there in five minutes. I'll leave a message for Mr. Sherman to call me."

By the time Gloria arrives Len has regained his composure and is sitting on a chair looking shaky and pale. It is soon apparent there is no body beneath the bedclothes, simply a balloon and a blond wig, carefully placed atop of an arrangement of pillows. Len hangs his head in embarrassment and Monique has to stifle both a desire to giggle, and also the disappointment that this may not be a crime scene after all.

"Well, it's a relief we haven't got a dead body on our hands," Gloria says.

"Bloody realistic though," Monique says. "Sorry, but I really need to use the bathroom."

"There's a book here on the bedside table," Gloria calls out as Monique closes the bathroom door. "Appears to be a crime novel authored by … Sheena Shitakovala."

"I read crime all the time, but I've never heard of her," Monique calls back.

Previously Len had taken only a cursory glance into the suite, but now, the drama having passed, Monique pulls back the shower curtain. She almost chokes on her own saliva. Scrawled there, in red lipstick on the white tiles, she sees a message.

WONDERED HOW LONG IT WOULD TAKE

"We've been played," she announces when she rushes back out. "This is some sort of trick. Miss big tits Shitakovala has been using us to test out a murder scene, or perhaps work out a plotline."

"You have a curiously vivid imagination, Monique," says Gloria. "I think you'll find it's just a sick joke."

Gloria's mobile rings.

"It's Sherman," she whispers, accepting the call.

Although Monique can hear a booming man's voice, she's

unable to glean the actual conversation. She and Len stand and nervously wait for the call to end.

"Mr. Sherman knows all about it," Gloria says, and signs off.

Len groans. "I'm getting too old for games."

"Appears you are correct, Monique. Miss Shitakovala has set up this scene as a test for a screenplay she's writing. We are, at this moment, being filmed by a time-lapse video camera hidden behind the television. It might be used as an art installation to publicize her work. Mr. Sherman has known about this for some time but, understandably, hasn't told anyone so as not to spoil the experiment. He's been compensated handsomely for the time and space, and you Monique, are to receive a generous bonus. Mr. Sherman has been especially pleased with your performance. Play your cards right and, who knows, one day you might be promoted to supervisor.'

"Bloody hell, I could be famous," Monique says. *Maybe you're not so bad, Gloria.*

"Do clean up the language though. Remember, you're on film."

Monique turns her good side to the camera and smiles. *Fuck yeah.*

AUTHOR'S NOTE

I started to write "Shitty Mushrooms" on a cold afternoon in January 2019. Having walked the paved streets alongside the canals of Amsterdam until my legs ached, my photographer husband wanted to continue and take more photos as the sun set. I needed to go back to our hotel room and put my feet up. Thinking a hotel might be a good location for a story I retrieved my notebook and played with some ideas.

I placed my story's hotel in London and made it jaded and faded, with cranky staff; most unlike the charming holiday hotel in which we stayed. I am not a habitual swearer and as far as I know. Neither was our actual chambermaid. However, she soon developed into Monique, who did swear and was a nosy, opinionated young woman who read crime fiction. The scene was set for a curse-filled tale with a tinge of mystery.

Goodness knows where the mushrooms came from!

PH

If you don't like something it's okay to shut the fuck up about it and find something you do like.

Marc Maron

Unnatural Shitbags

CAROLYN COLBURN

My husband says you know you're getting older when you wake up in the morning and realize you've injured yourself sleeping. When he asked me what I wanted for Christmas, I told him a new vanity in the bathroom. The current one has four 500-watt lightbulbs lined up above the *top* of the mirror, and any serial killer knows you put vanity lights along the *side*, for crissakes. Things are bad enough without having to deal with the ghost of Jacob Fucking Marley first fucking thing every day.

I knew I'd turned a corner when construction workers stopped whistling. It used to really piss me off when this happened, so I took to flipping them the bird. Which would really piss them off, making for some interesting exchanges.

Now it makes my entire month when some nearsighted asshole a half block away on a foggy day takes notice. Every once in a while a carload of hormone cases will discharge that distinct high-pitched jungle yelp in my direction, and I'll want to genuflect in gratitude. Usually this happens when the sun is going down and my back is turned (when glimpsed from behind from a moving vehicle, I can still pass) and my shades are on and my collar is up.

These days the only rise I seem to be able to get is from the garbage men, who wave gaily as they cruise the alley, probably because they're dumbfounded to find me standing upright given the number of beer and wine bottles they regularly find in our bins. The sound of our glass recycling hitting the inside of the truck resonates through the neighborhood like the Angelus. You can hear it a mile away.

I say, Demon Rum may not delay the aging process, but it delays having to think about it for the time being.

Still, taking my cue from the garbage men, and having nothing better to do, I decided to quit drinking. Stranger things have happened.

Actually I decided to quit drinking *for thirty days.* I'm "doing a thirty," as the saying goes.

This is day thirteen.

The first couple of days went relatively smoothly, and after a week of such madness, I felt so smug I wanted to celebrate with a case, er, glass of wine.

This seemed inappropriate somehow, so I decided to *phone a friend.* Except all my friends are soakers; I can't remember the last time I had a sober phone conversation; nix that idea.

So I decided to *ask the audience.*

"Hon ..." I purred to my husband in a voice I haven't used since the first Bush, "... are you up for a little ..."

But I couldn't finish the sentence, I didn't want to raise his hopes. For me, the word "celebration" is synonymous with "drunken orgy." Plus, my husband's also doing a thirty–the family that detoxes together, etc. What good is he?

All I had left was the *fifty-fifty* option. But deciding between a case of beer and a case of wine seemed, once again, inappropriate. I was at my wit's end. Literally. I had one wit left. And it was NA. What's a rummy to do?

So I took my remaining wit and my mineral water and located the nearest TV/Barcalounger combo, where I planted my dipsomaniacal ass and channeled Netflix. After seven hours of indecision, I Rokued *Two Weeks in Hell* and *Aryan Brotherhood Behind Bars* and settled in.

Sometime the following day I emerged, sober as the day I was born, which is pretty much the last time *that* happened. Between the Green Berets training program and a seemingly endless stream of humongous white tattooed shitbags, I'd had my fix. What this particular fix says about me, I don't want to know, but suffice to say I was loaded for beer, er, bear.

Which is a saying I utterly loathe. How about *loaded for Tea Partiers? Loaded for teetotalers? Loaded for tea drinkers?* Better yet, just make it *loaded* and let the party begin!

Believe me, "party" takes on a whole new meaning when you're doing a thirty (see above-mentioned Netflix selections.) For decades I've been accustomed to raising a few whenever life presents one of those special occasions: birthdays, weddings, funerals, Thursdays. Raising a few juice boxes to toast the rising of the sun, or the arrival of the mail, just doesn't cut the mustard.

Speaking of which, I've had some interesting cravings these past two weeks, mustard being one. Also salt, oregano, tofu, PAM, Crest White Strips, and duct tape. Most unusual of all, I had an uncontrollable urge for an O'Doul's last Friday. Which, I'm happy to report, I was valiantly able to overcome, lest I actually be seen buying the stuff. My god, I still have my pride.

For an old boozer like myself, this is proving to be a cathartic experience. Not to mention lucrative. For the first time since becoming an adult, I suddenly have disposable income. Typically, most of my income gets disposed down the nearest toilet—one doesn't *buy* beer, one *borrows* it—but now, here I am, swimming in cash! Front-crawling, backstroking, dead man's floating in it! What's a lush to do?

I opted for distraction. Is that one of the *lifelines*? It should be.

I pocketed my booty and grabbed the car keys and headed out, not to my friendly neighborhood liquor store—my home away from home where everybody knows my name—but to my friendly neighborhood grocery store, where I planted myself in the produce section and harvested as many fresh citrus fruits (and a couple sticks of celery) as a shopping basket could hold.

Which I dutifully lugged through checkout while "My Name Is Wanda! How Can I Help You?" eyed the abundance of lemons and limes and peered at me as if to ask, "Is that your *final* answer?"

No need to let Wanda in on my nasty little secret—*I utterly loathe fruit!*—so I gave her an acidic smile and loaded my purchases like wayward cue balls into my earth-friendly pockets.

Trust me on this, doing a thirty is *not* one of life's special occasions. When it comes to the excess citrus, I'm simply stockpiling for the next such special occasion: February! Because, as the saying goes, when life gives you lemons … make margaritas!

Hola! Seventeen days to go.

—

Recently a good friend of ours was hospitalized with a stroke, and it gave those of us of a certain "era" pause. The good news is that our friend not only survived this frightening incident, but his prognosis is for a full recovery, in spite of his having spent an intense two weeks in surgical ICU with a hole in his head, from which a tube drained blood and spinal fluid away but, thankfully, not his excellent mind.

During those two weeks, his friends and family kept track of him on Caring Bridge, a website devoted to connecting people regarding health matters. There we could read daily journal entries, view photos, make tributes, or, if we chose, post to a guestbook.

By the time our friend was released from the hospital, his guestbook had risen to well over two hundred posts, and given that he's a journalist, the posts from colleagues made for some great reading. These, alas, were scattered in amongst the usual plethora of God-centric outpourings, and after skimming a few dozen of the latter, I began to wonder if any of those people ever got up off their knees.

Still, I was reminded of W.C. Fields, a lifelong atheist, who, as the story goes, asked for a Bible on his death bed. When questioned about this, he explained that he was just "looking for loopholes." Every man for himself when it comes to staring into the abyss, I say.

My husband, however, took great umbrage to the whole setup.

"When I keel over," he huffed, "don't you dare put me on fucking Caring Bridge."

"You won't have much say in the matter," I snorted, "you'll be fucking keeled over."

"You mean you won't honor my last wishes?" he demanded.

"Who says they're your last?" I retorted. "Miracles do happen."

"I don't believe in no miracles," he grumbled, "and neither do you."

"What does that have to do with letting your loved ones know the score?" I countered.

"I don't have any loved ones."

"You'd be surprised," I cautioned. "In a crisis, loved ones come out of the woodwork, there's a loved one under every rock."

"That's just what I mean," he complained. "I don't want some wayward loved one praying for me and 'sharing' it on some fucking website."

We paused momentarily in this grumbling / countering / complaining. Something had gotten my husband's goat, and now that the goat was out of the garage, it was too late to lower the door. Whatever.

After a while, my husband shrugged.

"Okay, have it your way," he acquiesced. "When I keel over, set up a Caring Bridge site, I don't give a fuck. But don't you dare allow a guestbook."

"I don't think you'll have a choice," I pointed out. "I think it's part of the package."

"*There will be no fucking guestbook!*" he inveighed. "It'll make me even sicker having to read all that drivel!"

"But think of our friend's guestbook," I mused. "There were so many great postings."

"That guy has talented, interesting, *intelligent* friends," he admonished. "Their comments offset all that religious crap."

"Now you've gone and insulted our ... one friend," I warned. "I mean, you think after *your* brush with death, there'll be 237 posts on *your* guestbook? Think again, bubba."

"But I won't *have* a fucking guestbook!" he emphasized.

"We'll just see about that," I chided. "Come to think of it, maybe I'll open my *own* Caring Bridge site. Then well-wishers can sympathize with me for having to deal with a fruitcake like you! Whatta ya think of them apples?"

"When I keel over," he muttered, "you'll be at my bedside 24-7, you won't have time to go around opening websites."

"Whatta ya mean, 'I'll be at your bedside'?" I mimicked. "This is the ICU, don't forget. There's nothing I can do, my hands are tied, it's all up to the doctors now. I'll be down at the bar."

My husband stared at me.

"What?" I scoffed.

"Hospitals don't have bars," he sighed. "Cafeterias, coffee shops, gift shops ... no bars."

"Well what kind of fucked-up deal is that?" I bellyached. "Who needs coffee at a time like this? A couple stiff bumps is more like it."

"I'd say you got a couple stiff bumps," he observed, "on your head."

Which brought us back around to the recent matter involving our *friend's* head, which gave us pause, which made us feel like a couple of muttering/mimicking/bellyaching assholes for carrying on while our friend was recovering from having just spent two weeks in ICU with a hole in his head, not to be confused with the holes in *our* heads which, I might add, have been there considerably longer and show no signs of closing up any time soon.

I stood up. Did I mention we'd been sitting around the Christmas tree?

"Truce?" I asked.

"For instance?" he wondered.

"How's about a little Christmas cheer?" I offered.

"How's about, '*Two-Four-Six-Eight! Meetcha at the Pearly Gate!*'" he suggested.

"That's not what I meant," I replied. "Besides, you don't believe in no pearly gate."

"I'm talking about a drink," he corrected. "There's gotta be a drink by that name."

"I'll Google it," I promised. "In the meantime, how's about a couple stiff bumps?"

"Just what the doctor ordered," he agreed, and resumed Christmas-tree-gazing.

Meanwhile, out in the starless night, the snow careened mercilessly around a nearby streetlight.

—

The neighbors are getting a divorce.

"Lucky bastards," says my husband.

I don't think luck has anything to do with it. I think it's the househusband.

Call me Old School, there's something unnatural about a househusband. It goes against the laws of physics.

I grew up with a house*wife*. My mother. Who wore house*dresses* (do they even make those anymore?), who did house*work*, who ran a house*hold*. Here's where the physics part comes in: an apron (not to mention a babushka) just doesn't look the same on a guy.

Of course aprons and babushkas are Old School, right up there alongside ringer washers and party lines and 35-cents-a-gallon gasoline. Just the same, the househusband next door circumvented the babushka issue once and for all by going bald. I don't mean he *went* bald, I mean he *shaved* himself bald. This happened just after the divorce notice appeared in the newspaper, another iconic item on its way to that Old School in the Sky.

All I know is one day I was on my way out to the garage when I glanced toward our 20-foot privacy fence and a beam of light straight out of the Big Bang singed my retina. I peered through the periscope and determined the source: it was the sun reflecting off the next-door househusband's newly shaved pate.

I turned away in disgust and called my husband. He didn't answer, he was at *work*. I lowered the drawbridge, crossed the moat, threw some raw meat to the guard dogs and drove away in a cloud of dust, ignoring the friendly wave of the househusband across the alley hanging out the wash. I think he had a couple clothespins in his mouth.

We moved into this fortress 15 years ago, and since then, househusbands have cropped up around the neighborhood like creeping charlie. There's the bald one next-door, the one across the street, the one down the block, and the one across the alley with the clothespins, who replaced the one who moved away and was the forerunner of the whole infestation.

Meanwhile, back in the Jeep, I careened to a stop in front of the liquor store, ran inside and called my husband from the Beer Cave. This time he answered.

"I'm fucking freezing!" I said.

"It's over 70," he said, "I walked to work."

"That's what I *mean*!" I said. "You walked to *work*! You're at *work*!"

"Where are *you*?" he said.

"In the Beer Cave!"

"That's why you're fucking freezing," he said. Then he said, "You caved."

My husband and I have been on this low-alcohol diet for a few months: we only drink when absolutely necessary. For him that means holidays and special occasions. For me that means when I'm not sleeping.

"It's the neighbors!" I said. "The ones getting the divorce!"

"Lucky bastards," said my husband.

"Never mind that!" I said. "It's the househusband! He's fucking bald!"

That stopped my husband in his tracks. Nothing gets a guy's attention like another guy's hair loss.

"Whatta ya mean, 'bald'?" said my husband.

"As in *no hair*!" I said. "As in Lightbulb City!"

"But … "

You have to realize the guy we're talking about is in his thirties. He's a Cub Scout. A Little Leaguer. A small fry. A fetus. A week ago he had a full head of hair.

"It's obvious!" I said. "He shaved his head!"

"But why?" said my husband. "What for?"

"In fucking protest!" I said. "His heart's broken! His life's over! He's staring into the abyss!"

"I highly doubt it," said my husband.

A week ago, when the fetus had hair, we were repositioning the telescope one evening and accidentally discovered him and a blonde drinking wine and eating takeout at his kitchen table. Lo mein. With chopsticks. His wife's a brunette.

His wife's also a doctor. As in MD, as in never home, as in took time off to dump out a couple of kids and got right back in the saddle, as in *in need of a wife*.

Enter, your friendly neighborhood househusband.

These househusbands must have some online community somewhere, some chatroom in the cloud, where they gather regularly and swap gossip and life stories and microwave recipes, and share information re: up-and-coming neighborhoods targeted for infiltration. Househusband's List. Househusbands Anonymous. Something like that.

Except in my experience, there's nothing anonymous about these guys. They're fucking proud of their stay-at-home status, they wear it like a badge of honor. Make that jockstrap of honor.

"You're a real asshole," my husband said.

This was later that same day, following the Beer Caving incident. The temperature had also caved, suddenly and dramatically, never mind this was mid-May and earlier it had warmed up enough to thaw out the birdbath. By now the local robins are hip to the scene. As soon as they feel the plunge coming on, they immediately take wing, lest they be frozen to the concrete mid-bath.

My husband and I were sitting in our parkas in the living room, feeding the fire, drinking our respective drinks and eating Progresso Minestrone Soup and Old Dutch Fat Free Pretzel Twists. It'd been my turn to cook dinner. We'd already checked in with the telescope, but Telly Savalas had taken to drawing his drapes.

"I am not an asshole," I said. "I am a natural woman."

"Natural disaster maybe," said my husband, slurping soup and Amanda Marie's Just Peachy De-Tox Tea.

"Just think about it," I said. "Could you see *your*self hanging out in the house all day? Watering plants? Watching Dr. Phil? Not answering the phone for fear of robocalls?"

"Sounds good to me, but who'd pay for all this? Who'd foot the bill? Who'd bring home the bacon?"

"First of all," I said, "we're vegetarians. And B, I have a job."

"Yeah, right," said my husband. "You make the same as you did in 1977 when you were just another lounge act trying to break into waitressing."

"I've adjusted for inflation," I said.

"The only thing inflated around here is our waistlines," said my husband.

"Speak for yourself," I said, popping another fat-free Twist and washing it down with Corona.

"Besides," I said, "if you had all that free time, you might end up like Mr. Househusband next-door, clattering around your empty house, shaving your empty head, eating cheap Chinese with some empty blonde."

"Lucky bastard," said my husband, and stared into the fire.

Just then, a log fell.

AUTHOR'S NOTE

While I may have had my share of Kodak moments over the years, the larger portion of my life can be found drifting across the editing room floor like tumbleweed. As in, I've tumbled from scene to scene, decade to decade, era to era, endlessly searching for love, enlightenment, and that weed we used to smoke in the seventies.

Because the truth is, after the fifteen minutes are over and the curtain comes down and the lights go up and the rest of the staff heads for the nearest oxygen bar, it all comes down to this: house-cleaning. Housecleaning is what happens while you're busy making other plans.

"Unnatural Shitbags" is an excerpt from a full-length manu-script, a memoir, told in first person through a collection of inter-connected reminiscences spanning many years. While the voice is essentially humorous, the underlying story recalls what Mark Twain once said: "The secret source of humor itself is not joy, but sorrow."

cc

Another Day at the Fucking Office
KRYSTINA SCHULER

June 5

Elena grabbed her laptop and exited her condo. The heavy morning fog cloaked her trip across the street to The Daily Grind, where she ordered a latte from a hungover barista.

"Oh, hey," Elena said. "What's the wi-fi password today?"

The barista scratched his chin stubble and pondered as if she'd just asked him to explain the molecular structure of coffee. "Um...oh...yeah. *Mochalatte*, all one word, capital M."

With beverage in hand, Elena found a table, flipped open her laptop, and proceeded to play a couple rounds of solitaire. No way was she going to connect her personal laptop to a public network, certainly not for the task she had in mind, but that's the illusion she wanted to give.

A handful of customers vacantly surfed the web or read email. She could see most of their screens. Maybe they didn't know. Probably they didn't care. A lot of people she'd talked with assumed their data had been stolen long ago and didn't think it mattered if it happened again. Sometimes Elena felt like she was the only one who cared about privacy. She downed the last of her latte, then packed up and left.

Inside her condo, Elena collected her gear and dumped it on her balcony table. She was poised to jump into a gray sea where the lines between right and wrong, savior and criminal, blurred. Elena was keenly aware that once she did this, she would no longer be able to claim innocence or the moral high ground.

Elena connected her Raspberry Pi, a credit-card sized computer, to a small monitor, keyboard, and mouse. It was the sole machine she used when trawling the dark web. It was cheap and expendable if she had to nuke it. She was probably going to nuke it.

Elena selected the coffee shop's wi-fi network and typed *Mochalatte*. The browser screen glowed, and the cursor blinked in the address block. Delicate fingers hovered over the keyboard.

She'd only walked this path once before. In college, Elena had accessed the registrar's grading system to change the math grade of her best friend, Maddy, so Maddy could graduate on time. The pervy professor had held Maddy's grade hostage, because she had refused special "tutoring" sessions. Elena had nearly been caught, but in the end the administration couldn't prove she'd been involved. They also never figured out how the dean had ended up with copies of the professor's incriminating emails.

Since then, Elena only dipped her toes into murky hacker waters as an observer, keeping tabs on current vulnerabilities and how they were exploited, all in an effort to protect consumers from the negligent and nefarious alike. Still, the potential consequences of her actions made Elena's stomach queasy. Elena knew that if she was careless and the trail lead back to her, she'd be trading her cozy condo for a jail cell. Orange had never been her color.

She was out of options. For the last three years, she'd been trying to convince her boss to push for better security to no avail. The last attempt occurred two months ago after the BaileyWard Investment Bank breach. A third-party contractor had left a database improperly secured, allowing criminals access to personal data of hundreds of thousands of customers.

Headlines such as those sickened her. As a senior security analyst at Cypress Credit, Elena knew there were ways to make a system close to impenetrable. From her perspective, the least a company could do was secure its networks enough to make those headlines as shocking as they should be, instead of just another Tuesday news story. Her mind drifted back to the events that occurred following the BaileyWard breach two months earlier.

April 3

After reading the story of the breach in the morning newspaper, Elena finished her coffee, showered, dressed, and headed to work. A sour taste clung to her mouth as she listened to details of the breach over NPR. By the time she arrived at her office, her head was throbbing. As always, she navigated the narrow drive, arriving at a tall, black security fence topped with cameras, shrubbery with razor-sharp thorns that discouraged fence climbing, and guards at the gate. "Nothing like shouting, 'Hey! There's something important inside here!'" she muttered to herself. "Whatever happened to security through obscurity?"

She showed the guard her identification and scanned her RFID card at the gate. The card was also needed for floor access. Entrance to the data center required her fingerprint. Elena took a deep breath to calm herself. While she recognized the need for these measures, and welcomed them, she knew that all the security cameras and biometric scanners were little more than stage dressing compared to careless contractors, negligent or vindictive employees, or lax polices that left digital back doors wide open.

The radio broadcast about BaileyWard replayed in her head, distracted her from doing her job. "Fuck it," she said. "I can't just sit here." She locked her workstation and strode to her boss' office.

Sanj hunched over his computer, fingers tapping a rapid, staccato rhythm on the keyboard. Elena leaned against the doorframe and waited for acknowledgment, which would only come when Sanj was good and ready. He clicked the mouse and settled into the high-backed chair, finally glancing in her direction.

"Morning, Sanj," Elena said.

Sanj grimaced. "I suppose you're here to discuss the BaileyWard breach."

"No. I'm here to discuss the Cypress Credit breach."

"What breach?" His eyes widened, and the pitch of his voice rose. "We haven't had a breach."

"Yet." She stepped into his office and rested both hands on the back of the chair. It was pointless to sit. She knew the conversation would be over faster than a hundred-yard dash. Broaching this topic again was more to appease Elena's conscience than to secure a resolution.

"We've been over this before." Sanj leaned his elbows on the desk and folded his hands. "We're meeting the federal security guidelines for a financial institution."

Yes, please keep talking to me like I'm stupid, she thought. "Why not *exceed* them? Let's be the one company that isn't compromised."

"It's not that simple."

"Right, it's all about the bottom line." She wasn't an idiot. She knew it was often cheaper to pay for the consequences of a breach than to prevent one, but that didn't make it right. "What's going to happen to the bottom line when we lose customers?"

Sanj shrugged. "We won't lose enough customers to matter. Besides, consumers have short memories. Within six months the lost customers will be replaced with new ones. Someone always needs a new credit card or a place to transfer a balance."

And there it was. Businesses had no incentive to institute stronger policies if customers weren't willing to demand them. Creatures of comfort and convenience, the public continued to shop at their favorite stores, use their same old email address, or bank at the most convenient bank despite breach after breach. It was just easier than switching or demanding better, and the businesses knew it.

"And I thought I was the cynical one," Elena said.

"What do you want from me, Elena?"

"I want you to be the thorn in someone's side. I want you to be the squeaky wheel that gets the grease. Otherwise, we might as well be out there playing Fortnite with the millennials, instead of wasting our time pretending to secure this place."

He drew in a breath and released it. "We make the system as secure as we can with the resources we have." *A robot could have delivered that line with more sincerity*, Elena thought. Clearly, even Sanj didn't fully believe his own management-speak.

"So, what I'm hearing," Elena said, "is that we give the customers the illusion that we give a shit about their personal information, while what we really do is make sure the Band-Aids don't fall off."

Sanj's cheeks colored. He turned his gaze to his monitor, resting a hand upon his mouse. "Don't you have event logs to analyze, El?"

Dismissed as usual.

June 5

Elena thought for a moment, recalling the email she received yesterday from Sanj. A perfunctory message sent to reiterate the company's position and affirm that Cypress was doing what was required. As she sat in her condo in front of the Raspberry Pi, Elena ground her teeth at the memory. If Cypress thought doing the bare minimum was enough to protect them and their customers from a breach, they were mistaken. Maybe it wouldn't be enough of a wake-up call, but she was tired of the complacency, of corporations and organizations treating their customers like shit, of the public's acceptance that their data was there for the taking so why bother to complain; that's just the way it was.

A dog barked on the street below, drawing Elena's attention back to her balcony and the task at hand. Exhaling, she dropped her fingers onto the keys and let them fly. Infiltrating the legacy system was easy. The idiots assigned to archive its data never properly isolated it from the public network. With a few keystrokes, she walked through a backdoor that not only was unlocked, but left wide open with the lights on. Frankly, she was surprised no one else had discovered this vulnerability before, but she was relieved it wouldn't take much effort to make her point. Elena copied as much data as her flash drive could hold and split.

Because she had no intention of using the data she stole, she spent the next several hours overwriting it multiple times before wiping the drive clean. Excessive, she knew, but leaving only the slightest bit of data could expose Elena to the authorities or Cypress' customers to actual criminals. To alleviate her paranoia, which had become borderline clinical, she nuked the Pi and the flash drive, smashed them to pieces, and scattered the remains. Then she waited for her little adventure to be discovered.

June 8

"Oh, shit," Brian said, sitting in the cubicle next to Elena's. His already pale face turned chalky. "Shit!" Brian bolted to Sanj's office, not bothering to secure his station.

Elena glanced at Brian's screen. The highlighted line item on the log glared at her like the accusation it was. She shoved down her nerves, turning her attention back to her own work. She had to appear unaware.

"Brian, how many times do I have to tell you to secure your station when you get up?" Sanj said, as he rounded the corner. Sanj reviewed the text on the screen. His hand curled into a fist, and his lips disappeared into a fine, white line.

"What's all the commotion?" Elena asked.

Sanj glared at Elena, directing his irritation with the screen's data onto her, as if she was somehow at fault. Not that there was any way to know that, not from that log, and hopefully not ever. "Breach," he said through gritted teeth.

Elena literally bit her tongue, hard enough that Sanj could tell.

"Go ahead. Say it."

"Told you so," Elena said. And for a moment everything was right with the world.

June 9

A consultant arrived to conduct an investigation. Elena found it ironic that Cypress could afford to pay a consultant to investigate a breach, but couldn't increase the security budget to prevent one in the first place. She considered herself intelligent, but that kind of business logic was lost on her.

"Elena," Sanj said, "you're up. Bring your laptop."

The consultant had already interviewed half the department and audited their machines in search of Trojan horses, spyware, keyloggers, anything that might point to a source for the breach. Elena thought a person would have to be pretty stupid to use their business laptop to infiltrate their own company.

"I'm Rob," the consultant said, with Sanj seated by his side. "Please take a seat."

She handed Rob her laptop and sat, keeping a wary eye on him. Rob's meddling could end not just her career, but her life as she knew it. She'd go to prison, and when she got out, she'd never be allowed near a computer again. She wasn't good at anything else.

Doubt enveloped her. *I should have had a backup plan. Why didn't I have a backup plan?*

Rob started with small talk, softball questions about her education and job history. She was careful to supply only answers that could be found on her LinkedIn profile. Public record sort of stuff. *He's not a cop, and I'm not under arrest. Yet.* She clasped her hands in front of her to keep them from shaking and hoped her cheeks weren't as pink as they felt.

"Do you access other computers for work?"

"No," she said.

"Do you have personal computers at home?"

"Of course. Doesn't everyone?"

"If Cypress requested you make those computers available for review, would you turn them over?" He spoke as if the question he was asking was a reasonable request instead of a gross violation of her privacy.

"Not without a warrant."

Rob issued a tight smile, like he knew she was trouble. "Do you have something to hide?"

She met his eyes. "We all have something to hide."

"I don't."

She raised an eyebrow. "No?" Elena reached for the notepad and pen at the end of the table and shoved it in his direction. "I want you to write down all your log-in credentials for your bank accounts, personal email, and health insurance portal." There was no mirth in her request. She was dead serious.

"That's none of your business."

"Exactly."

She continued to glare at Rob, eyebrow raised.

"What were you doing on the morning of June 5 when the breach occurred?"

"What I do on my own time is none of your business."

Sanj groaned in a way that seemed to plead for her to be more agreeable, more cooperative. Rob adjusted his tie, leaned back in his chair. Her evasiveness put a target on her back, but if they wanted access to her personal computers and an answer to her prior whereabouts, they'd have to arrest her. She wasn't about to incriminate herself by accident.

"Are you done with that?" Elena said, pointing at her computer. "I have a lot of work to do."

"There's a new laptop at your station," Sanj said. "You can go."

June 12

Rob concluded his investigation. Elena watched him shake Sanj's hand, and she tried not to wither under Rob's penetrating gaze. The gaze either meant he knew something and she was screwed, or he suspected something and he couldn't prove it. Elena's fingers trembled over the keyboard, and the words blurred on the screen. Once Rob left, she fled to the bathroom and locked herself in the stall. Her pulse throbbed in her temples, and her stomach lurched. Her mind raced. *Is it over? Am I safe, or are these my final hours of freedom?* She wanted to stay in this stall forever. She wanted to go home. No, she wanted to get on a plane and fly somewhere without extradition rights. Instead, she returned to her desk.

Security guards pushed through the doors to her department an hour later. Sanj joined the guards, and he pointed in her direction. They walked straight toward her desk. Elena broke into a cold sweat and wrangled her breathing. *So, this is how it's going down?* she thought. Somehow she pictured proper police or mysterious men in black suits and earpieces ala *The Matrix* coming to take her away. She found the anticlimactic almost humorous.

Elena was about to stand up, but the security team walked past her desk.

"Karl, Chen, and Julia, get your things and come with me," Sanj said. Her colleagues rose with startled faces, hands fumbling at backpack and purse straps. Three other security staff secured their stations, protocol when anyone in the company was fired. Sanj's assistant gathered the personal items from their desks. Elena and the rest of the department watched as their colleagues were escorted out of the department, presumably to human resources.

A low murmur replaced the usual sound of typing and mouse clicking. Worried faces peered over desk separators.

Nausea overwhelmed Elena. *I never meant for people to get hurt. Sure, I wanted to teach Cypress a lesson, and was willing to face the consequences, but I never intended for Julia or anyone else to have to deal with the fallout, not like this.*

"Get back to work," Sanj barked.

Thirty minutes later, Sanj called everyone to the conference room to explain what had happened.

"As you know, Rob investigated the breach that Brian discovered. He determined the breach originated through an insecure legacy system, but was unable to trace the infiltration to its source, losing the trail in the Philippines. It was Karl, Chen, and Julia's responsibility to lock that system down. They failed in this task and have been terminated. That's all." Sanj exited the room before anyone could ask questions.

The teams dispersed.

Elena felt a minor sigh of relief. Fired, not arrested. Had they been arrested, Elena was certain she'd have turned herself in immediately. In her estimation, Karl and Chen deserved to be fired, operating with an inflated sense of infallibility. Julia, however, was actually competent, a fact often disregarded because of her gender. Shaking her head, Elena walked to Sanj's office and stood in the doorway.

"Not now, Elena."

She ignored him. "Is that it then? The investigation's over?"

"Yes."

Her intestines slowly unwound. "And then what? Business as usual?"

Sanj turned his attention away from his screen, meeting Elena's eyes. "You know I've assigned a team to isolate the legacy system, close access so this can't happen again."

"What about some of the other suggestions I've made?"

Sanj shrugged and turned his attention back to his monitor.

With that simple gesture, she understood nothing would change. Elena returned to her desk, feeling relieved but unsatisfied. She had taken a great risk not only with her career, but with her freedom. *And for what?* she thought. Sure, the last week had been chaos, with the department in crisis management mode. But now Cypress had the opportunity to do it right, better than they were legally required to. And they weren't going to. In his not-so-subtle way, Sanj had told Elena all that she'd done had been for nothing.

June 15

Cypress issued its public statement regarding the breach. To Elena, it felt like all the other *mea culpas* she'd read before. Same bullshit story, different day. Customer data was compromised. Security holes were now closed. Responsible personnel were fired. But hey, don't worry. Cypress would issue new credit cards and six months of free credit monitoring for anyone affected.

A handful of "How could this have happened?" news stories followed, told in earnest tones. Customers flooded Cypress' Facebook and Twitter feeds with righteous indignation. In the cafeteria, Elena overheard customer service reps moaning about the nightmarish morning they had dealing with panic-stricken clients threatening to close their accounts. For a moment, she felt vindicated. *Maybe this time there will be enough public backlash to force the company's hand*, she reasoned.

June 18

Elena sat at the kitchen table, tablet in hand. She swiped her finger across the glass, scrolling through the morning's top headlines:

- BaileyWard Posts Highest Profits in Company's History
- McGinley's Department Store Announces Security Breach of Customer Database
- Britain's Royal Family Confirms the Princess is Pregnant with Twins

Elena finished her breakfast and headed off to work. She did not ask Sanj questions. She did not draft an email offering solutions. Earbuds wedged tight, she reviewed logs, sent requests for remediation, and didn't care if they were actually addressed. Because a princess was soon going to deliver twins, and by day's end, everyone would forget about their recent anger over Cypress' breach. *Today*, she declared, *is just another day at the fucking office.*

AUTHOR'S NOTE

Confession time. I love to swear. My favorite NSFW word is fuck, so when I saw a request for submissions to an anthology that not only contained a variation on that word in the title but also required profanity, I was all in. I sat down to brainstorm the myriad ways fuckery can happen.

My husband is an IT professional. As such, network security and internet privacy are frequent topics around the dinner table. Both are fertile grounds for fuckery on a number of levels. As we discussed these issues, he suggested I write a story about a security expert who finds themselves thwarted on all sides. Thank you, my dear, for providing me with a premise and the technical details necessary to write this tale. Any errors are entirely due to creative license.

To be honest, this story represents a departure for me. I usually write romance, which contains a far different sort of fuckery and always has a happy ending. No spoilers here, but when you're finished reading this tale, you might want to change your passwords.

KS

If you go home with somebody, and they don't have books,
Don't fuck 'em!

John Waters

A Meditation
on Lust
and the
Karmic Tab
for Kinky Shit
HOWARD BROWN

Sex is fine as far as it goes, a consolation prize of sorts
that comes with the rite of matrimony. Yet, like so many
other things in life, over time it can devolve into a mundane,
anemic ritual; one performed missionary style behind
locked doors on Sunday afternoons while the children
are napping.

But lust, ah lust, it takes things to a whole new level. The
beast whose hunger can never be sated; which thrives in
the midst of mirrored ceilings, feathered masks, handcuffs
and other implements not generally spoken of in polite
company; the abnegation of love, fidelity, gentleness, and
procreation, it could care less what havoc it wreaks or how
many bodies it may leave in its wake.

Facilitating spontaneous coupling between unlikely partners,
it can bloom any time day or night: in darkened alleys, empty
stairwells, broom closets, car seats, picnic tables, restrooms,
even high above the earth on late night cross-country flights,
just to name a few.

But nothing in life is without a price, which makes one wonder
exactly what the karmic tab may be for dabbling in this sort of
kinky shit?

AUTHOR'S NOTE

This piece was originally part of a series of poems I worked on in 2009, in collaboration with an artist friend, for a coffee-table book. At some point, the project fell by the wayside and this particular poem languished in a computer file until recently. However, I periodically go back and revisit older, unpublished work to see if I can rekindle the spark that originally moved me to write it and perhaps improve on the original. Having become involved in Buddhist philosophy during the intervening years, when I reread the poem, I had the sense that it somehow fell short. As titillating and pleasurable as the acts described in the first three stanzas might be, since they are intentional there has to be an associated consequence–a karmic price, if you will–for the same. Thus, I added the last stanza, which puts that question to the reader and, hopefully, closes the circle.

HB

Bitch Delivery for Mister Fucker

RÉMI SAVARD

"Bitch delivery for Mister Fucker!"

In and of itself, the sentence is surprising enough. But coming from his wife, Jen, and directed at him while he rappels, suspended over the void, is worthy of attention. He looks up to find an object coming straight at him at near-terminal velocity.

It is a head. It is not a trick of his imagination.

A. Severed. Human. Head.

Jen had been up there for God knows how long, on the ledge, looking down at him rappelling. When he noticed her, he smiled. She responded with a smile of her own, then that one sentence followed by the "delivery."

She poses a simple question: "Guess who just popped by for a chat, Adam?"

It isn't just any human head, he realizes. It's Sonja's. A head he'd seen very much attached to a marvellous, naked body, perhaps one time too many. That, obviously, is now over.

Now, Adam. Back to now.

"She told me quite the story!"

"Jen, let me—"

"Fuck you, asshole!"

Adam knows Jen's interruption and use of vulgarity are warranted, and he's about to agree with her, tell her he's sorry and offer an explanation, but she produces a handgun, a potent silencing tool.

Everything blurs as Adam braces for a shot that will certainly end him. In a flash, though a little late, he reconsiders the wisdom of dumping the climbing helmet and its blinding sweat issues altogether. But survival instinct overcomes fear, and Adam dives to his right, bouncing off the rock face with ease. He feels the rope shake and moan in his hands, his rappelling gear tightening as his weight quickly shifts.

The shot comes.

She actually did it. Jen pulled the trigger. Holy shit. Gotta keep moving. She won't hit me if I move. She's fucking SHOOTING at me.

He remembers the shooting range–*great idea, in hindsight.* They'd been there every Sunday for almost a year, playing Al Dexter's "Pistol Packin' Mama" in the car on the way. Jen had destroyed everything that stayed in place, as deadly as can be for a stationary target. However, she'd struggled with moving ones.

Adam's mind, busy coping, lets his body do its thing. Years of living up there, in the Cliff House, as they'd christened it, had many benefits. Adam had mastered every rock, crack, and ledge the cliff's face has to offer. It had always been his daily meditation, while Jen practiced yoga on the ledge. They were both, in their own way, defying the void.

But what used to be good for his mental health is now essential to his physical integrity, his survival.

She killed Sonja. He accepts this fact with incredible ease as he goes back to his left, running on the rock, holding the rope with his right hand. He feels chafing on his groin, as these movements are faster than what he's used to, and place a greater strain on everything: arms, back, the harness. His mind. Adam has never been this strangely aware of both his thoughts and his tangible presence.

Fucking zen, Adam. You're fucking zen.

Jen fires three shots, punctuating each blast with a scream–"ASSHOLE!" "FUCKER!" "CHEATER!" The third bullet whizzes by his left ear. Adam switches sides again, abruptly, looks up, and sees Jen holding the gun with both hands, steady, trying to lead him. As she presses the trigger, Adam sticks his right boot in a crevice to stop his movement: the weapon cracks, his ankle breaks, and the projectile grazes his shoulder. He screams. Jen half laughs, half cries, and cocks the hammer again.

MOVE.

Against the pain, he pulls his foot out of the crevice–*you fucking moron*–and dives right as hard as he can on his left foot alone. Again, the .44 roars. A rock explodes inches from his head, as dust and gravel pelt his face.

Sixth shot. She needs to reload.

Wiping the debris from his cheeks and forehead, Adam

catches himself wondering how Sonja's face looks now, and whether she made a sound when she reached the bottom. *Did her head explode on some rock after the 350-foot drop? Did it make a sound like an egg cracking on the floor, or did the fall slow down enough going through the evergreens' canopy?*

Vibrations coursing through the rope bring him back. Above, only Jen's head is visible, moving frantically back and forth, her usually well-groomed chestnut hair in utter disarray, curls flying this way and that.

She's not reloading. She's cutting the fucking rope. She's–

The feeling of the rope weakening, thread by thread, makes mind and body one again. Pushing hard with both feet despite the pain, Adam plunges to the right, toward an overhang he's used as a resting spot countless times before. This time, he just hopes it'll provide shelter.

The rope snaps.

There's a brief, weird moment of weightlessness, like he's gliding through the air, until Adam feels the pull of gravity again. His left hand, from pinky to middle finger, latches on to the overhang as his weight bears down. The fingers, damp with sweat, strain as he shoots his right hand up, hoping to grip the ledge, but everything slips. Adam is left, quite literally, hanging there, a solitary object holding everything together for a second: his wedding ring, stuck on a sharp rock spike.

Adam pulls himself up, and as his right hand almost reaches the overhang again. Gravity and momentum then combine, adding to his mass, and the ring cuts through the surface of the finger. It effortlessly slides under the skin and, *like a condom*, he'll think later, strips the finger clean. The sacrifice buys his right hand enough time to catch the overhang at the last possible moment.

He has time to hear the ring bounce once on the rock below him. Adam screams in agony until his throat, too, hurts like hell.

From above, Jen howls, "I'm coming for you, asshole!" Through the tears and blinding pain, he looks upward, beyond the overhang. She's wearing her gear, about to descend.

"Jen!" he shouts. "Don't! You've never–"

The rest of his warning, *"–been good at tying knots,"* dies on Adam's lips as Jen goes over the ledge, rope in one hand, gun in the other. Adam swears he can almost see Jen plummet, gear and all, to a most certain death. He takes a few seconds to realize it fully: for once, it seems, she'd actually managed to tie something down.

A fact dawns on Adam with frightening clarity: climbing on the ledge is his only hope for survival, as his left hand is quickly losing strength. It is, however, also the best way to ensure a stationary target for Jen to shoot. Adam is also painfully aware that a broken ankle will, from now on, only contribute to slowing him down.

Yeah, fuck that.

As if on cue, Jen fires a series of shots at the ledge, raining fragments of stone on Adam's hands. He winces, bracing against the pain as tiny pebbles shower onto his skinned finger. Through the ordeal, amidst vision blurred by tears, Adam sees the error of his ways, but faces the horrible, honest truth: he consciously made the choices leading up to now. *Whatever happens from this point on is out of my control.*

"What's happened to your hand, Mister Fucker?" The question is painted with hatred, punctuated with another salvo. "Poor baby got hurt doing things he shouldn't have?"

Adam hears a familiar click-clack shuffling overhead. He peeks from below the ledge to find Jen reloading the weapon–reloading it fast. Adam had nourished the dim hope of using this time to distance himself from Jen. Or maybe, at the opposite end of the spectrum, of closing the distance and reaching up to her, disarming her. At the moment, though, Jen is powered both by anger and her firearms experience. It also was Adam's idea to get the Desert Eagle semi-automatic–classic, fast reload.

She's way out of reach. Shit.

Upon reloading, Jen looks down at Adam, spots him peeking, smiles a terrifying, inhuman smile, and empties another clip in his direction. The last bullet explodes on the rock, a mere inch beside his right hand.

Adam gasps in pain and surprise, reflexively retracting the hand to his chest. The added weight, shifted to his left hand, sends an alarm signal through his arm, up his shoulder, and into his brain. No sooner has it reached the pain center than his right hand returns to the ledge. Adam notices a gash on the back of the hand, opened, no doubt, by a piece of rock from Jen's last shot.

"Oh Adaaaaam …"

He peeks again to see Jen carefully lowering herself closer, always remaining just out of reach.

"I'm coming to help you, baby. I'll help you out." She laughs a hollow laugh. "I'll fucking help you *down*."

Adam watches, powerless. Jen wall runs to the right, where he loses sight of her behind the ledge, then she goes left, affording him a better angle on the whole affair. However, this also places Adam more clearly in Jen's sight.

Jen pendulums her way to and fro a few times, always staring straight at him at the apex of her leftward swing. After a push that causes her to grunt under the strain, instead of pivoting and going back to the right, she plants both feet firmly on a protruding rock and stops abruptly, knees bent. The estranged couple have a clear view of one another.

Jen straightens her legs as she retrieves the gun. Adam knows it's over, even before she raises the weapon. He closes his eyes.

"Look at me, you cheating fuck!"

He does. As a last resort, Adam tries to shimmy his way as far right as possible, but the pain in both his too extreme and his movements too slow. Nevertheless, this prompts a reaction from Jen: instead of positioning herself as far left as possible, hugging the rock, she seems to find it necessary to stand away from the cliff's face, as if to compensate for Adam's repositioning.

Jen pushes out as much possible, on the tip of her toes. Letting go of the rope, she grasps the gun with both hands, aiming. Adam mentally carves the invisible line leading through the air from the gun to his heart.

Fuck.

Jen's mouth contorts into a rictus, and Adam wishes he could forget it now, forget that face, not carry it along with him on the other side. Down the cliff.

Jen's body jerks as it suddenly descends a few inches. Rictus gone. Eyes wide. Jen, trained hands snatching at the rope, lets the gun fall silently. She bends her knees again, shifts her weight as close to the rock as possible, reducing tension on her lifeline.

Another light release.

She looks at Adam, her face a study in panic.

"Adam ..."

"Jen, did you use the flat overhand or the flat figure eight knot?"

"I–"

With a weird motion, feet shooting upward like she was ascending the cliff face and had slipped, Chaplin-style, on a banana peel, Jen plummets. Her hands clutch the rope, holding it tight against her chest. Without even the slightest cry.

Adam can't see her body as it reaches the canopy, but, unlike Sonja's head before, he clearly hears it break through, then hit the detritus. Adam closes his eyes.

"*Bitch delivery*? No ma'am, wrong address."

If he still had it in him, Adam would laugh, but instead conserves his remaining energy to hoist himself up on the ledge.

There's barely room to sit. *Still,* he thinks, *better than the alternative.*

—

As the sun sets, Adam shivers and reassures himself: *someone's bound to notice my absence–or Jen's–at some point. Or Sonja's.*

Either that, or there's bound to be a third delivery; same courier, same wrong address.

AUTHOR'S NOTE

This one arose from a competition in which my group was tasked with writing a thriller with a cliff as its location, somehow involving a wedding ring. I thought having the whole piece happen on the cliff's face would raise the stakes both in terms of tension and location writing. I was just coming out of writing a few screenplays, and the very visual, action-oriented style of "Bitch Delivery for Mister Fucker" stemmed from that bout of screenwriting.

I must admit that I have a love/hate relationship with Adam, the story's protagonist. He's no good guy, not by any stretch, but he's paying dearly for what he's done.

And then some.

RS

Full of Shit at His Age Now

PAUL MILENSKI

At his age now he thought he was full of shit and was not full of shit when he was younger, thinking then of course all by himself with no one to rub it off on, no one to have to say untruthful things for. But at his age now, he was working hard, learning to be young again, trying to be irreverent all over again.

He would see businessmen and professionals all dressed up in blue suits, neat and clean. Same haircuts, same shoes, and in the cold weather the same blue wool overcoats. They looked phony to him now although not all of them were, because they must have wanted to be this way, or they would not have been.

He did not give a shit how he dressed, had no pretenses that he knew of, except he was full of shit when he did dress that way and was not honest with himself about it.

He would hear someone say something truthful, what they were thinking and feeling, because they knew what they were thinking and feeling, and he would remember when he was young enough to do that all the time, without effort, without any confusion at all.

Today he was on the bus, his actual metaphor for change, his older self recapturing his younger self. He felt good about this, feeling he would not be full of shit anymore and trying to work out of it the best he was able.

Across from him on the bus sat this old lady, horse face, lipping her false teeth, taking them into her tongue, dropping them down, lifting them back into place. Behind her was a middle-aged man, ugly cratered face, the remnants of adolescent pimples, dark red and purple blotches from having been squeezed unmercifully during a time of total self-possession in front of a mirror or just sitting and watching television. He knew this was a form of self-abuse, an eerie proof of existence, so when you were done squeezing you could look at your fingers and under your nails to the see the results of your handiwork, the ugly red and purple parts of you.

Ugly people, poor people, the infirm, the angry, the old, the retarded, and the young–on their way to and from school–rode the bus. Everyone else was above bus riding.

But he wasn't above bus riding. He wasn't that full of shit. But his reasons for riding were not just getting from one place to another. He liked riding because he liked to watch the young school girls get on, walk to the back of the bus and talk to each other about their boyfriends and other boys, how they went out with Jimbo, or Bret, or Jason, or Michael H, and how they drank up at the lake, or in cold weather how they snuck into the garage or into the locker room during the janitors' change of shifts and chugged booze and doped it up and felt each other up unmercifully.

These were pretty, young girls, a little cheap, but prettier than they would ever be again, their bodies newly ripe, their lips glossed, looking vulnerable with little firm tits most of them and flat bellies and tight asses.

He liked these girls young and cheap. He was born around cheap girls, always felt comfortable with them, knew what they liked and how to flirt with them, even now that he was older and not so good looking anymore. He knew how to get them going so they would not just think that he was some queer old man trying to score on younger girls. About these younger girls he was not full of shit, about how he liked them, about how he knew them. They responded to him in friendly ways, not dismissing him and not making fun of him. If he wanted to, after giving time to them, most would have gone down on him regardless of his age, but he was not like that. He felt they should go down on their younger boyfriends, even if their boyfriends were unlikely to make them feel good, to do it for them right. That was part of being young, the mistakes that came with it, and now at his age not wanting to interfere with that no matter how much he might have wanted to. He knew how to smile at these young girls, not interfere with their talk of how they got laid in the garage, how they drank like fucking yahoos and then got laid again. It was a wonder their mothers didn't know, that their fathers didn't know, that the friends of Jimbo, and Bret, and Jason, and Michael H didn't know. It was nobody's business anyway–what they did or who they did it to. Nobody's. You just couldn't trust some of the slime that was around, like Maggie the Pig, who was always trying to get shit out of the guys by sucking them off so she'd learn who was sleeping with who, who was fucking just for the hell of it, or because they were really serious with somebody. There was always Louise who knew about everybody, but she was so hooked on *leak*, she wasn't telling anything. She was safe, poor shit.

The young girls were dressed mostly in tights and tight sweaters so their pointy little boobs stuck out. He liked these crazy young girls, their interest in one thing and one thing only, their honesty in looking for boys who would screw them, say they loved them, and maybe buy them a present or two, or take them bowling, or to a movie, or out someplace where they could pull out their fake ID, have a few drinks like they were older, then dance, before they went out to the car to get laid, to get their best dress stained, ripped right the fuck off them.

He was not full of shit about liking these young girls, so he rode the bus.

Early in the morning the junior college girls were on the bus, but they were not so interesting, being more into some image of themselves or being into what they wanted to be in the future and not what they were right now. But again, on Saturdays sometimes the young girls rode the bus from the city to the mall, so they could buy perfume, nail polish, lipstick, naughty panties, sex things, plastic necklaces, and earrings, flirt with the boys if they came around and maybe go for a ride to get felt up and maybe get high.

When he was young he was not so full of shit because he was like these girls, full of hormones and honest. He had no choice just as they had no choice. His hormones took over completely, so thinking just got in the way, couldn't really rise above everything that was sexual. It was awesome then, not full of shit, just full of hormones.

Now he was full of shit because he substituted thinking for lots of things he was feeling. And he still had hormones, even at his age, not as many, but enough, yet he held them back for mostly stupid reasons.

Behind the man with the pimples, among the young girls on

the bus, was this tall girl, more mature than the other girls, bigger tits, wider hips, bigger ass. She was still a young girl, talking with the other girls, but she was more mature. She had hickeys, a number on her neck and one right beneath her left ear. She was happy with her hickeys, kept pushing her hair back to show them off. He looked closely at her hickeys, and she smiled because she could tell he was not full of shit about that. He smiled back and she smiled again. Then she loosened one button on her blouse so her bra could be seen. It was purple, lacy, very sexy. She let her blouse slip on her shoulder so he could see the bra better. He nodded and loved that she was so full of hormones, so full of herself and showing herself off.

At the next bus stop a tall boy got on, walked back and joined her, pushing away one of her friends who sat next to her. "Hey, Freddie!" the friend said, but he just sat down anyway and smiled slyly.

Freddie kissed the mature girl on the lips, on her neck near all the hickeys, then he put one arm around her so he could use his hand to touch her breast. She smiled, not just for Freddie, but because she saw him, at his age, watching her with Freddie. So she did many more things: pulled Freddie's hair, stuck her tongue in his ear, ran her hand along his thigh. She was not full of shit about this. She was having fun.

He kept watching, and she was great, this one tall, mature girl, until a couple of stops down she walked past, brushed against him, smiled, and got off the bus with Freddie. He smiled back at her, because none of it was full of shit. It was all good, and a good start, to be at his age now and trying not to be full of shit, and maybe even trying honestly to be at some earlier age, like the tall, mature girl and Freddie, when it was all so much easier and truer.

AUTHOR'S NOTE

I write every day, so for me neither writer's block nor inspiration are issues. This being said, not all days are equally as profitable. Some days, regardless of the effort put in, seem in retrospect as warm-up days, where "all my darlings" need to be expunged, resulting in end-products that, though honest, are labored or even bland. Then, over time, the muse visits, as reward for persistence and diligence, and a story like "Full of Shit at His Age Now," appears full blown, with strong characters, in balance, and metaphorical. Writing can be difficult, but the rewards are great.

PM

If anyone orders Merlot, I'm leaving.
I am not drinking any fucking Merlot!

Miles Raymond
Sideways

The Red Fucking Converse of Sergio Menendez

FELIX PIRE

1: Bryant

"Please."

"Ay, please," I said aloud, as I rolled my eyes and power-walked past Ms. Bryant, the judgy old lady who cleans up after the apartment building where I live. I was a little crabby because this was an early morning performance-slash-rehearsal I was attending, and I couldn't resist. But then again, I find that early morning light looks good reflected off my skin tone, as I am a Cuban-American cis male who is built from head toe and can do splits so well your mind wound spin as to why I haven't already ended up in porn. And down below? *Please* ...

And so, this time, a rarity when I was feeling good about myself–I wanted her to *look at ME*! She's always giving me looks anyway about what I wear and what I act like. She says I act like a girl, I say *she* acts like a man.

For one, I always act like *me*. Gay li'l ol' *me*. And for duds, that day I was wearing my 1960s *push-your-butt-up* Levis jeans that button about an inch below the navel; a sequin pink-paisley vest of my own design, my usual black choker, and my green army boots–*muy casual*. So, *please* ...

Whenever I think about Ms. Bryant, it's usually along these lines:

Why don't you look at yourself old woman? You're an un-happy old crone who has devoted her life to fifteen cats and a smok-ing addiction that makes you sound like a car that won't start, as the sound of that same ball of phlegm that's been there for years keeps circulating in your black lungs next to your black heart! If smoking was banned for a year, I'm sure you'd go psychotic.

Ms. Bryant–she's like the gay shit-baby of Joe Camel and the Marlboro Man.

There was one thing that I'd always wanted from her, the one thing that she always took special care of–her *shoes*. Anita had this butch thing about wearing Converse sneakers, and her son, whom she disowned (and who later became a very popular clothing designer with the initials C.K.) had only given her one present in his adult life: the pair of ruby red, high-heeled converse that she now wore *every ... fucking ... day.*

Because although Anita only bathed once a year, when the *cake of caca* that she had on her was impeding her movements, her shoes were forever impeccable and shiny like two queen-sized jew-els. In turn, I always thought there was an element of mystery about them. About *her.*

Porque mystery?

I concluded that since her son had been such a success in spite of his mother's attitude and grossness, that she and he were somehow *charmed*. Like that Tinkerbell had blown a mouthful of fairy (and that he was) dust all over them, and not that they could *fly* but, somehow, they just *were ... fly.*

Does anyone use "fly" to mean cool anymore? I heard you thinking that, and I do, bitch–I do.

I'm thinking all this, when the idea smacks me that I'm going to be late for rehearsal, definitely. I mean, I'm late a lot. There is a note on my birth certificate that says I took eleven months to literally be born. *Please*. I mean, that's the way I am. I make fabulous late entrances. Because let it never be said that Sergio Menendez was early to anything–even to life! Fashionably late, that's where it's at. Forget it. I'm never early; that would be tacky. Of course it would. There are two things that I always make sure never to do prema-turely: arrive and ejaculate, okay? *Please.* To borrow from Meg Cabot's *The Princess Diaries*, "A Queen is Never Late, everyone else is simply early."

2: Kiko

Kiko barked behind me, telling me to hurry up because we were massively late to the club thanks to me primping and prepping my face with a slight veneer of make-up and creams to stay looking like my fav department store: Forever 21.

I know dogs are supposed to be just dogs, *pero* Kiko's been spiritually very close to me ever since I was little. He was the only thing I asked for from the nuns in the Miami orphanage.

"I mean, a boy must have a companion. Most of these boys don't go anywhere around me." I argued. "A boy and his dog are like a hairdresser and his most intimate client. And a dog is to the boy what a bartender is to an alcoholic, what the Lasso of Truth was to Wonder Woman." The nuns reluctantly agreed that it was necessary for me to have some company, since the other boys were afraid of me. They said I was weird and gay. I am different and very happy. They were right.

You see, I never enjoyed playing sports or getting into fights or anything like that, despite holding a black belt in kung fu.

I am the type of person that you'd get if you mixed Liberace, Carmen Miranda, and Mother Teresa; a very artistic pacifist who would rather wear a flamboyant outfit and sing a song to clam up everyone than create a scandal.

Of course, many times my *outfits* have been the source of scandal. Like the time when I was twelve at the orphanage and Kiko and I created that one pair of green rubber pants that exposed my left testicle. I chose the green and Kiko chose the rubber because he's kinky. I kept telling the nuns that it was an artistic choice, but they said that Jesus would not have worn them. I was taken to an empty classroom where they beat my left, exposed testicle with a ruler.

I was like, *more please.*

Anyway, I never planned to have kids of my own. I always wanted to adopt, so that took care of that. *Pero first*, I have to find parents of my own, no?

Kiko was finally allowed to live with me, and boy was I glad, because Kiko, a white poodle I dyed pink, would talk with me all the time and keep me company. People thought it was strange whenever I sat around discussing lip gloss and the dimensional possibilities of spandex underwear with a poodle at the age of eight, but what they didn't know was that Kiko and I understood each other.

You see, Cubans believe very much in past lives and the mystical part of existence. That's the magic part of the universe, where it can easily get out of hand and turn into fantasy if you're not careful and land you in a psycho ward next to Blanche DuBois.

Pero I do believe that we *crazy Cubans*–a phrase immortalized by Lucy Ricardo, who of course I *love*–we must be "touched" in some way. That's why she was obsessed with Ricky. Or maybe he had a great cock, 'cause boy was she after it! Isn't that what makes it all interesting? She's so brilliant, and then obsessed with some Cuban guy? He must have bewitched that funny-faced clown by just *being sexy*!

I'm no hypocrite I know I have a beautiful twenty-six-year-old face, and that I wield seductive powers, or I wouldn't choose to practically live at the gym so my butt can barely fit into the pair of jeans I'm trying to cram on.

Get this: Ironically, even though I was raised by nuns, they were Cubans, and so some of them hypocritically practiced a good deal of ritualistic Santería on the side. Sister Nenita had her own little altar to the African Saints placed behind an alcove in her closet. Santa Barbara, San Lazaro, you name it!

Although in public she denounced Santería as the worshipping of African pagans, at night you could catch Sister Nenita in her room, sacrificing chickens to Babalu Aye: "*Babaluuuu!*" She used to go off, and she had a deep voice. Everyone just thought she was a Ricky Ricardo fan and was watching *I Love Lucy*. But I knew better.

Kiko, I come to find out, after our many conversations together, was not only my pink pet poodle, but also my *third cousin on my mother's side*. A lawyer, who had died when one of his clients, upset about the shitty settlement that Kiko had reached with her millionaire ex-husband, came gallivanting through the office door, smelling of rum and Coke, and in the midst of an argument, removed and brandished her silver-spike heeled shoe above him (ala Jennifer Jason Leigh in *Single White Female*) and rammed it into Kiko's eye socket past his eye into his brain. It was instant death!

The police in Cuba released the murderess because they concluded that, considering she only got $200 Cuban pesos and a Sarita Montiel record collection in the settlement, any sort of retaliation on her part—even murder—was justified. Kiko once told me that he doesn't hold any grudges and that he doesn't mind, because he'd take the life of a dog any day over the life of a lawyer.

We were not yet to the end of the block when I heard a loud *shriek* from behind me. It was Ms. Bryant, whom I will now call *Anita* out of pity, screaming "MISTY!" This was followed by a harsh, grating sound of a truck slamming on its breaks and, seconds later, a loud THUMP!

I turned around to see. There was Anita, all four-hundred cellulitic pounds of her, on the ground behind the truck's first axle. I hate to say it, but Anita was always so drab, and when I saw her there with all that red, scarlet blood on and around her, despite myself, I thought, "Ay, that bitch looks so good in crimson!"

There she lay, seemingly dead, as Misty, her cat, sat patiently on the opposite side of the road, looking satisfied, licking its paws. With cats, you can't ever tell if this was a coincidence or if they orchestrated a *hit*. I can't tell, but Kiko, who's a regular Dr. Doolittle, tells me she was grinning. I can't say that I felt sorry for the old lady, but I jogged over just to be nice and pay my respects, maybe poke her with the stick of my eyeshadow brush.

A dream of a truck driver emerged from the hulking machine that had struck her. He was a tall, hunky, blond, muscular, hairy-chested, thick-thighed, big-bulbous-bubble-butt guy who was completely edible from head to testicles. He approached me, asking if I had seen anything. And although I was currently seeing a Greek god before my eyes, I gulped and said that I had seen it all, which was the truth to the question he was asking. I was seeing his name tag right now. Josh. The name of like, three of my exes.

I caught a look at Anita's shoes, which were shining dramatically with the light of the afternoon sun, blinding me momentarily, as they were half-exposed from the underside of the truck's cabin. The sirens were already signaling the near-presence of the ambulance, police, forklift, and whatever else they'd need to scrape the four-hundred-pound road pizza off the South Beach gravel.

Please. I'm not a cannibal, but if properly distributed, the meat on that woman could solve world hunger for about a week.

I looked to the truck driver, who had just murdered Anita, and he seemed out-of-his-wits nervous, so I naturally embraced him tightly and blew gently into his right ear to soothe him. His body tensed, but he let me do it; I think he was in shock. After semi-biting on his earlobe–okay, *nibbling*–I told him I'd make a two-part pact with him.

"I'm listening," he said.

"You let me have her shoes, I'll testify in court that it was completely her fault. That's part one."

"Agreed. What's part two?"

"In order to be able to live with myself for committing the atrocious sin of lying, and in order to appease my nagging Catholic mental anguish, you know, in order to survive that psycho-ultra-Freudian-cosmic-karmic emotional strife, you're gonna have to sleep with me."

"Don't push it," he said.

I took the shoes.

AUTHOR'S NOTE

In my mind, I clearly saw *The Outrageously Homofunky Adventures of Sergio Menendez*, as a feature screenplay. I wrote it in Hollywood during the mid-1990s, hoping to produce it as an indie comedy.

As I write this postscript in June of 2019, the screenplay is advancing to the quarterfinalist round of the ScreenCraft Sci-Fi & Fantasy Screenplay Contest. Alongside it, I wrote a few short stories as character sketches in Sergio's playful, uber-queer, Latino voice, flitting about his fantastical world. He is a frothy mix of amusing characteristics: the funny Cuban attitude I grew up with in Miami coupled with an overlay of uplifting magic realism.

Sergio, the name, I plucked from a kid I was in love with during the third grade. I spied on him on Facebook years later: happily married with kids. Nice. The *character* of "Sergio Menendez" himself, however–his speech pattern, and the magic of his world–coalesced when I wrote audition material for two television sketch comedy shows: *In Living Color* (I was cast, but the series was cancelled before I set foot on set) and *Saturday Night Live* (which, in 1997, while seeking work, a young John Leguizamo auditioned me for that slot [though it was ultimately given to a young Horatio Sans]). The audition for both of the shows was the same: Five minutes of original characters and impressions. *"Ay, please!"* Sergio immediately exclaimed, appearing in full drag regalia, snapping his fingers in a circle *in the face of my imagination!* After all, I'd written a movie (and more) about him when I'd first arrived in LA! The character: a goofy, endearing, fabulous Latino guy in his twenties and beloved as a drag performer at a South Beach, Florida, night-club, saunters through an almost utopian existence where gayness is a superpower, his pink pet poodle talks, and firemen flirt with him mercilessly.

The short story you've just read reveals what it sounds like in Sergio's head as he narrates a campy adventure with his trade-mark "rose-colored" view of his space. Wear your red rubber pumps while you read and I promise Sergio will *Crack ... You ... The Fuck–Uuuup, Queen!*

FP

"You like to say fucking a lot, don't you?" I muttered while adding the sweatpants to the cart.
"It's like verbal salt. I enjoy sprinkling it on everything."

Bijou Hunter
Damaged and the Knight

Fucking Songbird

K.T. VANDERLAAG

Starbucks 9:00 am
Leotards and foreheads
stitched to raise their eyes
Aging felines chatting
thru their blowfish lips
Pretending they have moist pussies
High hard breasts
at permanent attention
Create shadows over
what was delicious cunt
Now past the use by date

On break up number 25
She phones to fill me in
I am her break up friend
And then
My mother calls for coffee
plants new seeds of bad crops in my head

Our nights
filled with rising bile
I tell myself it isn't crap
In mauve moonlight
my brown sons
Call nigger from the stairs
Pierce the night and lays there
Like a used tampon

The daybreak and the sharp blue sky
Announces I am back

No longer dark
I look for fairy cloth to spread
Technology brings me snippets of love
Thru text my spirit moves
Each word aborted I bring to life
replaying
I'll be your bitch but not your wife

Whatever comes I have no wish
That is a lie
You fucked my soul
my heart no longer beats
Without the digging whisper
– give me more
I'll be your songbird
When you come

AUTHOR'S NOTE

This piece was written during my attendance at the Delray Beach Poetry Festival, which I attended for a week in 2009. It was an experimental piece that we were given the task of writing with ten or so disjointed words we had to incorporate in a poem. A few of the words required to include were *pussy, cunt, tampon, technology* and *fairycloth*.

The more constrained the requirements the easier it is for me to compose.

KTV

Daemon Fenroy, God of the Fucked

JANNA MILLER

Fenroy could feel the last of the sweetness sliding down his throat like a benediction, cleansing his sensitive palette in a deliciously cool and sugary swallow. It rejuvenated him and calmed him so that he could feel strength returning to muscles he had forgotten were his. He savored the brief memory by rolling his tongue across his now dull teeth and breathing in what remained of the delicate smell. It was of smoke and ash. Of chaos and war. Of a bittersweet end with the most refreshing hint of enduring misery.

It was the best meal he had consumed in centuries.

Fenroy cleared his throat and spoke in a low and raspy voice, holding tightly to the armrests of the chair to which he was chained. "New girl. Where did that come from?"

She busily swept the stone floor, disturbing dust in places that had happily lived for eons, and barely looked up to acknowledge Fenroy. Her voice was a little rough too, with disuse. "Where did *what* come from?"

Fenroy shook the wrappings on the side table next to him with impatience. "This, of course. This ... meal you gave to me when you entered."

The girl placed a hand on her back to help straighten herself up. She still didn't meet his eyes. They had all been warned not to.

Looking just beyond his left shoulder the girl replied. "It was from the trash pile behind the library."

"Is that right?"

"I was told to feed you any old thing, provided no one wanted it."

Fenroy did his best to contain a growl from deep within his stomach. A wisp of smoke escaped from one nostril. "Of course. The keepers know I'm not all that picky. They don't want to put you to any trouble."

"*Trouble?*" The girl moved her left foot back toward the door.

"No trouble. I'm no trouble. Obviously, I mean, they let you in here, right?"

The girl fell silent. Her right foot had followed her left one. She looked pointedly at Fenroy's chains.

"Oh, these?" He gave the metal links a little rattle and chuckled lightly. "These are just for my protection. Did you think they were for you? Posh. It's just that every so often or so I can become a little ... energetic. I have injured myself accidentally in the past and I take a long time to heal. No, no; these are for me." Fenroy tried to direct a frozen smile toward the girl.

She quickly departed and the metal door slammed shut behind her.

Fenroy muttered to himself. "Shit. It was the smile. I never can get that right."

No matter, he thought. It had been a long time since the librarians had so carelessly weeded their collection. Perhaps the girl would scavenge from the discard pile again.

—

Kayra was intrigued. She wondered what had changed the old daemon. Fenroy usually just muttered and drooled a bit. She only fed him and did some light housekeeping, there were others to move him from his chair. Sometimes he was at a desk, over on a longer chain that allowed a bit of walking. Usually the chair though.

She went through a few more cells, sweeping and tidying before she sought out her friend Hugh, who worked in the kitchen. He gave her a smile and handed Kayra a pastry. "Just baked it. Eat it fast, you know that they don't last long."

Kayra gratefully accepted the warm confection and ate quickly. In between bites, she asked Hugh what he thought of her experience.

"Fenroy's usually somewhat docile. Mutters and smokes a little, but that's all. How do you think he was different?"

She swallowed. "I dunno. Kind of wily. Dangerous maybe. He was trying to trick me into talking to him somehow."

Hugh laughed. "He should know better than that. Gregor and

Millicent have gags on most of the time now. You have to have ear-plugs on when you enter as a precaution."

"Mmm." Her mouth was full.

"Sookie, too. She's chained and gagged. I have to blend all her seaweed into a liquid so they can pour it directly into a tube in her neck. Fenroy really ought to be more careful. He's only chained."

Kayra considered this. "He was talking about dinner. Liked what I fed him."

"Did you take something from the library pile, like I told you?"

"Yes. It wasn't even very big."

"Was is a memoir?"

"No. Some history book. It looked awful."

"Hmm. History is usually fine. Just make sure it's thicker next time. The bigger volumes are the easiest for him. Less concentrated. First-person narratives are best. If he keeps acting strangely, we'll need to tell the Duke on his next visit."

Kayra thanked Hugh for the pastry and left to resume work on the remaining rooms. Her new rounds consisted of a light dusting and feeding of the wards in the lower dungeons. Before that, she had worked on a few of the upper floors. The demands of both were quite similar. The academics she had been used to, barely spoke to her. They were often so engrossed in whatever it was that they were do-ing, they forgot to eat. Kayra often removed trays that had not been touched while the academics scribbled away at their work. Now that she thought about it, it really wasn't very different at all.

———

Fenroy retched and coughed with his first bite. He looked accusingly at Kayra and spluttered at her. "What was that?" He spit a few pieces out from between teeth, wiping off his tongue.

Again, she looked over his shoulder when responding. "A book, of course. I took it from the same place as yesterday."

"Read me the title, please. I can't bear to look." Fenroy con-tinued to cough.

Kayra walked gingerly over to the side table. Still out of arm's reach, she bent sideways to read the spine. "*Dams Through the Ages.*"

"Argh! That's why it tasted like muddy water. Of course, it wouldn't be the other kind, How awful. Wait …"

Fenroy flipped to the back of the book. "Any deaths in here? Sometimes working far from home on dams can be dangerous."

He nibbled on the chapters before the index, chewing thoughtfully. "OK, a bit stale and without a lot of detail, but I suppose they will have to do."

Fenroy looked critically at Kayra. "Not your best work, my girl."

"I don't think I'm supposed to please you."

"Why-ever not? How will changing my dinner a bit hurt anything? There is little enough to look forward to."

Kayra glanced around his dismal room. Stone walls and floor, an iron bed, a shelf with folded clothes, and that ridiculous chair in the center. It was cold and bleak. Fenroy was old, too. She had heard that he was one of the first daemons here.

Kayra shrugged before doing another quick sweep of the room. Her fingers weren't tingling (this was usually a sure sign of magical interference). *He's not using magic to cajole me,* Kayra thought. She would consider his request. It probably couldn't hurt.

—

Fenroy dreamed.

The way was rocky and cold. The way was dark and treacherous. The way was lost. All was lost. Small struggling forms that could not stand. Larger forms wrapped against the wind that would not cease. Calls that seemed to be unanswered but, oh, they were not.

Fenroy heard. Fenroy always heard. And Fenroy came when he was called.

He heard the song of loss, of desperation. Of traveling from one impossible choice to another. Of feeling only agony but moving anyway. Of feeling nothing save for the smallest grain of hope that burned instead with a pulsing wish at every step: please, please, please.

He heard all of this and came to them. Eager.

Fenroy began to remember.

—

Kayra slept in a small, unused room in the attic. She could sleep in the dormitories but felt her loss of freedom keenly in such a crowded space. No one seemed to mind (really only the Duke minded about anything), so she settled in with the small belongings she had taken from around the compound. She was thinking about finding another room for storage.

Recently she had taken a few of the unwanted books. Settling in with one, she tried to form an idea of them herself. So far, she felt nothing.

Maybe it's the material, she thought.

She critically assessed her little collection. *Elder Crapshot: A Biography in Three Parts* had put her to sleep on three consecutive nights and she still didn't know what was going on. *50 Ways to Tie a Slipknot* was interesting for a few pages but soon became repetitive. She still hadn't looked at *Ode to a Jellied Eel: Prose for Bottom Feeders* or *The Fifty-Year-Old Tomato.*

Kayra wondered what boring tasted like and took a small nibble out of a corner of the *Jellied Eel* book. Chewing thoughtfully, she decided that it tasted like paper.

There was one more book though. She had been a little bit naughty and taken it from the main reading room. She wasn't supposed to take anything out from there, since she wasn't an academic, but no one really seemed to notice Kayra in her drab clothes and tied-up hair. It was the easiest thing to bring her broom and sweep, sweep, sweep over to the displays that ached to be touched (so rarely achieved). So easy to slip a tome into her pocket.

It was perfectly sized; small and compact and easy to hide. As she swept out of the room again, Kayra had felt the little volume weighing in her apron, knocking against her leg in the most satisfying way.

It was now that she reached for her hidden treasure, fingers tingling in anticipation. As soon as she opened it, Kayra felt an immediate sensation. It seemed to reach into her and pull her along from page to page. It guided her fingers without her even knowing it. And without her even knowing it was how she spent the entire night, reading page after page until reaching the end.

As the light of dawn begin to take hold in her room, Kayra

gave this one a little nibble, too. It also, coincidentally, tasted of paper.

———

Duke Winslow was exasperated. He had felt the twinge for the first time when he was in the middle of a toast to some soon-to-be better friends (which would now have to wait), the second time was while walking around the lake with a lovely companion (his leg had cramped up and the was walk cut short), and the third time as he was writing in his journal (spilling a half-filled ink bottle on the pages).

Yes, he was definitely more than annoyed. As he wiped up the spill with a now unusable tea towel, Duke Winslow thought he might actually be approaching furious. *How long had it been? A few years?* He paused and made a counting motion with his fingers in recollection. *Well, a few decades at the outside*, he thought. At any rate, it seemed like only a short amount of time.

Duke Winslow sighed deeply. He was going to have to cancel his tennis match.

———

Fenroy had been allowed his weekly exercise, in the small space of six steps end to end. He had hidden his flashing eyes from the one who moved him (though as encased as he was in magic deterrent armor, he would never have seen anyway). Fenroy had been docile, recalcitrant, and, frankly, as neutral as a daemon could be without arousing suspicion.

And now he paced and thought. How long had he been dormant, living this half-life of partial consciousness? He felt himself filtering through layer after layer of dead thought and cobwebs. It must have been an extremely long time. They had been keeping him alive, but not himself. Feeding him enough that he would not die (if he *could* die, he had never had the pleasure himself), but instead would exist in a sort of limbo.

This new girl had accidentally given him just a bit of nourishment. Not the best kind, not by a long fathom, but the dust of a kernel of calorie of the right direction. Sometimes, all it took was a drop. But the problem now was that he was hungry, so hungry for the next drop. He hoped he wouldn't do anything irrational. The balance was most delicate.

So when the new girl returned, Fenroy made a point of being quiet and polite. Kayra ignored him absolutely.

She swept, emptied the trash of leftover book casings, ran a damp rag over Fenroy's chair and table. Stepping outside briefly to put up her supplies, Kayra entered again with Fenroy's dinner.

"New girl," began Fenroy

She stopped mid-step.

He continued. "I was wondering if you have given any thought to our conversation earlier? Hmm?"

Kayra flicked her eyes upward and then down again quickly. "Again, I am not sure if I am supposed to make you comfortable. The cook left strict instructions."

"Oh, you know that healthy eating is constricting if you can't splurge a little. Honestly, can't I at least have a selection?"

Kayra considered this and went back outside again briefly, returning with several extra volumes. "These were all on the designated pile."

Fenroy strained forward slightly. "Well, that's very kind of you. I do appreciate just the faintest touch of kindness. Could you read the titles to me? I can't see them from here."

Kayra read the titles aloud, talking mostly to her feet. "*Weather Patterns in the Southern Hemisphere, Fishing the Indigo Lakes*, and *The Fall of the Dorman Empire*."

"Hmm. Not much of a choice here. I mean, what do they expect me to live on? But I suppose if I had to have something, it might be … well, *The Fall of the Dorman Empire*. Let's try that one."

Kayra waited for a heartbeat before advancing to put the book on the table. Fenroy had been leaning on the wall until the moment it touched the flat surface. Then, in an explosion of movement, he reached for the volume and brought it to his lips, inhaling sharply as he did so. Kayra watched him from underneath her hair.

"This really does have some potential. Exodus maps. Eyewitness accounts. And …" His voice deepened. "Interviews."

"Thank you, new girl. I think … I want a little alone time. Yes." Fenroy sighed a long, deep sigh. "I think I might want to savor this one."

———

Hugh attentively stirred a large steaming pot with a long paddle. The lumpy contents swirled gently, releasing the odor of mildewed socks.

"Here, hold this." Hugh handed Kayra the paddle. "Don't touch the end though."

Kayra gripped the wooden handle lightly, eying the smoldering end with some concern.

"How's our friend?"

Kayra considered this. "The best way I can describe it is that he is … waking up."

Hugh added in a few healthy shakes of red pepper to the pot, then retrieved the paddle from Kayra.

"Then we still have a little time," Hugh said.

"Time for what?"

Hugh turned off the fire and put on the lid. "Time to worry about other matters."

"Such as?" Kayra asked.

"Millicent has been complaining of a stomach ache. She seems to think it's the food. Woolsey is losing his third eyesight. Reynold has a sore throat."

Hugh added red pepper to several other dishes that bubbled on the stove.

"Are you in charge of these matters?"

"Well, no one else seems to be. I might as well try my hand at it. How much harm can I do? Let me know how things go with your fiend, okay?"

Kayra nodded. "Okay."

As she left, she looked closely at the pepper flake jar.

———

A beacon shone down twisted mountain trails.
In pulsing bursts of a keening wail,
the song emerged–high and sweet.
The air effused with longing.

The destination never reached.
A sweep of wind, a cloak of night.
The pause of ragged feet.
Here, right here, where hope is lost.
A darkened form arrives to feed.

—

Kayra looked around her attic space, which had become, if possible, even more crowded than before. The largest table had nearly disappeared beneath piles. A twisted plant grew toward a rough-hewn hole of sunlight in the corner. A smallish experiment bubbled gently atop a frying pan atop a wooden box. Cascades of drying seeds hung in strings from the ceiling. The platform where she had made her bed could just be glimpsed under different types of borrowed footwear. Presently, Kayra focused on various books, arranged vertically by color.

Moving a black stiletto and a soft, buckskin boot, she perched on the edge of the platform, hands on her chin. Kayra knew, of course, that color had nothing to do with anything, but she had just wanted to see how the books looked in this arrangement. She liked the ephemeral artistic presentation.

From atop the dark blue pile, Kayra pulled a smallish volume toward her. Its cover was stained so badly that she had almost classified it as brown, but if she looked closely she could see that the cloth was a dark, navy blue. The stains were … troubling. Possibly food, but possibly other fluid types. Kayra wondered if she could find out their compositions.

The spine popped and crackled as Kayra opened the cover. It smelled of must and was filled with thick and unevenly cut, yellowed pages. Flipping through, she could see that the pages were handwritten, incorporating several distinct styles and various types of ink and charcoal pencil. The cover had been sewn by hand, several times, as pages appeared to have been added like ungainly building extensions.

Flipping to the book's center (with a sound like a small stream breaking up in ice), Kayra opened to a page that was pockmarked with water stains. *Perhaps the author had been writing in the rain,* she thought. After reading the page, she discovered that this was indeed the case. The thick, charcoal writing described the mud, the torrent that would not stop as a small group traveled on and on, day after day. All ages, all abilities, traveling together, living and dying and suffering in unison. Looking briefly at other entries, she realized this was the journal of a diaspora. A journey of generations.

This book had not been from the discard pile. After her initial success, she had returned to the main library, with a more targeted plan. Kayra absconded books from certain sections and, in doing so, found more than she bargained for. This partially explained the newest collections in her full-to-bursting attic room. A chemistry book sat next to the frying pan, a gardening primer against a misshapen corner plant.

The book Kayra now held in her hands had been found beneath a glass plinth in a nave on the library's south side. The dust was so thick she had the perfect reason for being there. Retrieving a cloth from her apron, Kayra had wiped the surface with small, circular motions. When the book emerged from under glass, she felt like she had discovered a new and different world. Her fingers itched. There was no doubt that she would take it.

For the meantime, Kayra assembled the books she would bring to Fenroy tomorrow, added a dash of red pepper to the bubbling experiment on the frying pan, and pushed additional shoes off her bedcovers. Kayra picked up a lovely indigo book from the purple pile and snuggled in among the bedroom slippers to read herself to sleep with the sweet songs of chemical fires and explosions.

—

The Duke would have to hurry. He had left much later than he meant to after a ridiculous five-course breakfast that he had treated himself to for missing the tennis match. He realized now that it had probably been a mistake to tarry for so long.

He also realized that the heavy food added to a brisk horseback ride was unwise. So far, he had taken seven bathroom breaks, each with a differing consequence. Besides feeling generally unclean, The Duke had stepped on an ant hill, goosed himself with a spiky plant, dropped (and lost) a rather expensive bracelet, and stubbed a toe after kicking a large rock in frustration. The extra time in the sun had also given him the start of a prickly sunburn on his neck and forearms.

The compound was still hours away when the shadows started to lengthen. The Duke's belated sense of magical alarm was now painfully reminding him in twinges, tingles, and a few actual convulsions that further delay would result in some truly unfortunate events. The same sense told him that, without a doubt, arriving after dark would cost him dearly.

For the first time in a long while, Duke Winslow was starting to feel a little responsible for the compound in the middle of nowhere that was currently in peril, and what would happen were he to fail in his duties. The Duke set himself in the saddle and urged the horse to canter, feeling each and every bump and jostle acutely.

—

Much activity seemed to be happening all at once on the grounds. Minor explosions, Flashes of light. Some eerie singing that seemed to be compelling Kayra to take action, but she wasn't sure precisely *what* action to take. It was clear that the safest option would be to stay in her little attic room until it all blew over. She looked around. *I could always pick up a little,* she thought.

When her again eyes fell on the tatty blue handwritten volume, she picked it up once more, wondering if she ought to see what might happen. It could prove interesting. As if from a long way away, Kayra was reminded that exciting incidents used to happen to her. And that she liked it.

Decisively, Kayra put on a cloak against the chill of the coming evening. She grabbed the little volume, this time distinctly feeling the tingle in her fingers as they touched the cover. Concealing the book in her apron pocket, Kayra closed the door behind her and began navigating the steep staircase down to the main level and then below.

Strangely, Hugh was crouching in the hallway next to Fenroy's iron door. Hugh gazed idly at a plume of smoke that seemed to be changing into a physical form near the ceiling. He looked unsurprised to see Kayra.

"Hugh, why are you here?"

"Oh. I knew you would be along sometime soon."

"How would you know that?"

Purple lights flashed from under the door opposite the duo. "Just a feeling," Hugh said. "Also, I am quite sure that I ought to be here, too."

Kayra shrugged a shoulder and opened the heavy door to find Fenroy unchained and smiling at them from atop his small desk. Smoke drifted from both his nostrils and his eyes were a dull red.

"Both of you? How wonderful. I am truly excited and thrilled that you could both be here tonight. It's a little bit like a family reunion."

Fenroy clapped and jumped off the table, striding over to his visitors, though stopping several feet short.

"You brought me a treat, didn't you girl?"

Fenroy extended his hands and motioned for Kayra to step closer.

"I won't hurt you. You don't know this," Fenroy lowered his voice to a mock whisper, "but I really can't hurt either of you. Now, who's ready for some fun?"

Kayra pressed a hand to her apron pocket and felt electricity even through the fabric. She closed her eyes with the power. She was suddenly more than a little reluctant to let go of her prize.

"I need to know something first. How do these books nourish you?" Kayra asked. "I've done experiments and I really don't see the connection, except for subject matter."

"How about I tell you after you give me that little tome you're hiding."

Kayra cocked her head at Fenroy. "I think that I would like to know now."

For a moment, Fenroy's eyes flashed bright red as he took another step forward before being stopped forcibly by an unseen force.

The extra light in Fenroy's eyes dimmed and a placating tone quickly replaced it. "No matter. I would love to share it with you."

Kayra looked over at Hugh. He sat on the floor, knees bent in front of him, with a look of utter contentment.

"It is very simple really. It is just that I feed on a certain kind of misery."

"Misery in books?"

Fenroy made a dismissive sound. "Well, obviously, I prefer a living example, but the printed form is better than nothing. And some authors are so utterly descriptive, it really is as though you were there. A good turn of phrase can be as important as the actual event. People often discount presentation."

Kayra nodded at this last word. She did understand that. The book vibrated in her hands. She had decided to give Fenroy the book, but dragging out the moment gave Kayra a strange, surreal pleasure. Or maybe that was Hugh, she felt something odd from his direction, too.

Kayra reached into her pocket and withdrew the worn and beaten book, rubbing her index finger back and forth over its scarred exterior. Fenroy drew in a shuddering breath. She looked back at him plaintively, unafraid to make eye contact now. Kayra had a little something of her own to give back, it seemed.

Teasingly, Kayra opened the spine and let Fenroy glimpse the interior pages.

"Why can't you come any closer?"

Eyes only on the book now, Fenroy spoke without inhibition. "The chair is the last bond that confines me. I have come back into myself enough to break the other restraints. The chair pulls me near it. But … if you give me even a taste of what is in your hands, I can show you the how the smallest amount of my power can break me free. Break you two free as well. You know you are trapped, too, don't you?"

Kayra looked at Hugh who shrugged. Fenroy's last statement didn't make sense … and yet it did. *How long have we been here?* Kayra wondered. It was becoming clearer, though was not yet transparent. The noises and shouts outside the room became louder and more insistent.

"The book, girl. Please." The aching in Fenroy's eyes, unlike his smile, was real.

"You know me, you say," Kayra said. "Why call me *girl?*"

"Your body sometimes changes, though you are still the same inside. We have known each other a long time, you and me. At times, we have even worked toward the same ends."

Kayra felt as though this might be true, even if she didn't understand why.

For the first time since entering the room, Hugh spoke from the floor. "Go on, Kayra. Let's see what happens. Give the old bat his food."

Kayra glanced at the book-bound memorial once more and considered the possibilities. They eventually settled into two choices: to know or not to know. The itching moved from Kayra's fingers and hands up to the top of her arm. Even with consequences … how awful to not know what might have happened, could have happened. She began to reach her hands forward into Fenroy's. His nostrils now held little embers of fire and his eyes bored into hers.

A second, a millisecond before the book crossed over into Fenroy's hands, a figure entered the room at a run and shouted a word.

Everything froze.

The noises stopped, the lights diminished, and Kayra's reaching arms stood still.

Reaching.

The figure was bent over, sucking in heaving breaths, as though it had run faster and longer than it could actually handle. Coughing, it tried to straighten up, bent double again, and continued breathing and coughing. All the while, everyone in the room waited, like icicles.

Finally, the figure spluttered into a vestige of Duke Winslow. "How ridiculous! I'm gone for a few years, decades maybe, and you have all decided to take matters into your own hands. There is a protocol!"

The enraged Duke looked around the silent room and sighed. He waved a hand, and those within the room were again able to speak and move their heads, at least.

"Still nothing to say for yourselves? I am revoking so many privileges."

Kayra didn't know what to say. She felt like she was sifting through memories that she always thought were stories. Now that she could turn her head, she looked at the Duke more fully.

He was a mess. His shirt, blue satin originally, was shredded into tatters. His hair, typically braided and worn beneath a hat, was missing the hat and was filled with an assortment of grasses. His face had a deep gash over one cheek and a few lighter cuts across his forehead. The Duke's pants were missing altogether, his legs covered in a strange purple rash.

Receiving no response, the Duke turned on the trio individually.

"Hugh. I really had higher hopes for you. I honestly thought you could be rehabilitated with time. You had a job, a good position in the kitchen. So disappointing."

Kayra did speak up then, in defense of her friend. "Hugh didn't do anything wrong at all, what are you talking about?"

"How long has he been peppering the food? He usually starts there."

"He's a cook, of course he adds pepper to the food!"

"In vast amounts? Anyone complaining of stomach aches?"

Hugh interjected. "It was just a little fun. And anyway, the pepper is gone now."

The Duke sighed again, pointing at Kayra. "Because *she* took it, of course."

Kayra let her mouth hang open. *How would he know that?*

"This whole experiment is a waste of time. None of you seems to be able to help your own natures." He turned to Fenroy. "And you, given a perfectly good food substitute, still unable to change your attitude. Such a waste."

The Duke started pacing and talking a little to himself. "I guess I have to reset all the memories again. It just doesn't hold for very long. It would be nice to put you all in chains, but then, who would work here to keep it up? Certainly not me."

"Why in the world would you want to chain us?"

The Duke exploded with an exasperated ferocity. "Because you are all daemons, fallen angels, minor deities, and anti-muses. Trouble, every one of you! The world is better off without your lot!"

Fenroy snorted.

"We give you a world to live in, a world in which to function. And what do we get in return. One-hundred percent recidivism. Every. Single. Time."

Hugh looked mildly amused. "Me?"

"Wipe that smile off your face. You're only a minor trick-ster. Not even big time."

"I'll take it." Hugh looked smug.

"And you." He turned to Fenroy. "God of Misfortune on Journeys. How weirdly specific is that? Feeding on the fear and hopelessness of the migrating masses. You can get all the vitamins you need from stories, you know."

"It sounds better in my native tongue: God of the Fucked.

Also, you fed me garden journals and old train schedules."

Hugh raised his head slightly, "Oh, sorry, that was me."

Smoke from Fenroy's nostrils threatened to block their vision.

"Okay, and what about this girl here. Hmm? Care to tell her your little secret? She's not supposed to be here, you know."

The Duke picked at his hair. "What? She's destroyed lives, leveled cities, and started wars. What else I am supposed to do with her?"

Kayra looked confused. Reaching back in her mind, she felt a city in flames. Had she done that?

The Duke was quiet now, dabbing at the blood oozing from his cheek. Fenroy gleefully filled the silence.

"Her body changes occasionally, but I will always recognize her. She isn't an anti-muse at all, you hypocrite. Curiosity is a full-fledged deity. Better than you."

The Duke turned to Kayra, as she let the knowledge realign itself with her. "I'm sorry child. It is a more boring world without you, but it is infinitely safer. There is too much of your grandfather, Chaos, in you."

Kayra was shocked into a thoughtful silence. This did seem to explain quite a lot.

Fenroy continued. "Yes, Duke, so tell us what the world is like without, strife, indifference? Now that the balance wobbles, what do you do with your time?"

"Honestly, there is some singing and dancing, and a lot of dinner parties. It is quite nice. You are not missed." The Duke sniffed.

Kayra cut her eyes at him. "That's because no one knows better. Since now that I know it is my nature, can I ask why you keep us here?"

The Duke straightened up for a moment, but then noticed his lack of clothes and other maladies. He realized that he currently lacked the presence for that kind of haughty look. His voice, though, dripped with it. "Well, I'm Privilege, of course. Everyone else was on board with this, too, though. Peace. Logic. Benevolence. All on my side."

The three still-almost-frozen figures nodded. This also made sense.

"Listen, I'm sorry. I have to reset the timeline now. You will all go to sleep and wake up without remembering our little conversation. Then I will go home and forget my horrible trip here today. I think I can still reschedule my sporting events for next week."

"Yes," said Fenroy, coaxingly. "What happened to you? Looks like you had quite a time."

"You mean besides being sick, the fall down the hill, the tangle with the tree, and ..."

What happened next took only took a fraction of a second. Fenroy reached out to touch the volume. Kayra wrested it from his hands, returning it to her apron pocket. She felt her own magic in full now and erected a barrier of protection.

The Duke looked at his now unfrozen charges. "Ooo, sneaky aren't you, daemon? No, I will not tell you about my journey. And I will make sure you eat stories about small singing animals for a full year. Come Kayra, Hugh."

Fenroy's frozen smile quickly returned as the other two began to walk out of the chamber, leaving him behind. "But Duke ... before you go ... please ... of your latest journey ... if you can't speak it out loud, could I get it in writing?"

In the silence that followed, Fenroy thought. *God of the Fucked indeed.*

———

Kayra awoke in the dormitory feeling weakened. The other servants had already risen and were dressing. She looked at them blearily and sat up, rubbing at a headache. Feeling a reassuring weight against her leg, she reached into a pocket in her apron, letting her fingers brush against a battered book cover. She smiled. Today, she decided, was going to be an interesting day. Full of possibilities. Just the way she liked it.

She bathed quickly and ran upstairs to her old attic, packing a few interesting experiments, a choice of footwear, and one or two other little books that she thought would be good company. Thinking of good company, she grabbed the pepper and found her way down into the kitchens.

"Sorry Hugh, I had to borrow this."

Hugh looked up and met Kayra's eyes, feeling the usual

cloudiness dissipate at her glance.

"No problem. It really is the least of my tools."

"You ready to get out of here?"

Hugh's mischievous smile could light up a room. Hugh took back the pepper and stashed it, along with a few other unlabeled, more potent bottles, in a burlap bag.

"I've been meaning to visit the Winslow castle. I've heard they eat as many as ten meals a day. Can we stop there first?"

Kayra balanced the possibilities on her tongue. "That would be lovely."

AUTHOR'S NOTE

When writing, I love to have my characters dance on that grey edge of right and wrong, good and evil, since we all carry these larger concepts within ourselves in abundance. We like to think that we lean toward the light, but we're also fascinated with those who don't. In this story, I sought to explore what it would be like not to be able to help who we are, but instead always default to a concentrated version of ourselves. This is irregardless of where that grey line might be and what might be put in our path to push us to one side or another.

I also wanted to create a fantastical world where no one would think it odd if your toaster tried to talk to you, or that the gentleman on the corner sold imported magic spells. In addition, down a back alley, there's a cracked mirror that reflects a little bit of light from our own world–in case you recognize anything.

JM

The Shit Collector
MARK KODAMA

I. The Kitchen Mama

The sun has not risen yet. It is early morning at a house of prostitution in a small city in the southern part of the island of Honshu, Japan. The year is 1910. Shizuko, a beautiful woman in her late thirties, prepares breakfast. Her seventeen-year-old son, Minoru, opens the door. He is carrying cordwood for the kitchen stove. The morning is cold and both Shizuko and Minoru wear coats.

"Don't forget your mask," Shizuko says. "And here is your lunch."

"Mother, I have it," Minoru replies.

"Don't rush. Just take your time."

"Don't worry so much." Minoru says. "I will be home by afternoon."

"I really liked your drawings and new poems."

"Thank you, Mother," Minoru says.

"You are talented and getting better. Last night I dreamed that you were living in America and you were driving a grand, brand-new black shiny car with your pretty wife and two young daughters. America, Minoru. Dream of it. Then make it happen. Minoru, find who you are. Once you find who you are, don't let anyone else define you. Paint your own canvas in life. Your life is your own and belongs to no one else."

———

Shizuko is washing rice in the kitchen. Steam from the first pot of rice is already rising from the black pot, bubbling over on the wood-burning stove. Shizuko adds sticks of wood to the fire.

She can feel someone looking at her. She gazes at the reflection in the window and sees Kodama the Elder standing in the kitchen doorway. He swallows hard as he looks upon the former beauty.

—

Yong Ran Pei, the beautiful prostitute, sits on the balcony of the second floor of the brothel and watches the people moving in the street. Her face is painted white and lips red. She sings as she combs her long black hair that falls on the front of her white silk kimonos.

On the street, Fujinaka, the blind bookkeeper, cocks his head as he listens to Yong Ran Pei's lilting voice. "She is just like Shizuko was," Fujinaka says to himself. "Same history. Same fate. Well, some things should be left unsaid."

II. The Shit Collector

Minoru pushes a wooden cart that rattles along the cobblestone street. People cover their noses and run from the stink. A man covering his nose with a cloth quickly hands Minoru a covered bucket then disappears into his building. Ryoji, the brothel owner's son, looks upon Minoru from the second balcony of the brothel. He is dressed in a suit and tie and wears a thin mustache. He stares down upon Minoru with sadness.

—

Minoru arrives at the farm of Matsumura the Mayor on the outskirts of the city. Matsamura is fifty with jet-black hair. He is clean shaven with a medium build. Minoru is selling bags of dried human waste to the farmers. He has big hands and a kind face.

"I have a question for you, Minoru san," Matsamura says. "I hope it does not offend you."

"Yes?"

"Why are you always so happy?" he asks. "This world is so full of sadness and injustice. And the bad are rewarded while the good suffer."

"Why do you think I am always happy when I wear a mask

all the time?"

"I can tell by the way you walk–the way you move," the mayor replies. "And you are always singing such happy songs."

"I don't really know. It seems to me life is a gift and every day offers new presents."

"I like what you say," the mayor nods. "We will see you again next week. I would like to talk more with you."

—

"Why are you wasting your time and energy on Yong Ran Pei?" Shizuko asks her son. "Do you see this coat? Do you think it keeps you warm? No. That is only an illusion. It is the heat from your own body that keeps you warm. The coat only allows you to retain you own heat. Be like your body–the source of your own warmth."

"I'm not wasting my time," Minoru says.

"She is a prostitute, Minoru. She is not the kind of girl you marry. She is not even Japanese."

"I never said I would marry her," Minoru says.

"You don't have to say anything. I know you. I can see it in your eyes. The Chinese have a saying 'Don't play a musical instrument to a cow.'"

"What harm is there in it?"

"She will only bring you tears. Can't you see she sleeps with Kodama the Elder, Kodama the Younger, and the customers, all who have money. We don't have anything. See her new red silk kimono–a gift from Kodama the Younger. Her shiny new gold pendant–a gift from Kodama the Elder. What do you have to give her?

"Love."

"All your tears for someone incapable of love," his mother says. "Focus your efforts on improving yourself and you will find someone who will appreciate your gifts."

"Thoughts of Yong Ran Pei make me eager to get up each and every day."

"Youth is fleeting. The gifts will stop someday, then you will find you are just like everyone else. And then you will stop caring. People get older. Outer beauty is transient. Inner beauty is eternal. Dream of America. Taste it. Breathe it. When you get there, your past will not matter. You will be able to succeed on your own abilities. Prepare yourself and be bold when the moment comes. Be ready for opportunity when it presents itself. Success or failure in life turns on a few key moments."

"I will bring you with me," Minoru says. His mother looks beautiful again, like when she was twenty. She smiles as her breasts heave.

"No, Minoru. This is *your* dream. Maybe it could have been my dream once upon a time, but I am old, and my life is here.

"I will bring you with me."

"Yes, Minoru," Shikoku laughs, and Minoru's eyes light up. "I would like that. Some day we will climb to the top of the Statue of Liberty together. Now here is dinner for Kodama the Elder and Kodama the Younger. Please take them their meals."

Kodama the Elder enters the room. Kodama is small but strongly built. He is in his mid-forties but looks much younger and has jet black hair. "Hello, Shizuko and Minoru," he says kindly. "I hope I am not interrupting anything."

"Nothing important Kodama san," Shikoku says, her eyes looking down.

"I have more drawing paper and ink for your son," Kodama the Elder announces. "Minoru is very talented. We are all so very proud of him. And here is a book on Western paintings.

"Thank you, Uncle," Minoru says.

"I must be on my way," the brothel owner says. "I have business to take care of. I will be back tonight. Study hard, Minoru."

Please take your meal before you go," Shikoku says. "Minoru, serve Kodama san his meal. I prepared your favorite broiled salmon."

———

Matsumura the Mayor and Minoru stand outside the mayor's farmhouse.

"I have the answer to your question, Matsumura san," Minoru says.

"What question was that?" the mayor asks.

"The one you asked me last week."

"You mean about happiness?"

"Yes."

"What is the answer then?"

"I dream about America."

"How do you know about America?" the mayor asks.

"I read about it."

"I didn't know you could read."

"My mother taught me."

"Ah, the beautiful Shizuko. Who taught your mother how to read?"

"I don't know. I never thought about it."

"What a beautiful soul your mother has. She only thinks of you."

"America is the place where anyone can become president. You are only limited by your own limitations and the limits of your imagination."

"Ah, if only such a wonderful place existed, Minoru. The world is so full of pettiness and oppression."

Minoru points to the temple and smiles. "It does exist, and I will get there. To make great things happen you must dream them first.

Matsumura claps Minoru on the back. "Young man, I like the way you think. Dream, Minoru. Dream."

Suddenly, the two men hear a loud shriek. The mayor's wife runs toward them. "Ryoske, Bunni has fallen into the cesspool," she shouts in panic.

Both men run to the cesspool. Minoru, running ahead of the mayor, jumps into the cesspool and pulls the child out of the sewage.

"Get clean water,' Minoru shouts.

The young man carries the child out of the pond. They go to the well. They wash the child. Minoru takes off his own filthy clothes and then he washes his body. The stench is unbearable. The mayor's wife brings a bowl of cold water for Minoru.

"Thank you, Minoru san," the mayor's wife says, tears in her eyes.

"Yes. Minoru san," the mayor adds. "We owe our lives to you."

Minoru bows his head.

"A thousand thanks to you," the mayor's wife says.

"I will bring you some new clothes," the mayor says. "You

can wear my clothes."

"Please wash my clothes," Minoru replies. "I will wear them when they are dry. You are too kind to me."

"You will wear my clothes," the mayor insists. "I will tell Kodama san about this. His family once lived here as samurai family. What can I do for you, Minoru san?

"Nothing. What I did was nothing."

"You are too humble."

"Yes, Matsumura san."

"What do you really want? Please tell me."

"Nothing, really."

"You must want something."

Minoru hesitates and then replies. "I want to learn how to ride a horse and shoot a gun like a samurai."

"I will teach you myself," Mastumura says.

III. The Prostitute

Minoru sits stoically, cross legged, on the wood floor outside the room of the prostitute Yong Ran Pei. Laughter from a young man and the woman emanate from the room. The man calls to Minoru from the room. It is the owner's son, Kodama the Younger. He is short, slight, with a thin pencil mustache. Kodama, dressed in a colorful blue and white cloth kimono, sits upon a silk cushion behind a low cherry wood table, drinking sake from a black and red lacquer bowl.

"Minoru, fetch the red kimono in my room and bring it here."

"Yes, Kodama san," he says, eyes downcast. "Right away."

Minoru leaves and then returns quickly with the beautiful red silk kimono. "May I enter the room."

"Yes, come in," Kodama the Younger says as he eyes the young prostitute, Yong Ran Pei, who is sitting next to Kodama. She is half naked, her kimono covering her hips. Her silken hair half covers her firm young breasts.

"You see my darling, I am a man who knows few words," Kodama the Younger says, imperiously lifting his bowl of sake. "But I am a man of action."

Kodama the Younger gives the expensive silk kimono to

Yong Ran Pei. She squeals with delight, flashing an exquisite smile.

"This is beautiful," she says, feigning surprise. Although she is young, she is accustomed to receiving gifts from wealthy men. "Thank you Kodama san."

Kodama the Younger, noticing Minoru was still in the room, says curtly, "Fool, what are you doing still standing here like a country bumpkin? Can't you see we are having a private moment? Wait outside."

Minoru bows his head and returns to his place outside the room.

—

Minoru is lying in a flat bed with the beautiful Korean prostitute, Yong Ran Pei. Her gold pendant around her neck dances as she moves. Yong Ran Pei rises and folds her red kimono before placing it on a pile of other kimonos.

"You are beautiful," Minoru says, his eyes sparkling.

"I know," she says and laughs.

"I love you," Minoru says.

She looks at him for a moment. Her large dark eyes melting. She heaves a sigh. "I know."

"I have something for you," Minoru says, as Yong Ran Pei places her kimonos in the closet with her other gifts.

"What is it?"

"You must turn your back."

"What kind of present?

Minoru motions for her to turn her back. He hands her a package wrapped in light red paper and tied with a dark red ribbon. She opens the present. It is a poem with a drawing on it. She is delighted.

"You know I can't read. Read it to me."

They both sit up on the mat on the floor. Yong Ran Pei smiles at him.

Minoru recites his haiku.

"Your white knight is here,
Not atop a great war steed,
But walking on foot."

"Someday I will marry you and take you to America."

"Aiyo!" she says. "You are such a dreamer. And what makes you think I would like to go to America?"

"Because in an America even a poor man can own a mansion, wear the finest clothes, and eat steak every night.

"You talk too much.

"I just say what is in my heart."

"Minoru, you can't change your fate. Your fate is decided by the gods."

"You *can* change your fate. If you let other lesser people define your dreams, then your fate will be decided. Life is a canvas. And the canvas is blank. You must paint your own canvas with your own dreams."

"What makes you so restless?"

"Sometimes I feel like I am buried alive in a tomb. I either have to break free or kill myself.

"Minoru, you are a good boy but poor and from a poor family. Have you considered that I may have dreams of my own?"

"We are poor but why should we live in cages built by others. What are your dreams? Define yourself. Do you love me?"

"I don't love anyone. I don't believe in love.

"If you do not love anyone, including yourself, then how can anyone love you? Sometimes, love is all we have."

"I don't like you when you are like this, Minoru. Talk, talk, talk. It gives me a headache.

"Do you love me?"

She looks away. "No. You are a poor boy."

"I ask again: do you love me?"

"Sometimes, I love you."

—

"You are a good boy, Minoru," Fujinaka the blind bookkeeper says. "But someday you will learn the natural order of things. It is better you learn this sooner rather than later. The gods distain the impertinent.

"Alexander was king of Epirus. In Epirus, the River Acheron flowed. It was foretold that Alexander would die at the River Acheron. So, when Alexander invaded Italy with his mighty army he was sure of his success for he knew he would die at the River Acheron in Greece.

"When Alexander was crossing a river in Italy, the enemy appeared in great numbers. When Alexander asked his Italian companions what the name of the river was, they told him Acheron. Alexander then charged the enemy and died a noble death. You see, Minoru, even kings cannot escape their fate."

"Did my mother speak to you?"

"Yes of course. She is concerned about you. She has enough worries, don't you think? Life is difficult and not always fair. You must learn to endure."

"Yes. Uncle. You are right about everything."

"You must know your place. The Matsumuras ruled this community with the Kodamas sitting at their right hand. The Kodamas became too arrogant and fell from grace. They did not know their place. The nail that sticks up gets hammered down."

"Yes, uncle."

"Men who do not know how to live by the rules are men on their own. They are outlaws, animals, not fit to live in a society of men. Let me tell you the story about the monkey god. The monkey god was talented but undisciplined. The monkey god became so power hungry that he challenged the king of the gods himself for hegemony over the universe. Finally, the king of gods put a mountain on top of the monkey god, imprisoning the monkey god for a thousand years in granite. Grass bends and is eternal. But even the hardest stone gets worn down by rushing water and is washed away to the sea. Know your place. You cannot change your destiny."

IV. The Mayor

Mayor Matsumura invites Minoru to join him and his men to buy horses in Kyoto.

"I must ask Kodama san," Minoru says.

"I spoke with him already. It has all been arranged. I have a gun and a horse for you. We leave on Saturday. Be here at dawn." The mayor gives Minoru and handful of coins. "This is for you."

"Thank you," Minoru says. "I will give them to my master."

"Kodama san has been paid. These are for you, my young friend. When I look into them, I can see a thousand things going on behind your eyes. I see a great future for you, Minoru. Greatness can come from anywhere, even from the most humble."

—

Matsumura and his entourage pass through Rashomon Gate, and enter into the ancient capital. Nicha, a Buddhist monk, dressed in saffron robes, preaches to a hostile crowd that has gathered at the market to watch a tightrope walker cross a high wire strung across two temple towers.

"Friends. I herald the coming of the higher man.," the monk says. "God is dead. There is only beast and man. Rise above the common man, the herd. Live the life of the higher man. There is only beast and man. I am the monk, Nicha, from Nagasaki, the city of the Christian martyrs. I've come down from the mountains to save you. There are no sinners; no saints. There is no afterlife. Rise above the common man. Rely upon yourselves for your own salvation. I love followers who are leaders and leaders who follow. I love those who love to think and think to love. I love those who know their own limits and know that there are no limits. I love those who hate me and hate those who love me. I love those who fly free to be devoured by those who are caged. I herald the higher man who will smash the tablets of morality and create a new set of values."

"We have heard enough of this," a voice from the crowd calls out. "We want to see the tightrope walker."

"You have evolved from worms to man," the monk says. "Yet you still are worms. Man laughs at apes. Similarly, the higher man laughs at the common man. I see you laughing at me. Such icy laughter."

The tightrope walker emerges from one of the temple towers. He proceeds to cross the tight rope. When he reaches the half-way point, a jester emerges from the same tower.

"Out of my way," the jester says. "Make way for your better."

The jester jumps over the tightrope walker, causing him to lose his balance and fall to the ground, arms flailing in the air. The crowd gasps and scatters as the tightrope walker falls to his death.

The monk quietly speaks to the dying tightrope walker. The

monk then hoists the corpse of the tightrope walker over his shoulder and walks through the parting crowd toward Rashomon Gate.

Matsumura turns to Minoru. "Everything is always before us. Some people see it and others don't."

———

Matsumura, two of his men, and Minoru ride their horses on their return trip from Kyoto. Matsumura's men hold the reins of four additional horses that Matsumura bought in Kyoto. They arrive at a clearing at the end of the cedar forest. There is a small cemetery to the right of the men. The freshly dug graves house the bodies of the soldiers who died in the recently concluded Russo-Japanese War.

In the clearing at the crossroad, four bandits armed with carbines and dressed in tattered Army uniforms approach. The leader wears a back patch over his left eye. The left side of his face appears to be half melted. He has a withered left arm and he walks with a limp. He brandishes a pistol in his right hand.

"We are revenue collectors," the bandit leader announces.

"For which town?" Mayor Matsumura asks. "I may know your mayor."

"Is it not enough that we just say it?" the bandit says.

"What do you say we owe?" the mayor inquires.

"What do you have? Never mind. I will check for myself."

"Stop where you are," the mayor says through clenched teeth. "We are not going to give you anything. If you take another step you are a dead man."

Minoru thinks that if he were the bandits he would put someone behind them. Since they are evenly matched there must be a reason why they are so bold. He looks at the tree behind to the right and sees a pair of feet dangling from the branches.

"We are not looking for trouble," the bandit chief says.

"Neither are we," the mayor replies. "Step aside."

"As you wish."

The bandit then turns his back and starts to walk away. He spins suddenly, drawing a handgun. Without hesitation, Minoru shoots him in the chest. Matsumura shoots and wounds a second bandit who turns and runs.

Minoru then turns and shoots the bandit lurking in the tree.

The man falls and hits the bushes.

One of Matsumura's men shoots a fourth bandit who attempts to flee. A fifth bandit escapes unharmed.

Minoru dismounts his horse. He approaches the mortally wounded bandit leader who is crawling toward the cemetery. Minoru then shoots the man in the back his head.

"Good work young Minoru," the mayor says. The mayor throws him a white cloth handkerchief. "I was thinking the same thing. Wipe the blood from your face and hands. I thought they had a man behind us. I just couldn't see him. You are a young man of talent. A man of talent is always useful."

"Thank you, Matsumura san. You are too kind."

"Here. Take this horse. It is my gift to you."

V. The Brothel Owner

Kodama the Elder, Kodama the Younger, and Minoru stand together beneath the balcony of the brothel. Kodama the Elder and Minoru talk as Kodama the Younger stands stoically with them, eyes downcast.

"I am very proud of you Minoru," Kodama the Elder says and smiles. "You are a man. Matsumura san has told me all you have done. Be patient. I have my own plans for you."

"Thank you, Uncle. I am not worthy of your honor."

—

Kodama the Younger and the bouncer, Nomi, wait at the stable next to the brothel as Minoru approaches.

"You are a shit collector, Minoru. Nothing more. That is all you are. That is all you will ever be. I am from a samurai family. If we had not suffered such reversals, we would still be with Matsumura and you and your mother would be on the streets. That horse is mine. We own you. We own your mother. You are our servant. Everything that you own belongs to us."

"I am sorry, Kodama san, but you are mistaken," Minoru says, eyes downcast. "Matsumura san gave the horse to me for killing the bandits. He taught me how to ride and shoot a gun. If anything is unclear, Matsumura san can clarify it.

"There is nothing to clarify. It is you who is mistaken. The beast is mine. The girl is mine, too. You know your poem? It made great toilet paper."

"It is not surprising that you would think that is what it is for."

"You are very womanish. Poems. Drawings. You are a woman!"

"The horse is mine, Kodama san."

"You will pay for your insolence. Nomi grab him.

The large bouncer grabs Minoru from behind then ties him up, wrapping a rope around his arms. He then forces Minoru down on his knees. Nomi forces Minoru's right hand onto a stone. With the side of a steel ax, Kodama the Younger smashes the hand. Minoru screams in pain.

Kodama the Elder and Fujinaka the blind bookkeeper enter the stable.

"What is this?" Kodama the Elder asks.

"My God!" Fujinaka says.

Kodama the Younger and Nomi quickly stand at attention. They look at the ground.

"Send for the doctor," Kodama the Elder tells the bookkeeper. Kodama the Elder, his face red, looks up a Nomi who is a head taller than him. The bouncer trembles. Kodama cuffs him, knocking him to the ground. "You have five minutes to pack your belongings and leave," he tells the bouncer.

"Papa san, the horse is ours," Kodama the Younger says.

"That is for me alone to say. Did you break Minoru's hand?"

Kodama the Elder picks up the ax and raises it up to the light.

"I hit Minoru with the ax, Papa san," Kodama the Younger says, eyes downcast. Kodama the Elder slaps Kodama the Younger in the face and then punches him in the stomach. He grabs him by the hair and punches him in the face again.

"Papa san, Nomi is not responsible. He was doing as I told him."

"Each man is responsible for his own action." Kodama the Elder turns to Minoru. "Let me see you hand."

"Papa san, I take full responsibility," Kodama the Younger says.

"You are lucky that I don't crush your hand. Idiot! Get out

of my sight."

———

Kodama the Elder and Fujinaka are together on the street below the brothel. "This won't happen again. I'm going to hit them where it hurts. They will not fight anymore."

"What are you going to do?" Fujinaka asks.

"What I must do."

———

Minoru returns to see Yong Ran Pei but she is gone. Kodama the Elder, Kodama the Younger, and Minoru's mother are there to greet him. Minoru's right hand is bandaged.

"Control your anger," Shizuko says. "No more violence. Violence never satisfies anger. It only feeds a greater appetite for more anger."

"You boys are not to fight like that again," Kodama the Elder says.

"I did nothing," Minoru insists.

"Put it all behind you," his mother says.

"It does not matter," Kodama the Elder says. "She's gone. I sold her. There is nothing to fight about any more.

"Do you mean the horse?"

"No, the girl," Kodama the Elder says.

"Not Yong Ran Pei."

"Now do you see what you've done?" Kodama the Younger says. He is furious.

"Be quiet," Kodama the Elder says.

"She is all I have," Minoru says.

"And you did not really have her either," Kodama the Younger taunts. "We owned her, too."

"I told you to keep quiet," Kodama the Elder growls.

"Your mother is my father's concubine," Kodama the Younger says. "She warms his bed at night and warms his meals during the day. And you are our servant."

Minoru, enraged, rushes Kodama the Younger and knocks him backward out the second story window. Kodama the Younger breaks his neck and dies instantly.

The elder Kodama charges at Minoru. He punches him and then retrieves a knife. Minoru kicks him in the groin. Minoru runs to his room and grabs in pistol. With his left hand he shoots Kodama the Elder in the chest. Minoru then shoots the groaning Kodama in head.

Minoru turns to his mother who has witnessed the events. Her mouth is agape and tears run down her cheeks.

"What have you done?" she asks. "You must go now. Go to the mayor. He is a good man and will help you."

"Come with me," Minoru says.

"No, this is my home," his mother replies. She turns to one of the prostitutes "Send for the police and the doctor." Turning to a second prostitute, she says, "Call Fujinaka, the bookkeeper."

She turns to her son. "Go. I will see you in the next life. America, Minoru. Go to America, the land where dreams come true. Go quickly."

Minoru turns and runs out the brothel. He goes to the stable, mounts his horse, and rides to the mayor's farm.

———

"You must leave quickly," the mayor says. "Here is some food and money to get you to Osaka. Fujinaka has arranged for you to work as a sailor on a merchant ship called *The Phoenix,* bound for America. Meet him at the old inn."

"Thank you, Matsumura san."

"No time for thanks. You must go quickly. If you are caught, I never saw you."

"Goodbye, uncle. Thanks for everything."

"I hope you find your dreams in America. I think you will succeed. You are a capable young man. Now, go."

———

"Now that we are safely about the train, I must tell you something terrible that has happened," Fujinaka says.

Minoru is silent, still thinking of what had just happened. He looks up with vacant eyes.

"I did not want to tell you earlier because I did not want to impede your escape," the bookkeeper says.

"What can be worse than what has already happened?"

Fujinaka is silent for a moment, reluctant to further hurt the sensitive young man, but at the same time eager to unburden himself of his secret. "Your mother is dead."

Minoru stares back in silence.

"She hung herself shortly after you left."

"My God! Am I responsible, Fujinaka san?"

"It is complicated. You must judge for yourself. I will also tell you who your father is."

"Is he alive?"

"He was … until you killed him. Kodama the Elder was your father and Kodama the Younger was your half-brother. Your mother was his favorite prostitute. She was very intelligent and so he hired tutors to secretly educate her. After his wife died giving birth to Kodama the Younger, he asked your mother to marry him but she refused."

"My God. How could I be so blind?"

"The Kodamas had always protected the unprotected. That is why the clan had a falling out with the Matsumuras. A powerful member of the Matsumura clan raped a prostitute, so a Kodama killed him. At first the Kodamas protected the prostitutes and then they started running the brothels. Soon they became dependent on the trade. Your father was an uneducated man but someone who appreciated the value of education and who always did his best to be a just man.

"Your father loved you, too. He had you sell dung to the farmers and then held the money in trust for you. When you get to Seattle, you need to swim ashore. The captain will report you dead. Find the Waterfront Hotel. More money will await you there. I have friends there, you see."

"My God."

"As far as your brother, he was a good boy. He was just so jealous of you."

"Jealous of me? I have nothing."

"He had no mother to look out for him. And what kind of talent did he really have?"

"All I know is that he hated me."

"You need to be able to walk in another's shoes to really understand them. There is no time to dwell on it. We've got to get to Osaka. *The Phoenix* leaves port in two days for Seattle. Put all this behind you. It was your mother's dream to give you a new life. There was only oppression for you here, Minoru. You are a very capable young man. Seek your fortunes in America. I lived in America for 10 years. It may not be the country you think it is. But nothing is for free in this world. And that which is hard earned is more valuable than that which is given to you for free."

"Do you know where Young Ran Pei is?"

"Yes. But I will not tell you. All these people have died so you can now live. Minoru, make the most of your life. The gods control everything. The gods say people cannot escape their fates. But maybe you can. Good luck Minoru."

—

Minoru is naked on the deck of the ship in Puget Sound. It is pitch black on a moonless night. He holds a small bundle of clothes and shoes in his left hand.

"Death or a new life," Minoru says.

He then jumps from the deck of the ship into the frigid water of Puget Sound and swims for land. The small bundle of clothes is tied to his head.

AUTHOR'S NOTE

At the time I wrote "The Shit Collector" I had just finished reading Frederich Nietzche's *Thus Spoke Zarathrusta*. I liked the idea of *ubermench* or superman, someone who refused to live by the rules of a constrained society. Since Japanese society, especially during the turn of the 20th century, was rigid but rapidly changing, I thought it would be a perfect setting for my story.

As a person who collected human waste from brothels to sell to local farmers, the main character, Minoru, would be at the very bottom of this society and, therefore, would have the most incentive to want to break free from its rules.

I think most of us long to break free of society's prejudices, to fulfill their dreams, and to make the most of their human potential. It takes great courage to do this. I think this is what my tale is really about.

MK

broken
as
fuck
LOLA STEEL

some of us are broken;
we simply don't fit.
fucked.
we are born,
and from the moment we can think and conceive of putting our
thoughts into actions,
we strive to enmesh ourselves with our surroundings.
we know that it is safe there, in the space of blending in.
the space of being hidden.
secure.

we know the risk of not belonging.
the risk that it is to be alone, vulnerable, unsafe.
to be without,
tribe
herd
house
kin
clan,
alone.

we feel the fear
but can't find where it lives within us.
it is like our heartbeat,
simply there.
this fear of solitude, of aloneness.
it is deep, integral, unwavering.
so we blend in. we fit.
we craft ourselves to be unseen,
to be safe and secure in our invisibility.

to belong.
we know that it is a lie.
we know that underneath our surface that blends in, we are someone
else.
someone and something that aches to be seen, felt, touched.
we crave it.
we yearn for someone to see us.
not just what is on the surface but what is inside.
we are terrified to be seen.

yet more terrified that we will never be seen.
we are scared that someday we won't be able to hide.
and yet more scared that we will always remain hidden.
we are afraid that one day,
the truth of who we are will be written on our skin,
glaring in its raw honesty.
bared for all to see.
we have learned well,
creating a brilliant resemblance of what we see around us.

we are safe in blending in.
we are welcomed; we are embraced and held close.
we fit.
but we know that we don't,
that it's a lie.
we are stunning artists of illusion, birthing and carrying on our skins
the armour to move through
life, unseen and safe.
we scream silently inside all the while.

we rage and decimate ourselves where no one can see the wounds.
it tears at us, relentless,
ripping us apart slowly in a thousand invisible cuts,
from the inside.
it reaches for the surface of our skin that has so painstakingly been
tended to and guarded.
it demands to be seen.
for those of us lucky enough,
there is a day when the projected image flickers.

for some it is almost imperceptible at first,
our hidden unseen self smells the freedom through the cracks
and it smiles.
feeding on the exposure, it grows and rushes forward before it has a
chance at being halted.
those around notice the differences, tiny at first,
then more profound.
they back away, they retreat,
they distance themselves.

for others, it is an explosion.
violent destruction that destroys the illusion.
the unbearable suffocation and invisibility ignites,
bursting forth,
demolishing the camouflage.
the risk of being seen is nothing compared to the risk of being not
seen.
that truth, once shown to ourselves, cannot be unknown.

some of us are broken;
we simply don't fit.
we are fucked.
we are the lucky ones.

AUTHOR'S NOTE

At times, a piece of writing simply flows, and it reveals to you a truth that you never knew. This poem is an example of that.

"Broken as Fuck" was born from a conversation with a friend who expressed that he was "too broken" to ever hope for an intimate relationship. As we talked, we laughed about the reality that everyone seems to be broken in some way. This piece speaks to my own journey after that conversation to inspect, own, embrace–and see the beauty of–what I considered my own broken self. The things that make us "broken" also make us amazing, and those of us who are broken, are truly the lucky ones for how it shapes us.

LS

I curse when I get really upset. Letting off steam that way makes me feel a little bit better. I've been through a lot, but I have never had the urge to go postal. I thank fuck for that.

Oliver Markus Malloy
Bad Choices Make Good Stories - Going to New York

'Cause Dammit, I'm Still Alive

ANTHONY CRUTCHER

I wake up some mornings
with fog inside my eyes,
and bones stiff, stiff, stiff
from my ankles to my thighs.

Muscles are aching
and my heart is aching too.
Mind not connecting sometimes,
then I'm not sure what to do.

Coming and going–tired
exhausted half the time,
moving fast as I can 'til
Tired trips me from behind.

Day by day I must go on
fighting with all this jive.
My only choice–to fight you see,
'cause dammit, I'm still alive!

AUTHOR'S NOTE

This poem is the result of conversations that I have had with a friend who was diagnosed with multiple sclerosis. Over the course of several months, my friend would tell me what he was experiencing mentally and physically because of the illness. From these conversations I began to compose "'Cause Dammit, I'm Still Alive." I envisioned my friend's struggle of first trying to move in the morning, the frustration at being unable to function as during the pre-illness days, and the frustration of walking and then suddenly becoming exhausted as though being unexpectedly tripped. My friend explained to me one day the need to continue to function as normally as possible given the challenges of the illness. Hence the poem's title.

AC

Huffy Wee Fuckin Bampot

JAN McGUIRE

The City of Council Bluffs, Iowa, advertised, "Bike the Bluffs," to take place on a Sunday in May, two weeks before school was out. Between my graduate classes, grading student papers, and running my two teenage daughters around town, I hadn't done much more in the preceding months than walk on my treadmill and lift weights. Still, it was touted as a leisurely bike ride. Of course I could handle it.

My friends were wary when I invited them to join me. Linda declined with a lame excuse about nursing a painful knee, and Becky opted to browse at the farmer's market instead.

"It doesn't sound leisurely at all, and I don't want to feel rushed," Becky said.

I thought it was an odd comment because the event was clearly advertised as "a leisurely ride for the whole family." The ad stated that cyclists could ride at their own pace. It seemed as if my friends were acting like cerebral, little old ladies even though they were at least 10 years away from retirement. Unfortunately, Erin was working out of town and unable to join me, so I'd be doing the bike ride solo. I guess I didn't mind being "the woman riding alone." Besides, it wasn't really an event that lends itself to chit chat. Huffy wee fuckin bampot, we are all getting older, but I wasn't going down without a fight. This was foreshadowing at its finest.

———

I arrived, alone, comforted by the sight of children who were here with their parents. It was a leisurely ride. The event leader offered free flashing lights that clipped to bike handlebars for added visibility. The poor man hadn't even finished his sentence before being besieged by adults, hands outstretched and fingers wiggling like hungry zombies. A fit, middle-aged man sitting on his bike with an expensive haircut and a green biking jersey from the Tour de France, insisted on taking two. The leader dug into his now near-empty Walmart bag and fished out the remaining lights. My gaze turned to three girls, possibly ages eight, nine, and ten, waiting patiently, knowing they had no power to grab what remained in the bag. The ride leader stuffed a flasher in my hand. The two older girls snagged the last of the flashers, leaving the younger girl empty-handed. She walked sadly back to her waiting parents, and a toddler sibling packed in a bike trailer. I touched the back of her tiny white T-shirt.

"Take mine," I said, and handed over my green, stretchy, plastic flasher.

"Thanks," she said, smiling.

I already knew how to look both ways and, besides, it was a sunny 10:00 AM. I stared at Mr. Tour de France, quietly disgusted with him as he strapped flashers onto his expensive road bike. What a wanker. It was all poorly managed. The ride leader should have simply offered the lights to children, and then leave the adults to grabble over whatever remained.

We were soon underway. I began to walk my untested Jamis bicycle, the only female-owned bike company, with the front of the pack.

"Pink glove!" a voice hollered from the back.

I immediately looked at my fisted grip to see one pink bicycle glove and stepped off the trail onto the grass. I never wear pink but had purchased the pink gloves because they reminded me of my adorable daughters. It was disappointing to fall to the back of the pack, but I reminded myself that this was a leisurely ride. *Who cares if you're in the front or the back? It's not like it's a race.* I placed my bike on the grass off the trail and tried to walk nonchalantly back against the stream of cyclists to find the missing glove. *Why would somebody just holler rather than pick it up and relay it forward?* I wondered. *I was in the front for heaven's sake.*

With both gloves intact, I mounted my bike and rode in the back with a cluster of cyclists. A clear deficit. To my left I saw the girl I'd given my light to. She smiled shyly, I warmly smiled back.

—

Mile 1: I carefully maneuvered around the slower riders; mostly children and their parents. *Damn that pink glove,* I sulked, *I should have taken my Trek.* My twenty-year-old Trek was faster and took less effort to ride. Like me, 20 years ago, it was built for speed. I found myself immersed with dawdling adults.

Mile 3: I pumped my legs just a little more to get a head of the dawdlers. I felt anxious. Not that I had a plan, but the ride wasn't going *as* planned. If I turned around now, I still would have logged six or seven miles. A good first ride of the summer. But the only way I would have allowed myself to turn around was if nobody was looking. Too embarrassing otherwise. It was impossible.

Mile 6: I found myself between packs and knew I couldn't keep up my pace for twenty-two miles. I decided to just catch up with a group of forty-something men ahead of me. Then I would relax a bit and enjoy the view.

I was aghast when we arrived at a red traffic light and everyone slowed to a stop. Nobody went thought it. Couples and friends chatted without a care in the world, clearly enjoying the company of their companions. Car traffic was light, and even without the stretchy green flasher, I knew I could cross the street without consequences. Still, I was clearly a follower and sat with the herd, eavesdropping on the conversations of strangers. After several long minutes, the light turned green. My right leg felt tense as I thrust down on my perfectly placed raised pedal for maximum acceleration. I bolted to blow off the ridiculous red-light group, but the forty-something men were out of sight.

Mile 8: Decision time. I could go right and circle Lake Manawa, or cut the course and go left toward downtown. Again, I considered turning around to take the trail back home. I craved the super power of invisibility. Once an athlete, always an athlete. It's troubling to be out of shape and competitive on the same day. I took the path less traveled and couldn't stop myself from hooking a right. The humidity and heat around the lake surprised me, but the landscape was flat, so I increased my pace. I didn't see many people behind me after that, and I wondered if they had wisely turned left, or turned around.

Mile 10: An odd assortment of people popped up around me, lake property residents no doubt. I looked ahead for my forty-something men in their fancy biking jerseys, suddenly conscious of my own attire, which included a gray tank top and a wobbly bike helmet.

Feeling fatigued, I suddenly realized my body could no longer stay in shape through the winter by doing minimal exercise. I was exerting far too much effort around the lake and I, again, reminded myself this was not a race. This was a friendly, leisurely ride. A friendly, leisurely ride where nobody spoke or acknowledged me. I told myself to take it easy or somebody would soon have to call me a freakin' ambulance.

Mile 11: A mom, approximately 15 years my junior, in a black cotton tank top passed me sitting upright on her Pee Wee Herman Schwinn Western Flyer. I'm sure she did it on purpose. Pee Wee rode alone without a care in the world. I felt offended and made it my life's mission to pass by mile twelve.

Mile 12: With great effort, I passed her and continued to round the lake, wondering if I should have planned for a sag wagon. I wasn't having fun. Pee Wee suddenly zipped past me again as we came out of the lake area. I cursed my lack of fitness and wanted to be justified in blaming my age.

Mile 13: Pee Wee went off the trail in the direction of a nearby McDonalds. I wondered if she knew she was going the wrong way. She was doing too well to quit, and I naively kept looking behind me in hopes of seeing her return. I wondered if she was okay.

Mile 15: My incentive lowered. I was never going to catch up, and there was no one behind me. I didn't understand where everybody had gone. I went under the bridge, where I initially decided to circle the lake, and I saw my little eight-year-old friend with her green, stretchy flasher resting on the grass. The whole family smiled and waved at me. I returned a wide smile, pretending I was enjoying myself. This was my last chance to make a U-turn and head back. Instead, I continued peddling ahead.

My forty-something men were stopped at the next intersection. They talked about ordering lunch after the ride. I passed them, feeling a momentary sense of victory, but they passed me within the next mile. I wanted to chat with them, but as "the woman riding alone," I didn't want to seem like an intruder. I was always independent and frequently worked alone, but I missed my spouse and knew this leisurely ride would be more enjoyable with Erin. I wondered what secret knowledge Becky had when she declined this family ride. Perhaps she knew I couldn't ride leisurely, and thus chose to avoid me.

I usually didn't notice I was out of shape after the winter. It was typical for me to continue my summer activities without too much grief in the spring. I didn't think of using suntan lotion, and my pasty-white legs were feeling the heat from an unusual warm May afternoon. I was certain several riders had coerced friends or family members to bail them out. *"Meet me at the lake. Bring your bike carrier and I'll buy you a beer."* Quitters. I wish I had thought of that, but my kids were too young to drive, and Becky and Linda were sauntering around the farmer's market, probably sitting in the shade drinking organic wild berry tea. Damn it, I hoped my water would last in these desert-like conditions.

A large group ahead of me was suddenly visible as I rounded the path. I perked up like a dog spotting a squirrel. I gained on them, a group of older riders, possibly in their healthy sixties. They looked like they biked regularly and that this was not their first ride of the year. They had impressive bikes and jerseys and seemed to be chatting and enjoying each other's company. As a former track coach, I calculated the geriatric group was approximately four hundred meters ahead of me. A full lap around the track, and they were currently going my speed. They must have been near the front of the pack at the starting point.

Mile 16: I increased the rhythm of my tired quads to decrease their lead and eventually caught up to them. I had gone too fast for sixteen miles. I began to think devious thoughts of going off the trail and taking a shortcut back to my car parked at the start of the leisurely ride that was most certainly not a race. But there was no short cut. The trail was as close to a direct route as I was going to get at this point. My legs were lead and, after all I had done, my newfound geriatric bikers didn't seem to notice I had closed in and was flanking them. I am a teacher, for God's sake, not a creepy rider looking to run somebody off the trail or steal the contents of their fanny pack. *Somebody speak to me!* I was deflated. I was "the woman riding alone."

Mile 17: Jesus, Mary, I thought I was going to die! My legs had become numb and I didn't recall my bike seat ever feeling like a stone. I wondered if I would be able to sit down for the next few days.

Mile 18: A horrible image of people running marathons losing their ability to hold their bladder and having their sphincter blow out came to mind.

Mile 19: I rode with the forty-something men and really didn't give a shit. Enough already. At the next right, I took a left and rode into downtown. Not surprisingly, no one noticed. I peddled slowly, standing atop my pedals. I reached the foot of a hill and gazed around. The trail was only a few blocks away, but I didn't think anybody had noticed me all day, so I got dismounted my bike and walked it up the hill. The shame of it all. I promised myself to die with this secret.

Mile 20: I returned to the trail, an old man on a squeaky road bike passed me in a red, white, and blue cycling jersey and toe clips. I was in the home stretch to my car with the freakin' wind blowing against me. Always against me.

Mile 21: Pee Wee appeared out of nowhere and sailed by me once more. *Cheater!* I wanted to point my finger at her and alert the authorities, "She cheated!" But no one probably noticed her either. I thought about rolling down the hill into the river, but I would have drowned before anyone tried to save me. I checked my speed and was struggling at an embarrassing nine miles per hour as I fought the wind. I passed a jogger, excited by this triumph, but worried I wouldn't be able to create any distance between us. I kept pedaling, forging ahead by will, which was all that remained.

I rolled into the start/finish area. But there was no party; there was nothing. I wondered what happened to all those people behind me and ahead of me. My ass had fallen off around mile seventeen, so I stood up again on my pedals and coasted in the parking lot to my car, legs wobbly and begging for any motion other than circular. I carefully swung my right leg over my bike. My butt felt like I had just gotten off a fence post. I checked my speedometer: over twenty-two miles. I was sticky, sweaty, and just wanted to go home.

I spent the rest of the day in my airconditioned house, seated in my favorite chair. I sat and blamed my master's degree for causing me to become sedentary. I needed to blame something. My muscles shook as if I had spent ten hours on the vibrating exercise belt my mother had used years ago to burn fat. I was horrified this ride had been equivalent to what a two-hour workout with Jillian Michaels probably felt like.

Yet, the next day, I must admit, I wasn't sore at all and went for a six-mile bike ride to prove to myself that life would continue. I could bounce back.

I'm already planning to ride Bike the Bluffs next year. Already planning ahead. I'll grab all the stretchy green lights I can for the kids, and make sure my pink gloves are secured to both hands. I may bring my road bike. I have a new helmet, but I think I'll wear the same gray tank top in case anybody remembers "the woman who rode alone." I hope to stay in better shape for next year's leisurely ride, but I don't foresee any life changes coming up. If I can find a biking companion to ride with me, maybe we can park a car at the lake and grab lunch after the ride. I'll exchange a friendly hello with Pee Wee who also rides alone as she passes by, and I'll pass her a few extended miles later. I'll will ride the whole twenty-two plus miles at a chatty, leisurely pace, humming "Chelsea Morning," and I won't for one single, solitary moment worry or stress over where everybody else went or where I am in the lineup.

Yeah, right. Who am I trying to kid? I'll mount my bike on my indoor bike trainer over the winter and when Bike the Bluffs comes around again, I'll have my tires at a high performance 75 psi with the theme of Rocky in my head.

Just wait and see.

AUTHOR'S NOTE

"Huffy Wee Fuckin' Bampot" is based on a bike ride I took while working on my master's and coaching high school softball. There was little time for me to stay in shape during this busy period in my life, but I had never felt out of shape, even after long winters of inactivity. Naively, I didn't think aging would change that. Following an exhausting school year, I had read about a May bike ride on the trail along the Missouri River and thought it would be fun.

It would be easy; just pedal.

Sure.

JM

For the
Love
of Fuck
LES ZIG

"**Don't get me** started," Mazar ground out from between clenched teeth but, by the deepening furrow of his forehead, it was obvious that's exactly what was happening–he was getting started. "I mean … do I want to be a prick?"

Seated opposite him, Roche opened his mouth to say, *No, that wouldn't be you at all.* But it would. That was Mazar, who was rage and indignation bottled up inside designer clothes and stubble mixed in with a liberal dose of theatricality that smacked of martyrdom. And while Roche knew that his place was assured courtesy of THE PLAN, he still couldn't help feeling he needed to fit in.

"No–" Roche began.

"The facts are simple," Mazar said. "Tell me how the fuck anybody justifies a salary of millions for doing something they love?"

"Heh," Hennick said. Seated parallel to Roche, she was all angles, sharpened through exhausting gym work, and assembled to be tall and imperious and unapproachable, face twisted into sultriness that transcended any physical objectification. Her black suit with its high shoulders and pointed lapels could've been armor she'd donned to ride into war. "You see the budgets I've overseen. It's bullshit. You don't love it, don't do it. You *do*, then don't charge us millions."

"Right!" Mazar said. "Run into a burning building, risk your life saving people, be a cop and capture murderers and other perilous fuckers, even a teacher teaching the brats and twats of tomorrow. These are the sorts of people who should be getting the big bucks. But that's not the way it works. That's not the world we live in. We overpay athletes for playing fucking games, we give so-called musicians fortunes when real talents like Mozart and Beethoven died in squalor, and we financially bukkake actors for pretending to be somebody else. And why? For what? We're making movies. Right? *Movies*."

Mazar gestured lazily to a few of the original framed film posters of classics–*Casablanca, Citizen Kane, Gone with the Wind*– that littered the walls of his tiny bungalow-cum-office. The fluorescent lightning flickered above them, like it was pleading to be put out of its misery.

Roche shifted in the director's chair, trying to find a way to balance his portliness, while still coming across as comfortable and familiar. It wasn't easy, given he was 20 years older than his two companions.

"I'll tell you–" he began.

"What'cha going to do?" Hennick asked, rhetorically. "We've been in the system. We know the way it works–when it lets you *try* to work it. Is that our experience, though?" She snorted. "Remember I tried to get up that feature? Wanted to do it right. *Good*. No names. They took it from me and pumped it so full of names that every single scene oozed shit."

Mazar slammed his fist onto his small particleboard desk. The pristine leather attaché case that sat on the end jumped. "We should take a lesson from the porn industry. Their *talent*," Mazar paused to clarify the noun with air quotes, "gets paid fuck all. And you know why? Because, for the most part, they're still operating with studio systems, like Hollywood used to. *Talent*," more air quotes, "is contracted to the production company and told what they're making and when they're making it. No debate. Fuck ya." He shrugged. "You don't like it, out you go, because there's always some other fucker, hotter and hungrier, hopping off the bus hoping to make it big."

"Problem is when you get a star," Hennick said. Mazar was taken aback so violently by the notion, it was like she'd swung the flat side of a shovel blade into his face. "They *do* happen," Hennick continued. "For whatever reason, audiences decide this guy's a star, this girl's a star. Whatever."

Roche nodded vigorously. He'd seen it happen time and time and time again.

"Stars are fine," Mazar admitted, "provided you keep a rein on them. And provided they *are* stars. I mean, how many true A-graders are there nowadays?" He shot a finger at Roche. "Name one!"

Roche could've named every star, every up'n'comer, and every flavor of the month just a second ago. Now the names flitted from his head.

"That's right!" Mazar said, taking his silence for ignorance. "Filmmaking's become such a marketing exercise, you can turn any hack into a celebrity, and purport that any idiot with a couple of hit movies is a star. Then we're back in the spin. Because stars, even *pseudo* stars," Mazar rubbed together his thumb, index finger, and middle finger, "want *real* money."

"So that's what it comes down to," Hennick said.

"Yeah," Mazar said. "Money."

Mazar stroked his stylized two-day-growth and studied Hennick, and then Roche. Hennick was unmoved, but Roche felt the fire of Mazar's gaze–a fire that burned away all trappings of affectation and revealed Roche for what he was: a writer who'd never been anything but a plodder. Well, at least that was what Roche feared. Mazar grunted, and Roche braced himself for condemnation. Surely it would come.

"And who pays for that?" Mazar asked.

Roche blinked, failing to digest the question. Then it hit him: Mazar was still following his original line of thinking.

Money–who pays the money?

The office became too stuffy. The collar on Roche's plaid shirt grew too tight. He should know this. He was the veteran here. He searched his three decades of experience. The answer was obvious.

"The public," he said.

"That's right!" Mazar said.

Roche grinned.

"The studio!"

Roche's grin flattened.

"We have movies where fifty million of the budget is a couple of actors' salaries," Mazar said. "That's fucking ridiculous. For the love of fuck, I can't fathom anybody who deserves a fraction of that for any job."

Hennick nodded. "Bring back communism," she said.

"Why the fuck not?" Mazar said. "Why … the … fuck … not?"

"Or," Hennick held up a finger to halt Mazar's wind-up, "better yet, *filmmaking* communism."

"Even better!" Mazar said. "When I was trying to get my feature up, I struggled to get a cent. Meanwhile, the latest cunting mockbuster on the studio's slate was operating on two hundred million. They spent fifty fucking grand on donuts! Fuck me! And why? Because of the stars. Put a ceiling on how much these actors can earn per flick. They do it in sports. Salary caps! And what did we used to call *actors*?" He clicked his fingers and pointed at Roche.

Roche opened his mouth, as if ready to answer, mind racing. *Actors, actors, actors…! Wait, they used to be known as–*

Before Roche could verbalize a response, Hennick clicked her fingers and pointed back at Mazar. "Players!"

"Right! Same principle. Let's cap it. Sure, they'll bitch and whine they have to wake up four in the morning, work until midnight, maintain the routine for sixteen weeks, but like they say in the fucking mob, *This is the business you've chosen.* You don't like it, get out. You want to stay in it, stop your bitching or develop a speed habit to cope and keep up."

"It's the Bitching Age," Hennick said. "People bitch because they're given too many forums. Newspapers, magazines, paparazzi, therapists, social media, the list goes on."

"And fucking on. And … fucking … on. *Bitch-bitch-bitch, I had to wake up 3.30 in the morning just to get my make-up done.* Neglect to mention the money they're being paid, the mansions they go home to, or their million-dollar bank accounts. Fuck 'em."

"Fuck 'em," Roche agreed.

Mazar grinned viciously at him. "Fuck 'em all."

"Directors, too," Mazar said, almost as an afterthought. "Playing with studios" and investors' money, running around like tyrants, and then they take all the credit. Why? Because the actors did their job? Because the actors said the lines written for them– written for them and sometimes fucking spelled out phonetically for them? I mean, there's a fucking thought: what about the writer? We remember Shakespeare, Hemmingway, Tolkien, and all these great writers. How come screenwriters never get that sort of reverence for being the genesis of a movie? You know who gets it? It's always some cuntabulous director."

"For the love of fuck," Hennick said.

"What about you, Roche? Aren't you pissed by the lack of recognition?"

Roche considered the question. *Recognition for what? A string of movies that experienced moderate or no success? Jobs on average television shows? Failed pilots?* Roche was glad for the anonymity. Recognition might mean people started holding him accountable for his body of work. Of course, he couldn't admit this to Mazar. Mazar thought he had something because he'd come to them with THE PLAN. But he had to tell Mazar something. *Something.* Something.

"Fucking speechless!" Mazar said. "See? Because this is the system. We laud directors, but what are they? For the most part, what the fuck are they? I mean, it's like TV shows; they're all the fucking same. It doesn't matter who directs any given episode; they all come across the same. If one episode surpasses another, it's because of the writer, not the fucking director. The director's just a landlord."

"And the writer writes a better show," Hennick said.

"That's right," Mazar said. "The writer writes a better show! Same with movies. You have thousands of romantic comedies, thousands of mindless action flicks, thousands of dramas … the list goes on. And what separates them?"

"The writers!" Roche said.

"Nothing separates them!" Mazar said. "They're all the fucking same. How often does one stand out more than another? They're all competently made trash. And there's nothing wrong with that. There's nothing wrong with being commercial and making a living–that's what life's about. But don't tell me it's an art-form, don't laud the actor, don't laud the director, and–for the holiest of fuck's sakes–don't laud a single one of them for doing the job they're getting paid too much fucking money to do."

"If you're going to laud anyone, laud the writers," Hennick said.

"Right! As far as this example goes, they might be writing wholly formulaic tired old shit, but they're only writing what they're being told. And until you break their hearts and shred their spirits, they *try*. They. Fucking. *Try*. Give them free reign and somebody always butts in–studio or director, telling them what they've got to include. You've got to feel for the dumb fuckers. No offense, Roche."

"None taken!" Roche beamed.

"They're like dogs on a leash, horses under the whip, cocks in a condom. They're told the shit to write, it gets bastardized from gestation to birth by too many fucking opinions and unqualified interlopers, and then at the end of the unholy mess we deify directors and actors. It's the ungodliest of fucks."

Roche rolled his shoulders, feeling the tension in his back. The director's chair was comfortable, but not orthopedic. *How do directors survive it?* he wondered. Of course, they were puffed up on their own self-importance. That was a good one–he needed to segue it into the conversation.

"This chair–" he said.

"It reinforces this cycle!" Mazar said. "This cycle which has become this whirlwind of bullshit. How many reboots do we make? How many franchises do we chase up? How many comic books do we pilfer? We're fucking archaeologists of bastardizations of some greater form that has real cockplosiveness. Just like with … with … with …"

Roche struggled to find another analogy that fit the parameters.

"Computer games!" Hennick said.

Mazar thumped a fist on his desk. The attaché case jumped again. He rested his hand atop it, as if calming a jittery dog.

"That's an interesting one," he said. "Collaboratively, games can tell epic stories. *Why*? Because they're on the same fucking page. Nobody butting in. Imagine Monet was painting a landscape and some director came along and told him what he needed was to paint in a talking dog? Or, God forbid, a fucking love story! Or for the almighty fuck of cuntification, let's write to address market demographics."

"When I was in the studio system, all you got was …" Hennick lolled her tongue out, tilted her head back, and jerked her fist back and forth over her neck in a mock hanging. "You know how many fuckers I pitched that they bastardized into some unholy mutation?" She opened the fist into four fingers. "For the love of fuck."

"The. Love. Of. Fuck," Mazar said.

"I got that freedom in indies," Hennick said. "But for what? For *what?* To operate on a shoestring? I love my roots, but indies look like indies, like publishing a book on a roll of toilet paper. If a writer has some grand vision, how the fuck can it be realized? On an Etch A Sketch? Where's the justice?"

Mazar nodded. "Instead, we're left with the shit-churning in-dustry–paint-by-numbers franchises, derivative mockbusters, and misguided adaptations that we pour diarrhea into and expect to hold shape. We used to have classics." He gestured again at the framed posters displayed on the walls. "In 100 years, people will still re-member these movies. But what the fuck's anybody going to re-member from this era?"

Roche had to fight hard to make sure his grin didn't leap out onto his face. THE PLAN was THE PLAN was THE PLAN. He'd been right–especially in pitching it to these two. He leaned back, feeling now almost as if he belonged in the director's chair. Not that he ever would direct. Or aspire to direct. Or aspire. But he'd been the architect of this–THE PLAN–his one moment of true artistic ge-nius.

"As far as filmmaking goes," Mazar said, "what we need to do is create a utopian environment. First, our own crew. The best there is. And we treat them right. People treat you the way they're treated. And they stay *where* they're treated right. We don't want anybody who'd jump for a mercenary offer. Fuck that."

"Makes sense," Hennick said.

"Then, inflation aside, we have a fixed budget," Mazar said. "And fixed salaries. Actors coming in beforehand know what they'll be paid. Minimum negotiating. Like real jobs."

"You think that'll work?" Hennick asked.

"You can hope. I don't think it's impossible. After all, every now and again, some dick of a star takes a pay cut to appear in some indie or quality low-budget flick. So I think the attitude's out there. They're just scared of chasing it full-time because it depreciates them, and they get worried if they're depreciated, they'll lose their marquee. Not with us. There is appreciation in measure. You want more, shove a firework up your butt and blast the fuck off my planet. You want to be in something great, then here we are. Obviously, I'm not talking about anything unreasonable. But nothing fucking absurd, either."

Roche loved the idea … in principle. But he'd been around long enough to see the way things could spiral out of control. An actor worth a pittance could demand a ransom if his movie boomed. And studios knew ransoms could bring people in.

"Stars draw," he said tentatively.

Mazar and Hennick glowered at him, heads shaking.

Roche wanted to shrink, wanted to be swallowed into the very canvas of his chair. To have come so far, only to belittle himself now. He smirked nervously, as if to show he was only joking, but it came out as a toneless grunt.

"Where do you keep coming up with this unmitigated bullshit?" Mazar asked. "Stars drawing is a gimmick. Like a circus having a freak. Come see the fucking movie with a star. It's a gimmick, a fucking gimmick. We hype these fuckers and everybody believes our bullshit because that's what we are–the masters of marketing. That's the anal glitter we spray onto the faces of the public."

"The truth is, you get a good movie, people come," Hennick said. "The movie *makes* them. The *story* draws the audience in. It happens. Yet nobody seems to learn from it, or use it as a springboard to continue to do something original, to tell a good story, to break fucking molds."

"Let's use our power to create a new gimmick," Mazar said. "This one. Maybe it doesn't work the first time, or the second time, or even the third or fourth time, but we keep pushing it, we keep going at it. It's like a training a dog–through sheer repetition we drive the point home. That's what people come to learn about us: we don't spend a lot, we don't use stars, but, *fuck!* our movies are good!"

"So that's the hook?" Hennick said. "Quality?"

"That's right. But to make this work, we have to start again."

Roche sat there, teeth sunk into his lip, as if he was anchoring his mouth for the night. *Let Mazar and Hennick thrash this out*, he thought. *They're the dynamos. They're audacious. They're visionaries. And, quite possibly, they're insane. Then again, who isn't in this industry?* Roche knew that, over time, those who weren't insane were driven to insanity by the industry's machinations. And there was genius in insanity anyway. Roche knew that well enough.

Mazar unlatched the clasps of the attaché case, snapped it open, and spun it around, as if showcasing a game show prize. Inside, the case was filled with plastic explosives, as well as a timer with red digital numbers–currently on forty-five seconds and counting down.

"It's no good implementing a new system atop of an old one," Mazar said. "That's why computers are fucked–too much baggage from shit that wasn't working in the first place. Build shit on shit on shit, you know what you get? A shitstorm waiting to explode. It's similar to installing new software. It works, but the baggage is always there, cluttering everything the fuck up. But if you wiped all that shit clear, laid new foundations, started all over with a different system ..."

"... then you create something truly original," Hennick added. She laughed, her face softening to hint at whatever love had driven her into this business in the first place. "When we first discussed THE PLAN I wasn't sure. But you're right. You are fucking right. I just wish we had enough C-4 explosives to take out all of Hollywood."

"This is just as good," Mazar said. "Let's target a film festival where all the so-called cream will congeal. That's what they do. They congeal."

"Into muck," Hennick said. She grinned and her sultriness twisted into a cold, loathsome beauty. "What a plan!"

"And who do we have to thank?" Mazar asked. He pointed at Roche. "Our extraordinary friend, the writer!"

Roche grinned.

—

Within the Capra Screening Room of the prestigious White Star Film Festival, thousands of celebrities watched the unfolding short film with growing disgust. Black humor was one thing, but most in the audience found the subject matter to be extremely distasteful. Numerous producers and directors made mental notes to have the trio responsible for what they deemed a piece of unadulterated trash blacklisted. Actors vowed they'd never work for the triumvirate.

Hennick frowned. "So have you got a night in mind?"

Mazar broke the fourth wall and looked directly at the camera to directly address the audience. "How about tonight?"

He lifted the lid of the attaché case to show the timer, which was presently on three seconds. Mazar held a thumbs up.

Hennick turned to break the fourth wall and held a thumbs up.

Roche turned to break the fourth wall, and started to raise a thumb, but never got a chance to finish.

The detonation that engulfed the White Star Film Festival in flame was heard across the coast. Many who were indoors at the time mistook the reverberation of the explosion for an earthquake. But those outside at the time made no mistake about the source, courtesy of a blinding fire that mushroomed into the sky and spread across the night.

Most were surprised by what had occurred, and by the sudden wailing of sirens in the distance, the sound of emergency services rallying, the choruses of astonishment from passersby, the orange glow on the horizon.

Mazar, Hennick, and Roche weren't surprised at all. The trio sat on the hood of Mazar's old Mustang, which was parked on the beach. Each enjoyed a glass of champagne, and Mazar and Hennick puffed on cigars. They watched the tide come in, lap around the tires of the Mustang, and then pull out.

"So," Hennick said, "what do we make first?"

Mazar blew a smoke ring, then clapped Roche on the shoulder. "What've you got for us?"

Roche frowned and, for once, didn't have a single thing he wished he could've said.

AUTHOR'S NOTE

"For the Love of Fuck" began as a short screenplay (originally known as "The Execs"), written way, way, way back in 2002. Several years later, it was adapted as a short story. However, I felt that something was always missing from it. *WSOFIT?* actually gave me a new focus about how it could operate as a short story (and not just because of the fucking profanity).

So out came "The Execs," which underwent exhaustive revision, with lots of new material added. Now the story found life. Sometimes it takes time, and a new perspective, to get to where you want with your writing.

LZ

I am a snake on a rock. Don't fuck with me, I won't bite you. Fuck with me, and you're going to walk around with me hanging from your neck for the rest of your natural life.

Harlan Ellison

"You're fucking coming to hell with me, *puta*"
ALBERTO AMBARD

1

Pacing back and forth, I read the notice one last time. With each step, Maria, I wrinkled the letter little by little, forming a fist until, in a rage, I crumpled the paper into a ball and threw it in the garbage.

"Fuck them!" I shouted.

I turned to face David, hoping to get a reaction, but he just stood there like a tree.

"They've stolen it all," I said. "This is not different than what they're doing to the foreign airlines and to everybody, really. You guys are telling me we should be happy to lose nearly a half million dollars to these motherfuckers?"

"It's the Ministry," David said. "It's not like we have a choice."

"I have to agree, John," Daniela said. "Let's figure out the best way to …"

"No! Fuck, no!" I shouted, feeling the blood rush to my face. I seized the heavy stapler on the desk and flung it into the corner where a small palm paid the consequences.

Daniela froze, eyes wide open. I leapt up to apologize. She recoiled and leaned back before relaxing again.

"I'm sorry, Daniela. But this is bullshit." I said.

I know, stubborn and can't take a loss, that's me. But, Maria, can you blame me? Three years of work, half bankrupt and humiliated by a gang of thieves called the Venezuelan government.

Anyhow, Maria, the whole ordeal about the money is really no longer that important. I wouldn't even mention except that, in a way, it's why I'm here, desperately trying to talk to you. See, normally we'd leave the office at five, stop at the bar in the lobby for a drink or two, and go home. Instead, the discussion continued from the early afternoon when we first received word from the Ministry about payment for our project, until about 9:00 P.M, when Daniela finally said she needed to leave.

"Let's all go home and think it over tonight. We can discuss it further tomorrow," she said, before heading out to enjoy an hour or so with her family. Daniela deserves to take a long vacation; she's worked her ass off for three years on the project, figuring out the budget, managing the subcontractors, and, of course, dealing with all the stuff under the table, paying off the leeches.

"David, do you want to go downstairs to the bar?" I asked. "I need a drink badly. I've needed a drink since the moment we got the bad news."

"No, it's late, and actually, I'm going to stay a little longer, John. I want to make sure we have all the paperwork ready for tomorrow, so whatever we decide to do is set to go in the morning."

So you see, Maria, it was *this* answer, *this* moment, the decision to *not* have the usual after-work Scotch with David and the fact that we stayed so late arguing the unarguable that changed the course of my life.

2

The sound of the elevator bell announced its arrival on the P2 level and the doors opened. I stepped out, but stopped before advancing further. As usual, I'd forgotten where I'd parked the car and was scanning the lot. At the same time, I suddenly realized I'd forgotten to tell David about an accounting error. He was going to prepare the final documents for nothing. I had to let him know.

I found the car and headed toward it. Retrieving my phone as I walked down the ramp, I tapped the code to unlock it and found David in my contacts list.

The assailant sprung from the shadows behind me like a panther as I was about to make the call.

"Don't move, you fucking *puta*, or I'll put a fucking bullet in your brain!" His voice was nasal, but I sensed fear in his voice.

I straightened up, opened my eyes wide, and exhaled. I

turned to face the stranger but was shoved hard to the concrete. Instinctively, I thrust out my hands to break the fall. My phone fell on the hard pavement. My knees struck the ground, and now, raw skin burned where the thin cloth of my pants ripped.

I thought I'd black out. Breaking into a sweat, I felt my stomach shrink as goosebumps rose along my arms. My attacker's partner arrived and I shat my pants.

"We're going for a ride, sweet pea. If you behave, I'll fuck you gently. Some lube and little kisses on your back to console you." I glanced up to see a fat man with short hair, military style. I glanced at the second guy, the one who shoved me. He wore a mean scar across his cheek and a dreadfully large crucifix with a small photo of a St. Peter hung around his neck.

My mouth was so dry I could barely speak, but I pulled myself together. "Please, don't kill me," I begged. "Take whatever you want. I'm not armed. I've got two kids," I said.

"Get up!" the fat man ordered.

I scrambled to reach my phone but trembled so hard I fumbled it. The phone leapt from hand to hand like hot bread. I rushed to stuff it into my pocket and raised my shaking hands.

"*Puta*, stop pissing yourself. We like you smelling nice and clean. If you smell like piss, I'll assume you're a dirty bitch and fuck you like one," the fat guy said. I glanced at him, as the third and final member of the gang appeared, by far the youngest and obviously the quietest. They laughed.

"What?" I asked, not comprehending the joke.

I glanced down to see the warm, wet urine spreading over my pants. Humiliated, I looked up again.

I was shoved in the direction of a waiting vehicle.

"Get in the van, quickly, *puta*! I've waited long enough!"

Little did I know that while struggling with the phone, my trembling thumb had tapped on David's contact photo and that he'd picked up and could hear what was going on.

3

"Get in there, bitch!" the fat guy ordered. "You think we have all day? Put your hands behind your back and put your head down!"

He punched me hard. Immediately, I felt my nose crack and my whole face go numb. Squinting, eyes clouded with tears, I tasted blood, but had no time to feel where my nose should be. They pushed me into the van, crushing my face against the floor of the empty compartment.

"Ahh!" I exclaimed, as a zip tie tightened around my wrists, burning my skin.

The kid–the one tying my hands–held my hair and yanked me up, elevating me up like a cobra. He slapped my face.

"Shut up, *putica*! Save the screaming for when I'm pumping your ass. Sit right there!"

Even with a broken nose, I sensed a strong and acidic smell of body odor. I was shoved against the side of the van while the kid sat in front of me and the fat man closed the rear door from the outside. Only then–and I know, it's incredible, but this is how terror works–did I realize I wasn't the only victim. There were four others, each bound at the wrists like me.

I could barely think, bombarded with savage images of what the kid would do to me. Wedged into the tight space, with a stiff, aching neck, I crossed my legs to avoid being too close to him. My hands had lost all sensation and my insides felt empty, as if a vacuum had sucked out my organs.

The kid bound my ankles, brining me back to reality. I had no choice but to face him. He truly looked like a boy of sixteen, except for his eyes, which, full of spite, revealed a sad story: A little boy who lives in a shack with four unfinished walls, no water and five siblings–all from different fathers. He loves soccer, but the older ones bully him. So instead of learning how to dribble, he masters how to fight, just not in time to defend himself from his stepfather's beatings. One day, he's caught stealing and ends up in prison, where he's raped by cell mates. Robbed of his childhood and lost in anger, he now walks through the barrio and sees other children playing a sport he has forgotten he loved. His life is about express kidnapping, raping and killing, sometimes as coercion and others just for pleasure. He's a psychopath.

After binding my feet, the kidnapper lay back against the side of the van and started cleaning his fingernails. Sensing that I was staring, he lifted his gaze. I lowered my head immediately, careful not to provoke him, even nonverbally.

Next to me sat a stocky young man. Whenever I moved, I felt his sticky arm separate from mine. A woman sobbed in silence, her body moving up and down uncontrollably in waves. I exchanged glances with my fellow captives. Their swollen eyelids and red eyes made me wonder if I looked as terrified and desperate as them. Suddenly, I felt cold.

In front of me was the kid, and next to him, the two other captives. One of them, was either asleep or unconscious. *God knows how long he's been in this metal prison*, I thought.

The van violently lurched forward. The momentum forced the apparently unconscious man to the rear of the vehicle. He fell back and his head hit the floor hard.

Blood seeped out under his head where it had been cut open. I realized that I hadn't noticed the blood, some dry, some still wet and running from his head down to his neck, soaking into his shirt. The river pooled beneath his butt.

"You wanna know why?" the kid asked, pleased by my horrified expression. "He wouldn't fucking shut up. So I'll tell you just once. Keep your fucking mouth shut unless I tell you to open it to suck my dick. They call me The Bat for a reason. I love blood."

4

We were still in the parking lot. I closed my eyes and rested my head against the van wall, trying to calm myself. I felt each speedbump, and then heard the engine roar. We were the road now.

The feeling of movement took me back to the school bus rides of my youth and my friend Antonio. We often played a game by closing our eyes and guessing our location as bus the bus travelled its route.

Here, in the windowless, rolling prison, I revisited those days by trying guess where our abductors were taking us. But, of course, fearing the unexpected, I was distracted, conjuring images of mutilated ear lobes and, you know, Maria, never again seeing you and the kids. Never again seeing Diego on the soccer field. Never again feeling Rosana's weight atop my belly.

Engulfed in sobs, I joined the woman in her silent concert, our bodies convulsing in unison. It must have made her feel even more hopeless, because her sobbing soon grew into wails bordering on hysteria.

"Bitch, you either stop crying or I'll take my knife out and slice your lips open. Your call," Bat said.

I opened my eyes. Poor woman. The blood from the dead body was soaking her pants and socks. There was nothing she could do.

By now, I assumed we were on the highway because of how fast the van was moving. After a while I felt the van slow to a stop before turning right, left, and left again. The cable ties cut into my circulation, numbing my hands. My nose hurt and felt as if I had a giant heart pulsating behind it, every beat was painful.

"Where are you taking us?" I asked.

Bat ignored the question. "We're gonna phone your wives, husbands, children, parents, bitches, whatever. Pick wisely, because there's only going to be one call. One chance and one chance only to produce the money."

The guy in front of me spoke up, voice trembling. "W-What do you mean?"

"It means tomorrow at eleven we have our money or you lose an ear, or a finger. By noon you're dead. We know your finances, the cars you own, where you live. So, like I said, princess, you better make the right choice. They call the police, we'll know. And you'll die."

I wondered how much ransom they'd demand. What was the price tag for my life? For the first time during this ordeal, I felt an emotion different from fear or anxiety. I was angry, or I should say, I felt impotent, but just for a few seconds. Anxiety kicked back in when I counted the amount of cash available to pay for my life. I knew there was about sixty thousand in the bank and that you, Maria, could probably get another hundred thousand from family and friends. *Oh God. Please, kid, don't ask for more than that*, I prayed.

"You bitch. You go first." Bat interrupted my thoughts.

"Give me your phone. I saw you pocket it in the parking lot. You make the first call."

"I can't reach it with my hands tied."

Bat leaned toward me and cut the cable tie, freeing my hands, aiming his gun at my head as a warning. As I handed the phone to him I was startled to realize I was connected to David. The call was live!

For a millisecond, phone in hand, I tapped the screen frantically with my thumb, hoping to disconnect the call.

"Give me the fucking phone!"

Oh God, he's going to see the screen.

"You fucking piece of shit! You think you can play us,
you're dead."

"I didn't know, I swear!"

In films, when characters are about to die, they often close
their eyes and beautiful images come to them. Nothing quite that
poetic happened to me. Instead, I looked up the barrel, a tunnel with
no light at the end, and the pointed tip of a bullet Bat intended to put
between my eyes.

5

"Fuck, Wilmer! What's going on?" Bat yelled at the fat guy
sitting behind the wheel.

God exists, I thought. For whatever reason, "Wilmer" had
stopped the car just as Bat was about to shoot me. We were all
thrown to the front of the van, including Bat, who, while trying to
use his hands to stop himself from falling, almost lost his gun.

"The fucking cops! A stop point!" shouted Wilmer.

The sensation in my gut returned, once again filled with organs, muscle, and hope when the van started reversing at high speed,
seeking escape, before a rain of bullets stopped it.

The third kidnapper cried out. "Bat, get out and help! They
hit Wilmer, bro! Wilmer is gone!"

My fellow captives started to scream. Bat hopped out of the
van while we all kept down.

I don't know how much time passed, Maria, maybe a minute,
maybe ten. And I have no idea what happened after that, I mean,
from then until now that I'm with you. All I can tell you is that I was
down and, again, Bat grabbed my hair hard to pull me up once more—
his cobra.

He held my face up and looked at me with loathing, as if I
was the cause of all of his suffering. He aimed the gun. "If I'm going
down, you're fucking coming to hell with me, *puta*. This is *your*
fault."

6

"John, don't die. Please, don't die. The kids will be here soon. We need you. What's happened?"

I can hear the monitors beeping and the pump forcing air into my lungs, keeping me alive. I can hear you, Maria–your sad, desperate voice reverberating in the air–and smell your fear, powerful as a stink bug crushed under my nose. I am trying to open my eyes. See them move? I want to squeeze your hand, give you a signal that I am here, with you, and that I'll always will be. But for now, all I can hope is that my story travels through our skin, through my hand into yours. Your hand, so warm. God, I wish the kids were here with you so I could tell them everything I haven't told them yet in this, our last conversation. I love you guys so much, I love *you* so much, Maria. I am sorry! I should have been home more often, and you were right, this fucking project ended up killing me. Get away from this chaos, Maria, run away …

"John! John …"

AUTHOR'S NOTE

While kidnapping was always a problem in Venezuela as a result of the Colombian guerillas, the concept of express kidnappings (a method of abduction in which the kidnappers demand an immediate ransom) arose during the years of Hugo Chavez. A 2010 study from *InSight Crime* reports that the numbers of these types of crimes have increased since then, noting that in Caracas alone, there are approximately forty express kidnappings per day. It's estimated that seventy percent of express kidnappings are never reported.

The story you have just read is a fictionalized account of the abduction of John Alberto Machado, a fifty-two-year-old architect, who was kidnapped in the parking lot of his office building on a January evening in 2014. During his abduction, Machado had managed to dial a business partner via his mobile phone, and the latter, soon realizing his friend had been kidnapped, contacted the police. The offenders were stopped at a police post and eventually captured. John Machado was found–still alive–with a bullet in his head. He died hours later at a local hospital.

AA

My Neighbor's
a Fucking Monster
ANDREA GOYAN

January 24, 2019

Dear Neighbor (and I use that term loosely),

Your dog barked all night. Again.

As usual, he began with those tiny mewling yips, just enough to be annoying. They gradually rose to a howling crescendo whose decibel level rivaled that of a low-flying jumbo jet.

Then, when he paused, we all held our breath waiting, praying he was finished, but howling was merely the first act. He masterfully morphed into a furious full-scale barking assault determined to undermine the peace.

And his plan worked. We suffered another sleepless night.

He's good, maybe the best. He can keep the attack at a frenzied pitch for hours without losing his voice. At times, I'd swear he's part of a pack of wolves, not a lone canine. There are even moments, on days when his ritual begins earlier in the evening, that his baleful song drifts through our ducting. Our stove hood serves as a bull-horn amplifying each bark, so it sounds like he's in the room with me. My hand is still bandaged from the scalding water that sloshed over me when one of his falsetto yelps startled me as I boiled pasta last week.

There are times I'd swear the barking is in Surround-Sound. In fact, I do believe your dog is able to throw his voice. The talent is endless. If

I were a talent agent, I'd sign him without hesitation, because he'd make a killing in the voice-over world.

My dog has given up trying to beat, or even join, your dog in his vocal gymnastics. She realizes she's no match. Sometimes I think I hear her sigh. Or that could just be me.

But let's not forget you! You possess hidden Fucking Monster skills. My husband and I marvel at your ability to tune out the cacophony. Can you send me the name of whatever noise-canceling devices you use? They must be phenomenal. If we were friends, hell, if we merely communicated, sharing this information might stave off the inevitable.

Instead, another court date is on the calendar. We'll all stand before the judge and describe our woes. You'll leave proclaiming we're all out to get you. We'll leave hoping that the judge's ruling in our favor (for the fifth time) will finally stop the late-night concerts. We'll all be cowed by the power of our justice system and its remarkable ability to remedy problems and make the world safe.

And. Nothing. Will. Change.

So, I've decided to take a page from your book. I'll see your Fucking Monster status and raise you. As a master of misdemeanor violations, you've taught me a thing or two.

First, I am going to install speakers in my backyard. They will face your house. I'm going to play showtunes at all hours, at the highest volume, and when the police come knocking at my door, I will follow your excellent model and simply ignore them. I never knew that was a viable way to avoid the police until you showed me.

Second, to save water, I've decided to let my lawn die and park my cars over it. Hell, I'm going to rent out space to the Thompson's teenage twins, the ones who just barely passed their driving tests. I know it violates our city's codes, but your example has shown me that laws don't matter.

It's worked for you, and the inoperable cars you've left on your driveway for 15 years. Why, then, wouldn't it work for me? Let them assess liens on my house. They can collect their monies when I'm good and dead.

Third, I'm going to hang motion-sensor lights along the roofline facing your yard and house, dozens of them. I figure this, timed with your dog's movement and barking, will display and spotlight his complex canine choreography.

And, as for my garbage cans? I'm tired of wheeling them in and out of the driveway every week. It's such a hassle. I shall leave them on the street, but if I catch anyone using them, yourself included, I will dump the refuse in front of your home. Heaven help you if you drop your dog's waste in my trash bins; I'll throw it in a burning heap at your doorstep.

Sleep deprived as always,

Your Neighbor,
A Fucking Monster (in training)

AUTHOR'S NOTE

I doubt I'll surprise any reader by letting on that this piece was inspired by a true story. Because who hasn't lived next to a difficult neighbor? Loud music, crazy parties, screaming fights, stinking garbage, the list is endless. I imagine that many of us have dreamt of ripping said neighbor a new one, but since most of us are reasonable people, we don't act on those impulses. Instead, we obey the laws of our land and adhere to acceptable social standards. But what might happen if we loosened those constraints?

I thought this was a fun premise to develop. Since I wanted to work on a short comedic piece for this anthology, I felt like the story needed to remain one-sided, leaving no room for objections from the nasty neighbor. Composing a letter seemed the ideal way for my narrator to address her concerns and frustrations while staying calm, articulate, and (maybe) even funny. Plus, she could do it all from the safety of her own home.

However, I soon discovered that, as exhilarating as it was for her to vent those dark thoughts, doing so opened the door to her worst self. You can't fight monsters by becoming one.

AG

Resting
Bitch
Face
TERRI CLIFTON

Caroline stepped into the ladies room to fix her lipstick and step away from the crowd for a minute. It never occurred to Caroline that she was the topic of bathroom gossip. But there she was, gazing in the mirror above the sink, hair in place along with everything else, lipstick hovering just in front of her lips, when she heard her name, and laughter.

"Did you see Caroline and her Resting Bitch Face? Oh, my God, does she ever smile? Do you even think she can?"

"Some people are just cold."

"It would be a shame to be that frigid with a husband like Anthony; so attractive."

"And successful."

"Resting Bitch Face," the woman in the first stall said again, accompanied by a high, piercing laugh.

Caroline realized that at any moment the two strangers would exit their stalls. She'd be frozen there, face and all. In what felt like slow motion, Caroline left the restroom and blended back into the crowd. She placed as much physical space between herself and the laughter as possible, her only choice other than rushing out into the snowfall.

From a passing waiter with a tray of wine she grabbed a glass of Merlot and kept moving. Moments later, she stopped in front of the silent auction tables. With her back to the room, Caroline feigned interest in the auction items and bid sheets.

She wasn't frigid. She knew she wasn't. But Caroline recognized it as the way they saw her. She was familiar with the set of her jaw, the smooth false calm of her brow that refused to crease over the opinions of others, the many practiced ways she internalized her feelings. Caroline drank the Merlot and wrote a bid on one of several gift baskets, not bothering to examine its contents. Her vision blurred as she moved to the next auction item, and she was horrified by tears that threatened to form.

The music was loud and the room too warm, crowded with people who knew Anthony. Without looking, Caroline knew he was in the middle of a group somewhere, charming others. Somehow she was absolutely alone. Caroline was keenly aware that her *friends* were really just the wives of Anthony's friends. She was social with his clients, with the neighbors. Caroline's face might look as if she were resting, but she knew differently. She was simply waiting. All the years she'd taught herself to wait, patiently. It was just that she could no longer remember what she awaited, or why. Feeling ridiculous and angry at herself, Caroline gave a quick touch of a cocktail napkin to the inner corner of her eyes and placed a bid on the next item. And then the next, which happened to be the bid she eventually won.

—

Aided by the Merlot, she'd felt bold on the night of the fundraiser when upon learning that she'd won a gift basket for a twelve-week dance program entitled "Empowered You: Discover Your Happy Dance." She'd wanted to feel empowered. She'd wanted her happy dance. Even after the wine had worn off, she'd thought it might be fun, could do her some good. But seeing other women entering the dance studio, housed atop an antique store, in laughing little groups only made Caroline unsure. The space was larger than she'd imagined, with long unforgiving mirrors spanning the length of the room. The nervousness was nearly overwhelming.

It was a small town, and even though Caroline and Anthony had moved here a dozen years ago, she'd remained an outsider. She might have made some real connections and put down roots if she and Anthony had started a family, might have bonded with these same women over PTA meetings and soccer practice. Pizza nights.

Caroline sighed and stretched, faced forward, and focused on the dance instructor. It had been a long time. As she moved through the basic ballet class it was if some muscle memory from adolescence remained, and she found unexpected comfort in the patterns and positions. All the thoughts she'd brought with her into the room fell away for an hour. It was bliss.

—

Caroline endured her anxieties and aches, soaking them in long Epsom baths. It was worth it for the two classes a week that gave her release she didn't know she needed, shedding stiffness and sameness. She could feel her body working again, aware of her muscles and bones, of her heart pumping. From within Caroline, something shifted quietly, so that each time she emerged from the warm studio into the cold winter evening air, she felt oddly hopeful, celebrating the light, staying a little longer each session and humming as she walked to her car.

By the time she learned to Shag, Two Step, and Charleston, Caroline had learned how to laugh at herself again. Little by little, the woman in the dance studio mirror was returning to someone recognizable to herself. Daffodils bloomed, then tulips, and she tried Latin dance and tap. The world was waking up, and she with it.

The last Happy Dance experience was pole dancing. Caroline was relieved to see that everyone else looked as self-conscious as she felt.

"Leave your clothes on; lay everything else bare, ladies."

There were snacks and wine to celebrate the end of the course. The pole dancing ranged from hot to hilarious. To Caroline's surprise, it was difficult. Nervous giggles gave way to breathing through the cardio, but they were all stronger than they'd been eleven weeks ago, and they all approached it with the same gravity they'd approached all the other dances. The instructor taught spins with names like Fireman and Pinwheel, and after a couple of false starts and knocking her forehead on the pole, Caroline loved it and her fellow dancers cheered her on.

"Go Caro," they chanted, as she twirled.

She hadn't been called Caro since college. It was possible, maybe even probable, that parts of herself had grown cold, and dormant. It occurred to her in that moment that she would never have more than she was willing to receive from life. That she'd made her choices. She had shut out so much to avoid feeling discomfort or

248 WHAT SORT OF FUCKERY IS THIS?

pain, and it had never really worked at all.

Caroline felt empowered. It had been worth the hangover and every penny she'd paid for the auction bid to know that she still had a happy dance. Perhaps, she thought, even worth the words in the bathroom that had driven her to this. With a new sense of confidence and belonging, Caroline realized she had a chance to build connections and rekindle old ones, and she knew exactly where to start.

She needed to talk to Anthony, and soon, before her thoughts became trapped inside or evaporated altogether, before bravery faded. She refused to think of this as her new self. It was *her* self, the one she'd shuffled aside long ago. Her old self. She needed to reclaim it, not to return home and wait in silence.

Swallows dove over Victorian houses and the river as Caroline crossed the bridge and walked to Anthony's office, wondering what she'd say when she arrived. They'd drifted apart so quietly. Reclaiming their closeness would require speaking with forthright honesty.

The light in Anthony's office was on; an amber rectangle in the dusk. A car in the parking lot meant a late client. She'd given up trying to get him to slow down. The side door was open, and Caroline slipped in, thinking to make herself a coffee in the breakroom and wait But a few steps inside, the truth revealed itself. The sounds were intimate and hushed, but unmistakable. She reeled, feeling faint. The woman in the room with Anthony laughed. Caroline recognized the high, piercing sound at once and silently fled.

———

Caroline pretended to be asleep when, hours later, Anthony quietly slipped into bed. Caroline knew she'd never share a bed with him again.

Hours later and over coffee, the conversation was the same as always, the composure, unchanged. Caroline studied Anthony's face as she asked about his late night. Watched how easily he lied, and wondered how many times she hadn't noticed.

Caroline searched herself out in mirrors as a matter of course now. Useful tools, she thought, for seeing oneself if you dared. Suddenly she could dare. There was nothing to lose. And in the antique oval mirror in the breakfast nook she stared at her own icy blankness. *Resting bitch, indeed*, she thought. Under the surface she was coming to life.

Upstairs, Caroline realized her entire life could fit into two suitcases. The rest, closets full of dresses and coats and shoes, she emptied, stuffing everything into trash bags then stuffing the bags into her sedan. Caroline hated the car and its practical staidness, but today she was grateful for the giant trunk and cavernous back seat. She deposited the bags in the donation bins behind the nearest church. Caroline felt light, until she climbed back into the car.

A moment of profound awareness occurred to Caroline in that instant. *Maybe it is growth, maybe it's just time, but eras and ages pass, and days come when we can't maintain the status quo anymore. Life is moving on, I've no choice but to go with it. All I have is whatever lie ahead.*

Later that morning, Caroline withdrew roughly half the funds from the checking and savings accounts she and Anthony shared, with enough extra for a new convertible. The teller needed the bank manager's assistance and gave a nervous laugh as she stepped away from her station. Gooseflesh covered Caroline's skin as she recognized the laugh. Caroline glared, mind racing furiously, contemplating a withering response. *I won't play the part of the spurned wife,* she thought. *If I needed further proof that my life here is over, this is it.*

Upon completing the bank transaction, Caroline looked into the eyes of her husband's mistress. "Thank you," she said, with sincerity.

Caroline purchased a black Camaro and dyed her hair a pretty red. Anthony preferred her blonde, and for too long she'd let herself become a product of his preferences. It was time to discover her own likes, decide upon the direction of her life. Her only immediate plan was to find a beach and walk along the shore.

With the Camaro's top down, Caroline cranked up the radio and headed south on the highway in search of salt air. A quick glance in the rearview and she saw only lights and herself, smiling.

She was glad she left the top down. Now the world could see her, too.

AUTHOR'S NOTE

Sometimes characters stay with me for a long time before I manage to find their story or the proper home for it. When I saw the call for manuscripts for *WSOFIT?*, I wasn't sure I had any ideas, but an overheard nasty comment in line for coffee brought Caroline back to mind. I had my title, and Caroline finally got her moment.

TC

The
Self-Mindfuck
LUANNE CASTLE

Twice since early September, my school had subjected us to duck-and-cover drills. Because my first grade teacher had mentioned "Michigan storms," at first I believed the drills were tornado warnings. I dutifully hid under my flimsy Formica desk until the all-clear was given.

Following the second drill, a classmate set me straight. "It's because of the bomb, dummy."

Even then, at age six, I knew about the bomb. Months earlier, my father had transformed his warm and inviting basement workshop–a safe place where I watched him pound and saw and create–into a cement block bomb shelter. He rebuilt a ghost of his workshop in our garage, installing his bench vise and hanging a pegboard for his tools, but the magic was gone.

After pestering me for countless days, I had allowed Mark, the next-door kid, to peek inside our outfitted shelter. My father, brimming over with anger, spanked me that same night.

"You don't tell anyone about the door with the yellow and black sticker and what's behind it. That way, when the bomb hits, we won't have people pounding on our door."

Message received.

With the introduction of duck-and-cover into my life, I lived with bomb threats at school, as well as at home, cowering at every sudden noise or movement. Fear became my invisible friend, shadowing me everywhere. Sometimes I saw danger where there was none, like the time my parents went to the local golf course while I was out playing with the neighborhood kids. I didn't realize that our neighbor was "watching" me, and I felt terribly alone. Remembering my mother's warnings about kidnapers, I ran home and locked the doors, shut all the drapes, and hid under my bed until my parents returned home.

Fear became my frenemy. It was an unreliable witness.

One day in early October I missed the school bus and had to walk home alone. At six, this was my first time walking by myself. I trudged all the way down busy Gull Road from school, past the simple brick ranch that was our church, where my Sunday School met in the basement, and past the Catholic hospital that reminded me of the asylum in Anatole Litvak's *The Snake Pit*. The foliage had just passed that glorious time of October in Michigan. Brown leaves now outnumbered the red and gold; some clung desperately to the branches, and more formed a satisfyingly crackling ground cover. Breezes carried the sharp nutty smell of fall to me in waves.

When I turned down my street, I left the large oaks behind. I could count the trees on our street on one hand.

Although we lived halfway down Trimble Lane, Junction jutted out at a perpendicular angle across from our yard. The house directly across the street from us, therefore, was a corner lot. It was patrolled by a giant black Chow named Ares with a persistent and vicious bark.

As I neared my house, I heard and then saw the black-ruffed dog circling the perimeter of his home. Ares ran to the edge of the non-fenced yard, growing and barking. He lunged, pulled back, and then lunged again. Even from a distance I trembled. When I was an infant, my Aunt Alice's dog had bitten my eyelid. Although I had no memory of the event, my mother had told me that the doctors had to sew my eyelid together. Snapping teeth terrified me.

Mrs. Harris, a beautician, lived in the house just before the dog's yard. I stopped upon reaching her lot and looked for her, but it seemed she was away. I'd been in her house a few times, because she occasionally styled my mother's hair. Mrs. Harris had tall lacquered hair in a peculiar pink shade of blonde and her toy poodle smelled like permanent solution. Her poodle shook incessantly. Naturally, I figured it was because they lived right next to Ares. I stood uncertainly in Mrs. Harris' driveway, staring down the slope at the Chow. His eyes were lost behind thick, dark fur. His head nodded wildly in rhythm with his bark.

I didn't know what to do. I felt desperate for an adult. If I crossed over to our side of the street, would the canine make his move and devour me right there on the pavement? Would he follow me to our little patch of grass? To our cement front porch? I eyed the front of our white house, longing to reach the door or the open bathroom window.

Ares' bark rattled like gravel and preyed on my nerves. I held myself still and watched the animal suspiciously. His doghouse was located beneath the only significant tree in our neighborhood, an old maple. The neighborhood houses had been built in the forties or fifties, and other than the burned-down haunted house near Gull Road, all were single-story bungalows. Although my block had some run-down houses and yards, our house and others on our side of Trimble had a look of hope, with fresh paint and black silhouette palm tree or sun designs decorating the white and pink facades.

I searched down Trimble as far as I could see in both directions, looking for help, but the street was empty. I wished I could see down Junction. Unlike Trimble, Junction was a ragamuffin street, littered with kids and old cars.

I wanted desperately to be in the safety of my house, surrounded by the comforts of home–Little Golden Books, vinyl records, paper dolls, and baby dolls. Now that my mother was no longer working, an after-school snack always awaited me. Right now, she was probably setting out milk and graham crackers.

Ares wasn't giving up, and my stomach began to clench as if it were being pressed in my father's vise. I sank onto my knees on the dirt drive, stones digging into my skin, between the lips of the newly formed scabs I'd gotten riding my bike too fast two days earlier, and prayed that the dog would go inside. It seemed as if I were sucking on iron, as the taste of blood flooded my mouth. Eventually time began to collapse on itself, and I ceased recording it in my head. I sat and sat, both numb and alert to the barking.

I kept glancing to see if Mr. Blair might walk outside in his undershirt, a bent cigarette hanging from the side of his mouth, and wash his truck. He worked nights at the Chevy plant, and spent some afternoons scrubbing his pickup.

Ares began to grow hoarse and eventually stopped barking. I squirmed in an effort to pump blood back into my numb limbs. The beast responded, bark rougher and angrier than ever. At that moment, my mother stepped outside in her white blouse and pedal pushers. She called my name as she looked up the street. I wanted to yell, but was terrified of inciting the dog. Slowly, I stood up, all the while watching the snarling animal, ready to freeze if he made a move in my direction.

"There you are!" my mother said. "What are you standing there for? Come on!"

I sucked in air and bolted across the street to my front door, sensing the beast at my heels.

Once inside, I slammed the door shut and locked it. Mom had already gone back into the kitchen, so I peeked out the little diamond-shaped window. Ares sat at the edge of his yard, looking to one side and then the other.

My mother called out. "Come have a snack. How did you miss the bus?"

"How did you know I missed the bus?"

"It's late."

"I forgot my jacket and had to go back for it."

If I told my mother about Ares, she might interfere with my fear. If that happened, she might reassure me. I could lose the fear that, in essence, watched over me in a guardian angel sort of fashion. A witness, unreliable or not, was still a witness. And a witness meant protection.

Since I could never forget, I wondered if my mother remembered that the kitchen was directly above the bomb shelter. With a glance her way, I sat down in front of the snack she'd placed on the table.

"How was school today?" she asked.

Without answering, I dunked the cookie in the milk until it disintegrated entirely.

AUTHOR'S NOTE

In the summer when I turned six, my father dismantled his cozy basement workshop and built a secret underground bomb shelter out of cement blocks. This intrusion into our home was my first encounter with the Cold War.

Television regularly put us through tests of emergency broadcasting via CONELRAD, and at school, duck-and-cover drills were weekly rituals. The goblins in our nightmares were Commies, Reds, and Pinkos. The anxiety this threat gave me was palpable and made even more acute because I was supervised by nervous parents.

I had to wear a cumbersome lifejacket just to play in the sand at the beach. *Overprotective* was an adjective created for my mother and father.

I don't know if I would have been a fearful child if I had grown up in a different environment. Maybe part of it was genetic. But a fraidy cat I was–too scared to attempt cartwheels or to ride atop someone's handlebars. Living across the street from an intimidating dog was yet another frightening aspect of life in those days.

LC

"I think we should use some other greeting.
Something like 'what the fuck?"
"Okay," I said, "What the fuck?"
"Exactly. Right on. I love you."

Steve Almond
Which Brings Me to You

Fucking
Other Men's
Daughters
MARK HEIN

i <u>Power</u>

I am he
  the dark god
      the man in the shadows
I snatch away
      the girl
      from
      the mother
I force her to relate to me.
I make her queen.
I let her go back
      with red stains
      on her mouth
I know she will return
      to me.
I make her queen.

ii <u>Eden/ Chicago</u>

My father led me to the very bush
where he had lain and lost his innocence
so many ways:
bush
sprung from roots that grappled in the dark
of that wedge-shaped grassy ground
full fifty years before:
soil
gathered from the deaths
of leaves and countless grasses, blossoms dropped

each summer since the great Chicago Fire,
husks of insects, rotting candy wrappers,
particles of dust thrown up by hooves
and wheels, and rubber sweat from tires:
an ancient soil, grown rich
with generations of shedding, excreting,
dying.

And there, a tall boy, he held
his arms, which every night had held his mother,
around a frightened girl
whose brother said, *She's slow.*
She doesn't know. She only wants
the candy.
He put his trembling mouth
on her mouth filled
with chocolate, sugar and tear-salt,
lifted up her dress, pushed down his pants
and learned
how fast and frightening
and teasing a mystery can feel:
and learned
how nothing after
seems appropriate:
and learned
the crumbling earth had soiled his knees
and penis, marked her bottom
and her arms

And nothing–
not a thousand repetitions
in beds from Maine to Tokyo,
not prayer, not crusading
against the Hun, not
decades of life given
to teaching homeless children
and raising his own–
nothing
would wipe it clean.

iii <u>Love's Error</u>

That rosy golden light
      was everywhere–
dancing on the waters of the inlet
glaring from the piles and cables
      of the swaying bridge
winking off the snowtips of the mountains
and always gathering fatefully
      over one blonde head–

Ah! how was I to know
      this light's kiss was killing?
How could I uncrown her?

No more could she
resist lighting a candle each night
to peer at my sleeping form,
wondering
      what kind of monster?

Until the hot wax fell
      searing my face
the golden light burned
      her weeping eyes
and screaming, we fled.

Now each lies alone,
unable to bear mortal children,
untranslated.

AUTHOR'S NOTE

      This poem, like most others I write, weaves itself from domestic life and ancient myth. I've long been fascinated by how ancient archetypes dance and sing through the seemingly unprogrammed events of our lives.

The opening section, in the voice of Hades gloating over Persephone, summons the terrible mystery of rape that lies so deep in our wounding patriarchy. I can speak for this dark god, but without comprehending what he does or why.

Section two explores the roots of sexual compulsion as I came to understand them in my father's life. It memorializes a terrible ritual space he once showed me. (I don't reference it, but the bush reminds me of the one where Persephone disappeared.)

The third section records how love can fail between people wounded by this heritage. I was Adonis to her Aphrodite, passionately loved and quickly cast aside. She was Psyche, painfully discovering who her godlike lover really was. Burned, we fled, to tend (and perhaps learn from) our wounds.

MH

Shakespeare, Where the Fuck Art Thou?
PAULENE TURNER

My father says there are only two certainties in life–death and taxes.

I add a third to that list of misery–William bloody Shakespeare.

It's 2077 and we still study him as part of our school curriculum. I mean, seriously! How irrelevant can you get?

"What light through yonder window breaks?" Give me a break. We don't even have natural light here. Or windows. We live in an atmosphere-controlled dome with reflective surfaces that simulate Earth's sun. We aren't even on Earth, but part of a new colony on an asteroid called Beta, within Earth's orbit.

Even so, on Tuesday morning my Year 11 class will be tested on our *Romeo and Juliet* unit and the mark we get will count for fifteen per cent of the year's English mark.

"Why do we even have to read these outdated plays?" I ask my English teacher, Ms Orwell. "What relevance do they have for a teenager on Beta?"

"They have universal themes which offer insight for humans of any age, or location," she says.

"Insight? Yeah right. What did I learn from *Romeo and Juliet*? That the next time I pretend poison myself, I should text my boyfriend about it rather than relying on snail mail to deliver the news."

Ms Orwell grins. "Anyway, why shouldn't you go through the same pain as your parents and grandparents before you? Shakespeare is an experience the whole family can share."

I tried to study for the test. I really did. But I got distracted by Spacebook, and now I'm way behind. I need to do something drastic. Either a) study mega- hard or.. b) ...? I can't think of a B.

I sit on the bench beneath the frangipani tree in the school courtyard. It blooms with white flowers all year round–fake of course. Nothing like this actually grows under the Dome. I like the look of these trees, their sculptured arms, even when they're bare. But the smell? Not so much. So I go to the control panel on the tree trunk and change the scent to gardenia. Much better.

I tap on my *Complete Works of Shakespeare* app, select *Romeo and Juliet* and up pops a holographic page.

Two households, both alike in dignity, In fair Verona, where we lay our scene.

I read the first half dozen lines. I'm bored already.

Sighing, I look around and spot Homer hurrying across the Quad. He nods to me and blushes, as red as the sunset projected onto the western Dome wall each evening. Poor guy is really awkward in a girls' school.

He's eighteen and a first year uni student who works here part time as a driving instructor. Every afternoon, he teaches girls how to drive a Personal Mobiliser–which is a kind of flying scooter we all use beneath the Dome. But it's just a cover for the real reason he's here–his research, which he does the rest of the time, with the Head of Science, Mr Newton. The project they're working on is totally *hush-hush*, So, naturally, everyone knows all about it.

It's a Time Machine. Homer invented it–it's a universal first. But so far, no-one has so much as glimpsed it. Word about the corridors is that he keeps it on him at all times, even when he sleeps.

OMG. I think of an option (b).

—

When he passes by again a few hours later, I'm back in position on the bench beneath the frangipani tree.

"Homer," I call out. "Would you come here for a moment?"

I pat the seat next to me and smile sweetly. Like a shark. He sits down, not too close.

"Can I see the time machine?" I ask.

"What? How do you know about that?"

I give him some *Seriously dude* eyebrow action. "I just want a look. I won't touch! Promise."

He licks his lips and looks back hopefully towards the science lab. No rescue comes from that direction. Reluctantly, he reaches into his inside pocket and pulls out a flat rectangular screen, with gold and silver lights pulsing like fireworks.

"Wow!" I say, truly impressed. "So that's a Time Machine? But it's so small! How do you tell it where and when to go?"

"It's voice activated."

"Really? Just your voice? Or can anyone do it?" "Eventually, it will be modified for individual vocal tonation," he says, "Which is like a fingerprint, with only a sub-percentile range of error."

"But for now ... it only works with your voice?"

He folds his arm tightly around his chest and rocks back and forth, as he nods.

"So if you wanted to go to, say, the year 1587, Stratford-Upon-Avon in England ... the Pig's Ear tavern.. what would you say to the machine?" I ask.

"That's ... Shakespeare's time, isn't it?"

I shrug.

"Well, I'd say," he clears his throat, and booms: "Fifteen eighty seven, *Pig's Ear* tavern, Stratford Upon Avon, England. Planet Earth. See, that brings up satellite co-ordinates for the location. And the time-continuum interface code. Hmmm–there must actually be a *Pig's Ear* tavern?"

"So that's set for relocation now?"

He nods.

I slip over to the tree trunk and select "Autumn fall." As the white frangipanis flutter around us Homer looks up, mouth ajar. While he's distracted, I lean over to the screen, find a prompt marked "Jump," and press it.

—

Everything around us goes milky white. It's like we're inside a beam of light stretching to infinity. I reach out and touch the walls–they're cold and throb, like a heartbeat. There's a shooshing sound outside and the whole thing rocks and shudders constantly.

"You said you wouldn't press anything," says Homer.

"Ohmigod, ohmigod, ohmigod. Mr Newton, the Science Master, was supposed to take the first trip with me."

"Don't worry, we won't be gone long. And I won't tell him about it if you don't."

There are flashes of light through the fog and some crashing sounds, alarmingly close.

"What's that?" I say.

"Probably space detritus, or asteroids colliding. Then again, it could be the fabric of the world coming apart."

"Wouldn't that be more a tearing sound?" I say and grin. Homer doesn't smile back. "Oh Come on! How will you ever learn anything if you don't take a risk now and again. Surely a scientist like you can appreciate that?"

"If Mr Newton finds out …" he says.

"He won't. As long as you help me with my plan."

"Your plan? To do what?"

"To assassinate William Shakespeare."

—

The trip takes about twenty minutes–not bad considering how far we've come. When the noise and movement stops, and the fog ebbs, we are in a forest at night.

I've seen pictures of these in books. I touch the tree trunks–they're surprisingly rough. Pines needles crunch beneath my feet. And there is a smell–clean and earthy. I love it. The Pine scented hand wash in the school bathrooms doesn't come close. It's a little chilly too–which is a new experience. Our temperature-controlled Dome is mild all year round.

I look up through the treetops to an inky blackness, freckled with vibrant pinpoints of light.

"Have you ever seen a real sky?" I ask Homer. "It's … beautiful."

Homer looks up. "We shouldn't interact with anyone in the time period or we might change the future in ways we cannot imagine," he says. *Mr Buzzkill.*

"Don't worry. We won't be affecting anyone's future.. just the one."

I tramp through the forest. Homer trails behind, sulking.

"You're not really going to kill William Shakespeare, are you?"

"Yes I am. I'm not just doing it for myself, but for all students who have suffered under? his pen across the ages."

Between the tree trunks, we see light coming from a fairytale-style cottage. It's made of rough stones with a thick thatched roof. A chimney pumps smoke in the black sky. A painted wooden sign with a smiling pig face proclaims it as *The Pig's Ear*.

"Well, would you look at that," says Homer, scratching his head. "We actually made it."

"Yeah. You must be smarter than you look," I say.

"I'm not so sure about that." He grins and a shadow slips into a dimple on his right cheek I haven't noticed before. "Why this place anyway?"

"The *Pig's Ear*? From my research, Shakespeare was a regular here."

I take two dark cloaks out of my bag. I 'borrowed' them earlier from the Drama department. Homer and I put them on to conceal our Beta tunics (shiny silver jumpsuits with a blue V in the middle–what else?) and go inside.

The tavern is warm and smoky from a fire blazing in a stone fireplace. It's stunningly beautiful and hot–I've only ever seen one real fire before. Candles burn in metal sconces on the walls, giving the room a golden glow. The bar is busy, with mostly bearded guys in puffy knee-length shorts and quilted jackets, drinking from ceramic tankards. And the smell?

"What is that heavenly aroma?" I ask.

"It must be roasting meat," says Homer.

On Beta, we know meat causes heart disease. Our nutritionally balanced pills contain complex proteins that cause no arterial damage. But they don't smell half as good.

"This is so cool," I say.

"It might be if we weren't here to snuff someone out."

Edgy and restless, Homer runs his hand through the top of his hair for the zillionth time–and his wavy fringe just stays up, like a coxcomb. I hold back a giggle.

"So, how are we supposed to find him?" says Homer.

"I guess we'll just hang here, and hope he turns up at some point. If he even exists, that is."

"'*If* he exists? Surely his existence is not in question. If he didn't exist, who wrote all those plays?"

"There are theories it was someone else," I say. "Someone close to him. A friend using Shakespeare's name."

"Barmaid! Another round for my friend and I!" My eye is drawn to the speaker, a couple of benches away. As he tips his tankard back to drain the last mouthful, a waterfall of frothy liquid cascades into his beard.

"Oh. My. God. That's him," I say. "That's William Shakespeare."

I'd know his face anywhere. Hair wavy and dark to just below his ears, receding hairline, a pointy beard and curled moustache. He looks just like the Icon on the Shakespeare app–only younger. He's in his 20s now, not yet a theatre legend.

"You're not really going to kill him, are you?" says Homer.

"Yes, I am," I say, though I feel a tad less sure now I see him in the flesh.

"So how are you going to do it?"

"I have a ring," I say. "The top flips up–there's poison inside. I'll distract him and slip it into his drink. He'll fall asleep and never wake up again."

Homer takes my hand and studies the clasp near the fake green stone. "How ... Shakespearean."

"Look at those young lovers? Aren't they sweet?" We turn and see Will Shakespeare and his companion, a bearded guy about the same age as him, staring right at us. I snatch my hand back from Homer.

"What are your names children?" says Will.

"I'm Juliet," I say, totally weirded out.

"I'm Homer." His voice cracks with nerves.

"Juliette and her Romeo," says Shakespeare. "Meeting in a tavern. In hooded cloaks. A secret meeting I presume? Perhaps the families do not approve?"

"His name's Homer, not Romeo," I say.

Shakespeare doesn't hear. He holds his mug aloft and calls: "Ophelia, what's keeping you, woman. And try to get our order right this time, will you?"

"Coming sir." The barmaid, Ophelia, has flowers in her hair and is crimson-faced from overwork.

I sigh. "Well, if I'm going to do this, I'd better get on with it." (Or … *If it were done.. then 'twere well it were done quickly. Ahhhhh.*)

"No wait," says Homer. "If you kill him, you might get the result you want, but what will happen to your soul in the process?"

I'm amazed a science nerd has such sensitivity, until: "Hang on. Isn't that the theme to one of his plays?" he says.

"Macbeth," I reply.

Is there nothing new under the sun? No thought or idea that can't be traced back to the jottings of this guy before me, his beard soggy and wiry as a pot scrubber, guzzling ale and harassing the barmaid.

I force myself onwards towards Shakespeare's table, hoping no-one notices my ragged breathing as I steel myself for the task ahead.

"How did your last play go, Christopher?" I hear Will ask his friend.

"Not that well," says Christopher. "A half-full house was the best we had during our run."

"Trouble is there are so many writers these days," says Will. "I need to find some way to make my work a bit different to the others."

I'm just about to slip the poison in, when I pause. "Can I make a suggestion Mr Shakespeare? Why don't you try writing strong female leads? Women who are smart and brave, and their own person, not just some cling-on for a male hero? That would be different."

"Yes, it would be!" he says. "And it would probably get me locked up in an asylum." He hoots with laughter.

"Can I ask one more thing?" (*before I kill you*). "How come you speak like that?"

"I speak English. How else would I speak?"

"I expected more thees and thous, and shouldst? That sort of thing?"

"Wherefore shouldst I speak like this? Thinkst thou I be a simpleton, sweet Juliet?"

Now his friend Christopher cracks up. "That's funny. Sort of like talking poetry? You know, it could catch on."

"Really? You think people might actually like that backwards syntax?" says Will. "Come round to mine tomorrow and we'll scribble a few pages, try it out."

"Oh I can't," says Christopher. "I promised my brother-in-law I'd help with his beekeeping. Though I'd much rather write with you. Should I cancel him …?"

"To bee or not to bee, that is the question," says Will.

This is too much. I flick the catch on the ring, glimpse the white powder inside. Will's drink is right there. Unguarded.

—

"So … you did it?" says Homer, his forehead buckled with concern.

I shake my head and sigh. "I couldn't."

"That's fantastic," he says and wraps his arms around me. As we step apart, our cheeks are a matching crimson.

"To true love!" Shakespeare raises a glass across the tables. "Juliet and her Romeo! The fairest lovers in England. Though thou shouldest love more than fairly to say thou were fairly loved."

Oh not the puns. I touch my ring. "I'm going back in."

"No," says Homer, "You're not."

I sigh. "We'd better go, then. I have got a test to study for."

As we move towards the door, we're almost bowled over by a tall man in a black jumpsuit, shiny as an oil spill, who strides up to Shakespeare and announces, as if he's on stage. "I do this today, not just for myself, but for English students everywhere, throughout history."

And he plunges a gold knife into Will's stomach. Then he runs off.

"Will! No!" Christopher cradles his friend's head in his lap, as Shakespeare's blood soaks into the hay-strewn floor. I see his lips move, as if he wants to speak, but no sound emerges. No grand death speech for the Bard himself. Then he goes limp.

I kneel down and check his pulse. Nothing. I double check. He's gone. William Shakespeare is dead. There's no doubt about it. And then, the weirdest thing happens. The gold blade stuck in his belly … just dissolves in midair. Like fairy dust.

Christopher turns to me, eyes bulging: "Was that a dagger I saw before me?"

—

I burst out through the tavern doors into the icy night and find Homer staring off into the woods.

"The guy in black ... he was running and then ... he just vanished," he says. "It has to be a time machine–more advanced than mine."

"Which means..?"

"He was from the future. More future than us."

—

We arrive back on Beta at almost the same time we left, as the last frangipani flutters to the ground by our feet. Homer leans down, picks it up and hands it to me.

"I'm glad you didn't kill him, Juliet," he says. "I don't think I could go out with a murderer."

Is he ... asking me out?

"Saturday night? Pick you up at eight?" he says.

"Sure thing ... Romeo."

I lean back on the bench, amidst the scattered white flowers. And smile. That didn't turn out so badly. Shakespeare's dead–thankfully not by my hand. Which means no more test to worry about. And I have a date for Saturday night. *All's well that ends well.*

"What are you smiling about?" says Ms Orwell, sneaking up behind me. "Shouldn't you be studying for the Shakespeare exam?"

"But ... Shakespeare? What?"

"Two-thirty tomorrow. Marlowe Hall. Don't be late."

But ... but ... William Shakespeare was dead. I confirmed it myself.

So whose plays are we being tested on?

AUTHOR'S NOTE

"Shakespeare, Where the Fuck Art Thou?" was originally written for the NYC Midnight competition. The entry had three requirements:

Genre: science-fiction

Setting: an assassination

Object: a driver.

An idea leapt to my mind. However, I suspect it had been lurking there since high school when, like school students the world over, I was compelled to read Shakespeare as part of the English curriculum. Most people, of course, only dream of doing what the protagonist in this piece dared to do. But, as Shakespeare might have said, the course of true assassination never did run smooth.

PT

On Fucking Oneself

DESIREE HARVEY

I

It must be the spring between my junior and senior years of high school. Pre-Tom Tatum, so I'm romantically unencumbered. I'm not sure how I've ended up here. I am laying back on a bed with my skirt around my waist. My underwear has been pulled down and taken off, but not by me. A man's head is between my legs. I don't want to be here. I don't want him to be there. But for some reason I can't find the words to tell him to stop. If I've protested up to this point, it's been treated as foreplay, the words girls must say to feel better about eventually giving in, to make it seem as though they don't usually give it up so easily. That they're not this kind of girl.

Truthfully, I don't think I'm this kind of a girl. I've only had sex with two guys at this point in my life, both of whom were long-term boyfriends. I've never considered this person as a potential sexual partner. I don't think about him in that way. He isn't someone I'm sexually attracted to. Not to mention the long and complicated romantic history he has with a good friend of mine, or someone who used to be a good friend at any rate. They're not together, but he's the father of her child and one day Jules wants them to be a family again.

Whose room is this anyway? There's still music playing downstairs although it's too muffled to hear distinctly. I don't even know how I ended up in a bedroom with this guy. I can't imagine a situation where he suggested we go upstairs together and I agreed to it. It's a nice enough room, done in soft colors, the bed neatly made up. All of the lights are on, which makes it even more difficult to deny this is happening. How long has it been going on? It feels like forever. Maybe it's only been a few minutes.

Why didn't I say no? Why didn't I say anything? Maybe it's all the coke I inhaled earlier tonight. Or the six bottles of Boone's Farm I sucked down. Was I taken advantage of? Who can say. He's probably as drunk as I am, as high as I am, as fucked up as I am. I don't know that either of us has any control over our faculties.

The night began innocuously enough. Me and a handful of guy friends. Lots of booze. Lots of coke. Maybe some marijuana in the mix. Listening to music, smoking cigarettes, talking excitedly. This sort of thing happens all the time. Daily if I'm being honest. Or if I have my druthers. We don't normally hang out in this house. It's his parents' house, and he doesn't live with his parents, but it's bigger and more well-appointed than any of the places we normally inhabit. I'm sixteen. Most of the guys that were here earlier are in their twenties. The father of my friend's child is seven or eight years older than me. I don't remember the specifics now. Does it matter? In one capacity or another, I've been determined to play at being a grown-up since I was an adolescent. Maybe my behavior, my appearance, are convincing to onlookers. Emotionally, I'm still very much a teenager, perhaps even an adolescent, even though I would never admit this to myself if I could see it, which I can't.

I often dress provocatively. Too much so? Hard to say. Does it matter? Should it matter? I'm regularly sent home from school for wearing short skirts. I try to leave the house wearing a loose sweater sans bra from time to time but my parents always intervene. It's like they have nipple radar. I can't hold a candle, though, to the slightly more shameless girl a class ahead of me who wears nothing but thigh-high stockings under her short skirts and lets whoever would care to do so glimpse the unholy when she crosses and uncrosses her legs, god bless her fearless heart.

Tonight, the experience of having this man's head between my legs brings me to tears but I try to hide it. I don't know why I try to hide it. It doesn't make any sense to me now. Because my head is turned to the side, he cannot see my face, and sobs can sound much like moans of pleasure in a drunken, coke-fueled haze. I think he is trying to be tender, doing this because he thinks it will be enjoyable to me. Surely he believes it will lead to intercourse. What's wrong with me that I can't put a stop to this right now? That I've allowed this to happen in the first place?

In some part, the coke is to blame for my current plight. Under normal circumstances, whenever we are all just drunken stoners, I leave when everyone else leaves. But tonight I stay behind when the other guys leave. Despite minor protests and some surprise on the part of the others. Maybe they knew better than I did. Why would I put myself in this position, you might ask? Because if there were any coke left, their departure meant more for me. But if it was gone, which it would likely have to be for everyone to have left, I stayed because I hoped, maybe even suspected, that he'd held some back. My instinct was correct, and we did it all. The only reason I'm still here is because I thought it would be uncivilized to snort the last line and then immediately split.

This might be the first time I consent to being alone with a man of dubious scruples and motives because I suspect he will give me drugs, but it won't be the last. Over the course of a year I will gradually become strung out enough that I regularly put myself in ill-advised situations, although all I'm offering is a female presence. Sexual quid pro quo is always out of the question. Is that a line I would have crossed eventually? I'd like to think the answer is no, but who knows. I'll be in rehab inside of a year. The unspoken but lingering question remains: if a girl or woman continues to put herself in precarious situations, who's to blame for what happens next, if things get out of control?

Back to tonight. I finally cannot take it anymore and ask him repeatedly to stop. I don't think he hears me at first. It takes all of my strength to insist, even though I can't stand what's happening. Too much has already taken place. I've waited too long. But I can still stop it from going further.

Fending off men who try to touch or kiss me when I'm asleep or trying to sleep is routine. This is not because I'm some hot commodity–it happens to every girl I know, regardless of her age, measurements, intelligence, beauty, or relative chastity or promiscuity. It happens less when drunk men or boys are aware that you have a significant other, particularly an ill-tempered, tough-talking or physically intimidating one, but that won't always save you. We girls accept this behavior as a fact of life, even though most of us hate it. That doesn't mean we all give in. I'm an advocate for a sharp elbow to the ribs or a move to another room. I'm in awe at the handful of girls I know who can settle the matter with a well-thrown punch. So definitive. So badass. I'm so stupid I want to do it in a way that doesn't hurt anyone's feelings and ends with me apologizing to them for requesting that they remove their hands and/or lips from my person and allow me to sleep in peace. I apologize tonight, too, before I scramble out as fast as I can and begin walking the short distance to my parents' house. The quiet night and fresh air don't make me feel better about what happened, but I'm so relieved to be out here instead of in there. So relieved to be alone with my thoughts, even if they're agonizing.

Maybe this is all my fault. Because it wasn't a room full of drunken teens and twenty-somethings passing out wherever they could find a place to crash on a floor or a couch. Because I stayed alone with this man. Maybe it implied something I didn't even understand. I'm normally so expert at navigating these murky waters, flirty enough to get what I want without offering much other than my company, and that of my pretty friends, in return. Not so flirty that the male in question mistakenly senses a window of opportunity.

I will lose touch with some of these friends as my drug habit evolves. Jules and her baby haven't been around much. We will drift apart but I won't know why then. Looking back now, it's probably because of all the late nights I spend doing drugs with an almost exclusively male group of users, including the father of her child. It can't look good from the outside. Nothing like this will happen between he and I again, but we will continue to do drugs together from time to time, always surrounded by others. I pretend this night never happened, try to erase it from my memory. I don't know if something gets back to Jules or anyone else—I've never told a soul.

—

Some months later I'm at a party outside of town, someplace we're all planning to spend the night. Something feels wrong. I think it might be related to the fact that we're in a different locale, and some of the guests at this party are unknown to me and maybe even unfriendly toward newcomers. Something is simmering beneath the surface of this early evening, but I can't put my finger on it, and anyway, my policy is to commit to the party and power through, bad vibes be damned. Dumbass. Even interactions with a handful of people I know well seem to be missing their typical bonhomie. Eve, a Taiwanese hippie chick I regularly party with, pulls me aside after an hour or so.

"You shouldn't drink too much tonight."

"Why not? We're just getting started. And it seems like everyone here could stand to loosen up a little."

"Jules wants to get you really drunk."

"So?"

"So that when you pass out she can shave your head."

"Why?"

"So you won't be pretty to him anymore. She'll be here in a few hours."

Him, of course, is Antonio, the man who's broken Jules's heart over and over, the one I never want to be alone with again. I didn't realize Jules and I were on the outs, but now that I know, I don't want to face her. I don't want to be a part of some charade where we pretend to be happy to see one another. I don't want to stay here waiting around to find out what she's capable of. In fact, I want to leave as soon as possible now that I understand the reason behind the hostile atmosphere. I'm glad I'm still sober, glad I can think straight. I feel scared and betrayed though. That's rich, isn't it? But how many of my "friends" knew about Jules's plan and said nothing, allowed me to come to this party without warning? And what do those people think happened between me and Jules and him? I don't have a driver's license, much less a car, so I'm stranded until I can convince someone to drive me home. To leave the all-night out-of-town party that has only now started to accelerate.

Eve seems like a natural choice to assist in these efforts, but she doesn't want Jules to know she's the one who tipped me off. She's done as much as she can on my behalf. Hatching an escape is further complicated by the fact that I'm suddenly unsure of who my friends are, and I don't want anyone who's conspiring with Jules to know I'm aware of what she has planned. I'm fairly certain I can trust Jeff, and I give him the scoop. I don't have to beg or cajole. Even though he's arrived only minutes before, he's willing to turn back around and take me home.

Safely in his pick-up and headed back east, I thank him profusely and we talk about the bad vibe of that night, of that place. He says he's as glad to leave as I am, but it's possible he's just being nice. Because that's the thing about Jeff: he's true blue. In all of the time I know him, all of the nights we spend being stunningly intoxicated together, he will never treat me in a way that makes me feel unsafe, uncomfortable, or disrespected. He is not among the midnight molesters.

I don't know if Jules and I are ever in the same place at the same time after that. I'll regret that this friendship is over. I'll wonder what she knows, or what she suspects. I'll wonder if she deserves some sort of revenge after what happened between me and Antonio on that night a few months back. Does it matter that she's legally an adult, far closer to his age than mine? Probably not. This is not an accusation. It's also not an excuse. I wish none of it had ever happened. And I wish I could make more sense of it now than I could then.

II

My mom has been suspicious of my behavior for some time. When serious red flags arise, she surprises me by taking off from work for the morning and driving me to our family doctor for a drug test. Somehow, these tests are always negative although I've regularly smoked pot for years. I think I must have a Dionysian guardian angel looking out for me.

The final time my mother surprises me with one of these tests, it's the morning after a big coke- and booze-fueled bender, and I have no faith in my ability to pass the test. There's also no way for me to avoid taking it. Sometime in the days that pass, as we await the results, I ask my mother what she expects to find. She's right about the booze and grass but hasn't allowed herself to consider anything more serious.

I fill her in.

The details I provide are going to lead to a stint in rehab, but not before that last drug test does, in fact, come up completely clean.

Go figure.

After I've spilled the beans, my mom is on the phone with her HMO, making arrangements for me to go to the KeyStone Center for Addiction and Mental Health Treatment. I have no idea what this will entail but presume the party will be over, at least temporarily. Also, I'm not allowed to leave the house except to go to work. How then to arrange a last hurrah? Serendipitously, a shockingly good-looking guy from out of town walks into the restaurant where I work. I don't remember if he gave me his number or if I gave him mine. An actual male model, he's not my usual type but he is tall and strong and, as I mentioned, extremely attractive. Tousled black hair and icy blue eyes. He is, naturally, confident. Refined. Smooth-talking. And, as always, much older than me.

The Friday night before I'm scheduled to go to rehab, we talk on the phone. I visit the house where he's staying. Somehow this, too, is within walking distance of my parents' house, the odds of which are highly unlikely considering they live in the boonies, but there you have it. Easy to sneak off to when my parents have left for the evening. I leave them a note:

> Dear Mom and Dad,
>
> I know I'm not supposed to leave the house but I'm going out of my mind sitting here alone. I'll be on my best behavior and back in a few hours. Try not to worry.
>
>   Love,
>   Desi

I actually always leave a note when I sneak out–something to cover my ass and alleviate parental overreaction in the event that my absence is discovered. Typically, the note I leave tells tale of an unspecified emergency involving one of my friends. It's occurred in the middle of the night and I don't want to wake my parents, but my presence during said emergency is desperately needed. I promise to be home in time for school in the morning and apologize if I've caused undue concern. Some such nonsense. At one point, I just start using the same note over and over again, hiding it under a book in my bedside drawer during daylight hours and leaving it on my bed before I crawl out the window at night. This time I leave the note on the kitchen table. I've already told them my biggest secret when I confessed to my cocaine use. I'm headed to rehab next week–what do I really have to lose?

The house where I meet this guy is a lot like my parents' home and less like the homes of my friends. With its actual furniture and tasteful décor, it appears to be more than just a place to crash after a night of debauchery. Perhaps actual grown-ups–or, at least, young adults–live here. We sit on the plush gray living room couch, candles glowing on the coffee table and bookshelves, music playing softly in the background. I guess everyone in southeastern Pennsylvania is currently doing cocaine, because he has it, too.

I, of course, partake.

At some point, I get up to walk across the room and look through the CD collection, mentally taking note of the usual suspects–Stone Temple Pilots, Nirvana, Red Hot Chili Peppers–and after a moment I can sense him approaching me from behind. I'm not sure what I'm doing here tonight or what I expected to happen, but he makes the first move, wrapping his huge hands around my waist and expressing amazement that he's able to do this. I shrug in response to his comment, but the feel of his hands on my body is electric.

We make our way to a hot tub where we are joined by two of his friends, neither of whom I've met before. It occurs to me that no one knows where I am–I kept that note to my parents vague and haven't talked to any of my friends in this pre-cellphone era. The friends of this man are saying things to me that are far more menacing and lascivious than what other men I know might say and, in some cases, are downright insulting. My sensibilities aren't delicate per se, but I'm nevertheless taken aback when one of model guy's friends asks me whether I spit or swallow. I silently hope his testicles get sucked into one of these ferocious water jets, but wonder if, as a drunk girl in her underwear hanging out in a hot tub with a bunch of male strangers, I should expect to be treated differently.

I have a vague sense that this situation is perilous, and I convince model guy we should spend some time alone. Even though I sense this danger from his friends, and he doesn't exactly come to my defense when I'm being asked if I'm into three-ways, or how many guys I've fucked, or if I've ever had oral sex end with a pearl necklace, I'm still thinking about his hands around my waist and have been gazing at the water bubbling over his carved chest and muscular arms, which I want to feel around me again. I want to feel his weight on me, see what a man of this size can do that other men I've known cannot. We find a couch in a dark room somewhere.

In my experience (which is limited to a handful of times during my summer of love with Tom Tatum), sex on cocaine goes one of two ways for men–a hard-on that lasts an incredible amount of time and the stamina to fuck for hours, or the complete inability to sustain an erection. Maybe it's different with small doses, but I wouldn't know about that and neither would anyone else in my orbit.

Model guy falls into the wet noodle category, despite many determined and creative attempts on my part to assist him in rising to the occasion. On the one hand, it's a disappointment to find out that this beautiful man is no more remarkable than his pedestrian counterparts–no sexual superpowers to speak of. The disappointment of unfulfilled desire, though, is quickly overcome by fear. As I'm coming down from the coke, and he's suggesting a return to the hot tub and the company of his leering, lecherous friends, it becomes impossible to ignore the voice inside of me, urging me to flee. I finally listen to it, pulling my jeans and blouse over my wet underthings as calmly and quickly as I can. Fearing that I might be followed, I actually run part of the way home. Maybe I'm overreacting. No footsteps or headlights behind me–am I just being paranoid?

Dirty and used. Do I have a real reason to feel that way? But I do. Another wild night comes to a rapidly sobering close as I head home. Another dangerous near miss. How long until my luck runs out and I can't get out before it's too late? For better or worse, this is the last I will see or hear of model guy. And since we didn't have intercourse, I won't even count him among my conquests in the mental list I keep.

III

I think I did it for the first time in autumn of 1993 or winter of 1994. My junior year in high school. I'm not proud of this now, but back then, I start many nights with a fifth of Jack Daniels in one hand and a twenty-ounce bottle of Coca-Cola in the other. By the wee hours of the morning, I typically find myself with an empty bottle of whiskey and more than half a bottle of soda. I'm not alone in this behavior–we all party way too hard. Drinking this much, though, is a way of life, a badge of honor. And we're too young, our bodies and spirits too resilient, to know what a real hangover feels like. It's all still fun and games.

I'm currently enjoying the first significant block of time I've had being young and single since becoming sexually active two years ago. Post break-up with my second love, the dark and stormy Ronnie O'Reilly, I see no real romantic or sexual possibilities on the horizon, and it's fine by me–at least for now. I'm in the trailer home of a coworker, surrounded by many other women who also work at the same fine dining establishment as I do.

Although I can't say I'm an expert on trailers, having only been in a few at this point in my life, this one feels very much like a home. Framed photos of our host's family and friends fill tabletops, and the walls are decorated with sconces, mirrors, and watercolors I recognize from the Home Interiors parties my mother used to throw. I'm here for a similar kind of party tonight, but one that does not take domestic ornaments as its *raison d'etre*. This is a sex party, or more accurately, a sex toy party, showcasing lingerie, electronic devices, scented and flavored creams and oils, handcuffs, and nipple clamps.

It doesn't sound particularly groundbreaking now, decades later, when many such businesses are openly promoted and I have the opportunity as an adult to fearlessly visit novelty sex stores, be they online or brick and mortar, whenever I wish. As a teenager in the 1990s, though, this party is a gift, because it gives me the opportunity–for the first time I can remember, maybe for the first time in my life–to think about my sexuality in terms of what pleases me, without any connection to a specific man's desires.

It's difficult to describe the joy and freedom I experience in being a part of this group of women who are discussing all manner of women's things. The opening chatter is innocuous enough–favorite lipstick shades, signature scents–but we soon move onto the good stuff, the really important stuff. A waitress from the restaurant confesses her difficulty achieving orgasm during oral sex. A pastry chef recommends the alphabet technique while some of us nod in agreement and others exclaim in delight or surprise. Another waitress, Glenda, talks about how much her four-year-old daughter masturbates:

"I walked out of the room for one minute the other day and she had the hairbrush stuck down the front of her underwear again by the time I got back."

Astonished, I ask which end of the hairbrush.

"Doesn't even matter. You wouldn't believe the things she sticks in there."

The other women laugh and share tales of their own children's shenanigans. No one is scandalized by the masturbating toddler. The pleasure of being able to talk with such openness about absolutely anything, but especially about our experiences with sex and with our bodies–all of those things men either can't relate to or don't understand about its mysteries and miseries–inspires a sense of liberation I've rarely felt before. It's as though I'm being initiated into an unofficial sisterhood, let in on a magical, beautiful secret.

We drink red solo cup after red solo cup of a delicious punch that contains far too much grain alcohol. The sugar and the booze only add to my general feeling of euphoria, but I also have to pee frequently, and I'm not alone in this need. It rarely strikes me as noteworthy when women go to the bathroom together. Oftentimes, I imagine, we are eager to snatch that precious time away from the prying ears and eyes of men so we can share stolen moments of support, camaraderie, and confession. And given how much fun we're having now, and how increasingly intimate our conversations grow, it doesn't seem at all odd to me that a woman I met once only briefly before tonight, Jen Pierce, who graduated from high school the year I was a freshman and is the daughter of my coworker, Ann, volunteers to go to the bathroom with me. It's all of a piece with this spirit of conviviality.

Once in the bathroom, I'm the first to relieve myself. To my surprise, as I do so, Jen pulls out a mirror, spills a small pile of white powder onto it, and uses her driver's license to divide the pile into individual lines. Four of them. I think it's coke but ask her anyway as, before this moment, I've only seen it in movies. My suspicion is confirmed. I'm taken aback by how open and cavalier she is about this brand of drug use. When she offers to share, I thank her but decline. She asks me if I'm sure. I tell her I think I so. I'm not in any way pressured to do this; an offer is simply made. And after the tiniest hesitation, I have a *fuck it* moment. Armed with a bill of American currency tightly rolled into the shape of a straw, I follow her instructions, snort one line into each nostril, and then head back to the party as if nothing of note happened.

But something did happen. I wonder now: Was anyone else high on stimulants that night? I'm not really sure. I don't think Jen was doing coke with anyone else–I think she went to the bathroom with me in hopes that she'd find a willing accomplice for the evening. Great instincts on her part, as I'm openminded about many things and naturally friendly toward most people. Even though we're only just getting to know one another, long before we first walk into that bathroom together, Jen and I enjoy a very lively conversation about people we both know or have known, mostly the same group of men who have apparently been hanging out with high school girls for the better part of the last decade. Soon this turns into the kind of party I usually experience with my male friends, except everyone here has a vagina and no one is trying to fuck anyone else. It's marvelous. Jen and I take a few more trips to the bathroom together as the evening progresses. At the end of the night I go home elated, and after a few energetic and joyful hours sequestered in my bedroom, fall into a dreamless sleep.

Not long after this party, I'm made aware that at least three other women who attended are habitual meth users, and at least one other–unbelievably enough, Jen's mother, Ann–will become someone I split eight balls with in the future. When I'm not doing coke with my guy friends, I will do it with Jen on some nights, and with Ann on other nights. It will be quite some time–several months–before each knows the other is also using. The absurdity of the situation is not lost on me, and I'm relieved when the cat is finally out of the bag come summer. By then, Tom Tatum will be around and we'll have tenacious, frustrating, and unfulfilling sex on Ann's living room floor the same night she and her daughter do coke together for the first time.

But on this night, at this party, each time we emerge from the bathroom, I feel amazing. Happier. Lighter in every conceivable way. Full of ideas and energy. Desperately in need of cigarettes and more punch. But otherwise so very exhilarated. I love cocaine immediately. Lucky for me, it will turn out that many, many people I know love it, too. And over time, I will be initiated into another secret society of sorts.

AUTHOR'S NOTE

I began writing creative nonfiction in 2017. Once started, I couldn't help but look back at an earlier iteration of myself I had underestimated, silenced, misunderstood, and blamed for so much of what I thought had gone wrong when I was a young adult. The more I remembered about this self, the more I liked and forgave her. Aided by hindsight, I wanted to understand who she was and the world she came from.

But this story isn't just about me and it isn't just about then. I see a connection between that time and this one, some similarity in political, social, and cultural forces. A familiar disillusionment shared by so many of the people around me. I'm trying to decipher the confusing messages I received as a young woman of the specific time in which I grew up, and to determine how those messages have or have not changed with the passage of time. Writing at this moment is both seeking and release. Catharsis through time travel.

Always a work-in-progress.

DH

Dear Josh,
We stopped by to fuck you but you didn't answer the door.
Therefore you are gay.
Sincerely,
Tiffany and Amber.

Daniel Clowes
Ghost World

Stop Fucking Up the Gene Pool

NOEL ALCOBA

I once asked my Dad what he would wish for if he met a genie.

"Nothing," he said. "I'd look that genie in the eye and say, *'Get your ass back in that bottle, Mister!'* My advice? Find something you enjoy doing, do it well, and you'll be happy in your life. Be your own genie."

With those words, he straightened the nametag on his apron, adjusted his eyepatch, and donned a black pirate hat.

Dad was forty at the time, and the most absurdly happy person I ever knew. Now that I'm forty, I thought I'd be where he was. Not bartending in pirate garb, but being happy with where I was.

I followed his advice and found something I enjoy doing. I do it well. As a geneticist with my own company (named Gene Genie in honor of my dad's wisdom), I earn enough to grant my own wishes, including a new house in the gated community of Sandpiper Cove. I should be dancing a jig like Captain Dad of the *HMS Optimist*.

But while I'm sure Dad had his fair share of obnoxious customers, he never had to live next to the likes of Rudy Huber. Unfortunately, there are some wishes that can't be granted, even with money. Like it or not, we can't just wish away the douchebags of the world.

I considered Googling "how to make your neighbor disappear without killing them," but the search results would involve some manner of actual killing. I wasn't too keen on having my search history alert Homeland Security. Besides, Dad didn't work double shifts with a fake parrot on a puffy sleeve just so his son would grow up to be a killer.

Lucky for Rudy I didn't have the stomach for it.

I met Rudy on the afternoon I moved into my home in Sandpiper Cove. He introduced himself revving the engine of his envy-green Maserati in his driveway, instead of offering to help me unload my U-Haul. He kept the engine running and finally emerged, in a silk dress shirt that barely contained his juice-pumped, spray-tanned muscles. He extended a giant hand as if it were a gift from Mount Olympus.

"Name's Rudy. Rudy Huber," he yelled over the motor's intestinal gurgling, not bothering to await my response. "You must be the new neighbor. I was wondering who would end up buying the *smallest* house on the block. I'm kidding! It's fine, if you're into dollhouses. Seriously though, you need a larger deck. And a third story. Make it four. Also a wider garage. Better yet, two garages."

How did he manage to fit such a bloated head into his shiny little penis-on-wheels?

"Let me know when you decide to beef up your little clubhouse." He crammed himself back into his car, dropped it into drive, and sped off. I caught the vanity plate, which read GOLDEN, and I wondered if he had bladder issues.

After the exhaust cloud cleared, Ainsley Plover from across the street introduced herself.

"Here's what you need to know about Rudy," she said, offering me a crash course on Rudy Huber 101. "He played linebacker in college. He could have gone pro but injured his, oh, something unpronounceable. I'm sure it was painful."

Like most of the overly enhanced Stepford mommy-bloggers of Sandpiper Cove, Ainsley had that Pez-dispenser physique one maintained by following a rigorous workout. I imagined it involved flexing every muscle in her body in vain attempts to smile without shattering her forehead. That, plus a strict diet of gluten-free steam and birdseed.

A quick glance down at my waistline reminded me I was in no position to judge anyone's health routine. I deliberately chose to live here, so I would have to adapt, even if it meant trading baconburgers for alfalfa pellets and millet.

Ainsley leaned in to whisper, even though no one else was within earshot, "After the football thing fell through, Rudy became a male stripper. Wild huh? Called himself Guy Golden. He still has the figure for it, if you ask me. ANYWAY he took a bunch of business seminars, ended up making, like, MILLIONS, selling hormone smoothies. Or magnetic socks. Or both? I don't know. Whatever it was, it worked out REALLY well for him. Now he's got the biggest house in Sandpiper Cove. He even owns one of those fancy new hot tubs where the water changes color based on your mood!"

By 'mood' she probably meant the water changes color when it reacts to pee. That would explain Rudy's vanity plate.

Within a week (and only after exhausting my supply of excuses) I found myself simmering in that very hot tub. It was one of the many stops on Rudy's "check out my enormous mansion" tour. It was also an excuse to showcase his trophy wife, Kandace, who was busy downing Merlot from a bowl-sized goblet, and taking selfies.

"Every time she does duck-lips I feel like throwing her little chunks of bread!" said Rudy, elbowing me.

Probably the way most people felt like tossing Rudy pig-slop every time he opened his mouth.

"I paid for those," Rudy whispered, pointing out his wife's double-Ds, as if I hadn't noticed them already. They were twin palace heralds announcing her entrance before the rest of her arrival. *Her Bustiness, Lady Cleavage of Silica!*

I'm sure that somewhere beneath the nipped and tucked plastic, Kandace was a nice girl. She even might have been my type at one point.

"Multi. Level. Marketing," Rudy said, while taking a swig of Coors.

"Excuse me?" I said.

"You know, M-L-M! I can tell you were wondering how I could afford all this," he said, waving his can hand in the air, christening me with beer.

No, I thought, *I was wondering if your bloviating was powering the hot tub.*

"You should try it," he belched loudly. "If you do it as well as me, you could get yourself a bigger place. Like this. Eventually. Maybe even a cufflink like Kandace, here."

Kandace was in her own world, making faces at her drink. But I got a strange sense she was really studying me through the lens of her wine glass.

"Wait. You *are* into chicks, aren't you, sport?" Rudy asked. "Come to think of it, I don't believe I've seen a Mrs. ...whatever you said your name was ... around."

"*Soto*," I said, "There is no Mrs. Soto. Not yet, anyway."

"Sodo? Is that Mexican? Chinese? Chinexican? That would make you a car thief that can't drive for shit! Get it?"

Genetically I was Inuit, Fennoscandian, Iberian, and Han. I kept those details to myself rather than offer fuel for his gum wad brain to devise some hybrid punchline of my ancestry.

"I'm American," I said.

"Uh-huh. Sure. Why hide who you are?" he said, rising from the hot tub. "Look at me. I don't hide the fact I used to table dance for chump change in the Tri-Cities! Check this out. I was known for this one move." He started to gyrate, then teetered and flopped back down, creating a small tidal wave.

I was relieved to see the water remained the same color.

"Trust me. Women would take on a second mortgage just to see me do that move. And *you* got to see it for free. Anyway, this place is so big I even have an extra room just for my old dance costumes."

Which was the next stop on the Rudy Huber tour. I never thought I'd live to see a spandex gladiator costume, much less a tear-away astronaut suit. *Hooray!* I thought. *Two more items off the bucket list. Dad would be so proud.*

By the time we moved the one-sided conversation to his barge-sized deck, Rudy managed to offend every demographic group fortunate enough *not* to have him in it, from foreigners to college graduates. He peppered the insults with jabs about my house, my height, and my sexuality.

"You have kids?" he asked, as if it were a fraternity initiation challenge. "Of course you don't. The fuck am I thinking?" He pointed to a scrawny teenager in a lawn chair, hunched over an iPhone. "That there's Aidan, my son."

I was hoping Aidan was a neighborhood kid who happened to wander into the Huber yard by mistake, but The Fates have a cruel sense of humor. They allowed Rudy to breed.

Aidan tuned us out, clamping down his headphones like an adult-cancelling helmet.

"Aidan's small for fifteen," said Rudy, "gets it from his

mom's side."

The less he inherits from you, I thought, *the better for the gene pool.*

"He's into soccer," huffed Rudy, "Insists it's *futbol,* but who's he kidding? It isn't *real* football. No hands? No contact? No sexy cheerleaders? Puh-lease!"

"Actually, I played midfielder throughout high school," I said. Aidan shot me a curious glance before cranking the volume on his headphones.

Rudy continued his rant as if he didn't hear me. "Honest to god, I would've rather had a girl if knew he was going to have such a hard-on for that Euro-crap, twinkle toes, pretty-boy sport, instead of American football. Am I right?"

You tell me. You used to shimmy in a golden cape as gawkers folded dollar bills into your sequin thongs.

"By the way, Ainsley across the street says you're a gina-cologist," he said, draining another Coors.

"A what?" I asked.

"A gina-cologist. You know, *gina,* as in *vagina.* And why not just call yourselves vaginacologists?" he pondered.

"Actually ..."

"My wife is looking for a new gina-cologist. Aren't you, honey?"

"No, I'm not," said Kandace, refilling her wine glass. "I like Dr. Scoter just fine ... and it's pronounced *gynecologist*, not gina-cologist."

"No, I'm pretty sure it's gina-cologist. Besides, I didn't ask you. Just get Dr. Vagina and me two more beers, will you? Jeez, I should hire a Mexican to fetch my beer. At least he wouldn't correct my English."

He wouldn't know where to start.

"Clearly, I'm in the wrong field," said Rudy. "Wouldn't mind doing the vaginacologist thing. But I'm already making more money than God."

And you still can't afford brains. "I'm not a gynecologist, I'm a geneticist," I said.

"But that's the same thing. Genitals right?"

"No, *not* genitals. *Genetics.*"

"I know what a geneticist is," Kandace said, from behind the fridge door. "You look up family trees."

Close. It seemed Kandace might be the brains in this power couple.

"That's too bad," said Rudy. "If you were a vaginacologist you'd be looking up women's legs instead of family trees."

I cleared my throat "You're thinking of genealogist. They do family trees. I'm a geneticist. My company analyzes DNA."

Rudy blinked like a toddler trying to comprehend Latin.

"Like Twenty-three For Me?" Kandace chirped, beer cans in hand. "I've seen their commercials. You, like, spit in a cup, then they can tell if you're, like, half Indian. Or Mormon."

"Not exactly…"

"I don't need some fucknut looking at my spit to tell me I'm half *anything*," said Rudy. "My ancestors are from Ireland and Germany. That makes me one hundred percent American."

No, Adolf McDickhead, I thought, *you mean one hundred percent American cheese.*

The more he talked the more depressing it was knowing I could not simply wish him away. But perhaps I could grant myself the next best thing and put Rudy in his place.

"You know," I said, "my company could find out if you come from nobility. Your ancestors could have been famous!"

"Yes, like the Lannisters!" piped Kandace.

Oh, so close.

"Or maybe even the Lancasters," I suggested.

"The who?"

Granted, it wasn't precisely the kind of DNA screening my company did, but Rudy wouldn't know the difference. I could throw in terms like *single nucleotide polymorphisms* and *centimorgans*, and whatever I followed it up with would sound genuine.

"So," Rudy said, "if I give you my spit, could you see if my ancestors were, like, ancient warriors or something? Vikings?"

Fish, meet hook.

"Sure," I smiled.

I could get his hopes up, then tell him he descended from one of history's biggest assholes, like Vlad the Impaler. But knowing him he'd take probably wear that like a badge of honor. No, I could tell him his ancestor was Vlad's less famous idiot brother, Gleb, the sheep-poker.

Better yet, pop his racial purity balloon. *Gee, Rudy, your DNA shows that you're half-Mexican.*

Who needs a genie? I'm a genius.

—

Later that week Rudy showed up at my door with two test tubes of saliva.

"One's for Kandace. Typical chick, wants to know if her ancestors were princesses," he said. "Honestly, I don't really care. All I want to know is how much warrior blood I got."

"Sure thing," I said, "I'll just have you sign some legal release stuff, then in a few weeks we'll see if you're related to Ragnar Lothbrok."

"*Magma-what?* Whatever. And get me another spit tube. For Aidan. I want to see if he's got that, you know, gay gene."

"As opposed to the Rudy gene?"

"I don't know what that means."

Of course you don't, you mallet-headed steroid bucket. But why waste breath explaining? I thought.

I gave Rudy a third DNA kit. The sooner I ran the tests the sooner I could slap Superbigot down to earth by telling him he descended from farm animals. With Tourette's.

—

Disappointingly, the test results showed nothing ethnically diverse in Rudy Huber's genes. He was so thoroughly Teutonic you could set his chromosomes to music and get Wagner's *Ring Cycle.* Or Rammstein. I was also surprised to learn that Kandace had actual human DNA and not some barcode off the Mattel assembly line.

However, one's ethnic makeup is not the only specifics DNA can identify. DNA can also ascertain paternity. I examined the whole family's results. Something in the numbers looked disturbingly familiar.

I braced myself, and compared them to another set of chromosomes I kept on file.

I double-checked.

Then I triple-checked.

Shit.

—

Kandace Huber stood in her driveway unloading grocery bags and boxed wine. I rushed over to help.

"When was Aidan born?" I asked.

"November 1, 2003," she said. "Why?"

I counted back nine months.

"Just curious. By the way, were you ever at the Tacoma Dome, around, say, February 2003?"

I tried to look past her cosmetic enhancements, subtracting 15 years and adding in the hazy filter of one-too-many martinis. I believe she was a brunette back then, and obviously less busty. I distinctly remembered how she kept the drinks coming and laughed at all my jokes. She left my hotel room and we never even bothered to exchange names.

"Maybe?" she said, shrugging. "Rudy and I have been to so many vendor fairs over the years. All over the country, really. Why do you ask?"

I was about to answer, when out of the corner of my eye a soccer ball hurtled toward me. I pivoted just in time, deflecting it with my chest, bobbed it off my head, juggled it from knee to knee, and rainbow kicked it twenty feet into the air.

At the end of the ball's arc stood Aidan. He trapped it between his foot and shin, then gracefully lofted it up into his hands.

"Beast," he said, issuing a nod and a smile.

Kandace set down the boxed Zinfandel and faced me. Fifteen years ago I was slimmer and had longer hair. Did she recognize me at all?

"I was wondering ..." she said.

So was I. "Yes?"

"Aidan's high school is looking for a part-time soccer coach. It's only twice a week, for a few hours. Would you be interested?"

—

"Sure enough, DNA says your ancestors were big, axe-wielding Vikings," I said, popping the tab on a cold Coors.

"I knew it!" Rudy chugged his beer and let out a self-congratulating burp. "Maybe after Aidan goes through his growth spurt, some of that Viking blood will kick in. He still has time to get over his soccer phase and tryout for varsity football next season. Maybe he'll be a linebacker like his old man."

I looked out onto Rudy's expansive lawn, perfectly happy it was so vast, providing ample space for Aidan to practice his ball handling footwork. I took a hearty gulp, burped back, and tapped Rudy's can in a toast.

"I'm sure he'll find something he loves doing," I said. "If he does it well he can be whatever he wants to be."

Maybe a midfielder. Like his old man.

AUTHOR'S NOTE

Growing up, we moved from country to country, so I was always the new kid. But to me, everyone else was the new kid. There was never a shortage of new people to meet. And no matter who I met, sooner or later I would discover something funny about them. That's how I approach my characters. I watch them in my head for a while, and wait for them to do or say something funny.

While readers may find the Rudy and Kandace characters to be over the top, they're loosely based on actual people I've known. Truth is stranger than fiction, after all. Although their names have been changed to protect the innocent, I'm sure they're guilty of something.

NA

"Fuck you," said Czernobog. "Fuck you and fuck your mother and fuck the fucking horse you fucking rode in on."

Neil Gaiman
American Gods

Attacked by
a Fucking Fish
... a Love Story
LESLIE WIBBERLEY

The thirty-pound Chinook salmon squirmed in Daniel Robert's hands, flipping and flopping in an attempt to escape his grip. He frowned as the salmon's open mouth came perilously close to his groin.

Today was Daniel's first day at the Wannock Salmon Hatchery. An award-winning journalist, he was here to study their groundbreaking work. He'd spend the next month learning everything he could about the hatchery's operation, for the article he'd been commissioned to write. But, if this day was any indication of how those four weeks would unfold, he suspected he might regret his decision to write that article.

The huge salmon flapped across his bare thighs, cold and slimy. Not for the first time Daniel wished he were wearing the same heavy-duty raingear worn by the hatchery workers. His flimsy exercise shorts offered zero protection. In his defense, the weather was hot and humid as hell, and he'd only planned on observing and taking notes today.

But when he arrived that morning, Dr. Sarah Mackenzie, PhD, the stunning, young environmentalist in charge of the hatchery, raked her smoky grey gaze up and down his body and announced, "Today you'll be helping with sperm collection." She'd flipped her long, blonde ponytail over one shoulder and dared him to object.

"With *what?*" asked Daniel, caught between trying to imagine what the hell that entailed, and trying *not* to imagine what the long, lean body beneath her rain-gear would feel like pressed against his.

"It's called milking," said Sarah. "And the only way to truly appreciate what we do here is to get your hands dirty."

—

"For God's sake. Just slide your hand down its belly and press," said Sarah, interrupting Daniel's thoughts. She was holding a small plastic bag underneath the salmon to catch the semen.

Her exasperation irritated him. "I'm trying," he snapped, "but this fish is slippery as hell, and I'm not exactly dressed for the occasion."

Sarah's eyes narrowed. "Agreed, but not my problem. You're here to learn, and learn you shall." She shook her head. "For heaven's sakes, you do research for a living. You should have been better prepared. You were coming to a fish hatchery, not a bloody hot yoga class."

Glaring, Daniel said, "Precisely, I'm here to do research, not jack off a fucking fish."

Her eyebrows rose. "Jack off?"

Daniel shrugged. "Encouraging sperm to exit the body of a male fish, ergo, jack off."

"Lord, give me patience."

Despite her impatient tone, Daniel was certain Sarah's lips had twitched in a hint of a smile. "Also, I can't believe you couldn't have found a spare pair of rain pants to give me."

They locked eyes for a moment. This time Daniel definitely saw a spark of humor in the doctor's grey eyes. When her lips twitched upwards again, he knew she totally could've given him something to wear.

Damn, the woman was playing him. As much as he didn't want to be, he was impressed.

"Just give me the damned fish." Sarah reached for the salmon, but as Daniel tried to hand it over, the fish slipped out of his grasp and landed head first on his lap, open mouth snapping at his crotch.

The sharp teeth snagged his tender flesh. He let out a blood-curdling screech. "Holy shit! That fucking thing bit my balls."

Daniel jumped to his feet. The salmon tumbled to the ground. He held his hands to his crotch, cursing.

Sarah lifted the distraught salmon and returned it to the holding tank. "What are you talking about? These fish don't bite."

Daniel pointed to the blood trickling from the inside of his shorts. "Then what the hell is this?"

Her eyes widened for a moment, then she snorted with laughter. Which did *not* impress him. "I've never heard of a salmon biting anyone in the balls. Ever. And I've been working with fish like these for years."

Daniel was furious, partly because he was in pain, but mostly because he felt like a fool in front of this beautiful and accomplished woman. "This is serious. I need to go to the hospital. That thing is probably crawling with bacteria, and I'm sure I'll need stitches." Daniel tried to walk away straddle legged. Blood dripped down his legs with each step. "Shit. I don't think I can drive."

A burst of laughter came from behind. He spun around to find Sarah bent over at the waist. "I'm. Sorry. I realize. You're. In pain." She struggled to get the words out between laughs. "But, d-d-damn. This has got to be a first."

"I'm bleeding to death, and you're *laughing*?"

She wiped a few tears from her eyes. "Don't be stupid. You're not bleeding to death."

Daniel pointed to the blood still running down his wide spread legs.

Shaking her head, Sarah said, "Fine, I'll drive you. But you can find your own ride home. I have work to do."

She called out to an older man wearing a pair of green hip waders. "Hey, Dave. I need to take our intrepid journalist to the E.R. Can you take over here?"

The man nodded and Sarah headed to the parking lot without waiting for Daniel. He waddled after her.

—

Sarah started the truck and pulled out of the parking lot. *Unbelievable. First this guy shows up wearing those ridiculous yoga shorts, and then he lets a fish bite him in the balls.*

His injury was unlikely to be serious, though from his screams it was hard to be sure. Trust this fool to let something like this happen to him on his first day at the hatchery. He had a lot to learn if he wanted to survive the next month.

She sighed. As much as his cocky attitude annoyed her, Daniel Roberts, an accomplished journalist with more than one award for his work, was certainly no fool. After he'd sent an email asking to visit their organization, she'd read about him to make sure he was legit. The hatchery needed all the publicity they could get, and a well-researched article could do wonders for their funding.

She felt a smidge of regret for making him do the milking without the proper gear. But he'd pissed her off by showing up so unprepared. He needed to take their work seriously.

Daniel fidgeted in his seat. "Can you please hurry? I'm dying here."

Sarah darted a quick glance at him. Even though she'd temporarily sworn off men, she' be willing to break her self-imposed vow for those stunning emerald eyes and that incredible body. Those obscenely tight shorts of his did little to hide Daniel's finer points. In her opinion, intelligence and beauty were always a deadly combination. "Don't worry. You'll live."

A few minutes later, she pulled the truck up to the front doors of the hospital. "Do you have someone to pick you up?" she asked, taking pity on him.

"My mom," he answered in a gruff voice.

"Your parents live in River's Inlet?"

Daniel nodded. "Yeah. I live with them."

Sarah's eyebrows shot upwards. "With your parents?" *Please tell me he's not one of* those *men.*

Lifting his chin, Daniel said, "Yes. I moved in a month ago."

"Oh, while you write your article." *Okay, a temporary arrangement wasn't so bad.*

"No, indefinitely."

Her brows furrowed. Shit. He *was* one of those men.

Daniel bristled. "You got a problem with that?"

"Nope. Not my business. I'm sure lots of men your age live with their parents."

A strange expression clouded Daniel's green eyes. "And why not? I've got a bedroom all to myself. Mom does my laundry, cooks my meals, and even makes my lunch. What more could a man ask?"

She shook her head, unable to hide her disappointment. The last thing she needed was to get involved with a mama's boy. Staring pointedly at the door, she said, "I have to head back to the hatchery. Have fun."

"Thanks for the ride," he said as he slid out, not sounding particularly thankful.

—

Daniel waddled to the Emergency entrance. Why hadn't he told Sarah about his dad's stroke? And why throw in that bit about his mom taking care of him? To give her more time with his dad, Daniel had taken over the cooking—and the cleaning.

Must have been the way she looked down her nose at him. Judging him.

Daniel had read a lot about Sarah before he'd taken this assignment. She was a rising star in the environmental world, as brilliant as she was beautiful. Her opinion of him mattered more than he cared to admit.

Once inside, he checked in with the triage nurse, a young man whose name tag read Jason Wong.

"What brings you here today, sir?"

Daniel explained that a fish had bitten him in the genitals.

Jason eyebrows shot up. "May I ask what type of fish?"

Daniel frowned as he noted the hint of a smile playing at the corners of Jason's mouth. "A Chinook salmon," said Daniel. "Though I can't see how that could possibly be relevant."

"Well, if it was a goldfish, not such a big deal. Right?" This time a broad smile flashed across the young man's face.

Daniel glared at Jason. "Not funny."

The young man ducked his head, but not before Daniel saw him smile again. Did anyone take this injury seriously?

Jason took Daniel's blood pressure and temperature, then handed him a clipboard and said, "Take a seat and fill out these forms. A doctor will be with you soon."

Daniel shuffled over to a row of plastic chairs, wincing as he sat. Time to call his mom. A quick fumble through his backpack failed to produce his phone. He dumped the contents on the chair beside him, to no avail. Shit. He must have dropped it at the hatchery.

—

Sarah pulled into the parking lot, unable to stop thinking about Daniel.

The man intrigued her. He certainly didn't seem the type to freeload off his family. Why would a respected journalist with multiple award-winning publications want to move in with his parents, especially in a town as small as River's Inlet?

Of course, *her* move to the little town just over a year ago had been the best decision of her life. Her work at the renowned hatchery was exciting, and the people in the small community were warm and welcoming. And after her disastrous relationship with a man who preferred variety to fidelity, the lack of romantic prospects in town suited her fine.

Was it possible Daniel had just as good a reason for moving here? Climbing out of the truck, she forced her thoughts away from him, and walked over to the nearest tank, where Dave was standing.

"So, is our boy going to make it?" asked Dave.

She shrugged. "Not sure. I didn't wait around to find out."

Dave waved a cell phone at her. "Found this on the ground. Daniel must have dropped it in all the commotion."

Daniel's phone! The rush of happiness that hit as Sarah realized she had a reason to go back and check on Daniel caught her by surprise.

"You should take this to him," said Dave, a twinkle in his eyes.

"Why are you looking at me like that?"

"Like what?" Dave was grinning now.

"Like you just handed me the Holy Grail."

Dave shrugged. "I may be old, but I can tell when a woman is interested in a man. And for the record, I'm pretty sure the feeling is mutual."

Sarah took the phone without commenting and headed back to her truck.

"Be nice, and maybe he'll ask you out for dinner," yelled Dave.

—

Daniel used the payphone in the lobby to call his mom. As soon as he mentioned hospital, she let out a shriek and said, "I'll be right there."

He started to explain that he hadn't seen the doctor yet, but she hung up before he could finish.

They called him in to a treatment room just as he ended the call.

The attending physician cleaned Daniel's wound and said, "I'm going to give you a local anesthetic before I put the stitches in. It may sting a little."

Understatement of the year, thought Daniel three stitches later.

"Come back in seven days for stitch removal," said the doctor holding out what looked suspiciously like a sanitary napkin. "These will protect the area and keep it clean and dry. Change them every day, more often if there's weeping."

Daniel's mouth fell open. He wasn't serious?

"The nurse will see to this and bring you a script for antibiotics and painkillers."

Ten minutes later, modesty in tatters, Daniel's nether region was safely ensconced in a pair of sanitary napkins. He tugged his shorts on. They bulged as if he were wearing a diaper.

"Hello, Daniel? Are you decent?"

"Sarah?" asked Daniel, surprised that the sound of her voice sent his pulse racing.

"Yeah. I brought your phone. I was worried you wouldn't be able to call your mom. Can I come in?"

"Of course."

Sarah stepped inside. "So, you all fixed up now?"

He crossed his legs to hide his...*packing,* but before he could answer, a frantic female voice called out, "Danny!"

—

Sarah turned to see an older woman with a stylish, silver bob and pink tracksuit rush into the cubicle. She flew to Daniel and kissed his cheek. "My poor baby. Are you okay?"

"Yes, Mom. I'm fine. Relax."

Good, God. He's blushing. For some reason Daniel's adorably pink cheeks made Sarah's knees go weak.

Daniel's mom continued, "I'm sorry I took so long, sweetheart. I couldn't find anyone to stay with Dad, so I had to get his wheelchair into the van on my own. He's waiting outside."

Wheelchair? What's wrong with his dad? Sarah cleared her throat, and the older woman jerked around in surprise.

"Oh. Hello." She thrust out her hand. "Doris Roberts, and you are?"

Daniel answered, "Mom, this is Dr. Mackenzie, from the hatchery."

Doris beamed. "How lovely to meet you, dear. Danny's told us all about you."

Sarah shook Doris's hand, "Please, call me Sarah." *Daniel told his mom about me?* With a smile for her son, Doris said, "He's quite good at this writing thing, you know."

Sarah smiled at the woman's obvious pride, still wondering about Doris's earlier comment. "So I've heard."

"He's such a good boy. Came all the way from New York to help with his father. My poor husband had a stroke a few months ago. It's been hard managing on my own, but now that Danny's here, things are so much better."

Sarah's gaze flicked to Daniel. He shrugged, and if possible, his cheeks turned even pinker. Her heart melted a little more.

"Danny," said Doris, "you should invite Sarah over for dinner sometime. When you're all better." She turned to Sarah. "He's a wonderful cook."

"I'm sure Sarah's too busy to have dinner with people she hardly knows." Daniel's emerald gaze burned into Sarah's, and it was clear he hoped she wasn't.

His lips were so smooth, so pink. Heat flooded Sarah's body as she imagined how they'd taste. Tingles of anticipated pleasure spread across her thighs and into her belly. She answered, her voice husky and breathless. "I'd be delighted to *come* for dinner."

And maybe, for dessert, some wild, monkey sex.

———

Daniel grinned at Sarah's emphasis on the word *come.* Despite his injuries, his body responded to the heat smoldering in her beautiful, blue eyes. He cocked his head and gave a slow wink, to indicate her message had been received.

Her wide, answering smile filled him with the oddest sensation–a sense that today's entire bizarre sequence of events was supposed to have happened, and that somehow, this woman was his future.

—

How odd, thought Sarah, as she flashed Daniel a smile, *why on earth does it feel as if I've come home?*

AUTHOR'S NOTE

For the past two years, I've participated in the New York City Midnight Flash Fiction and Short Story Challenges. In these contests, participants are given a genre, a setting, and an object, and must finish the story within a specific time frame and word count.

I love writing to constraints. It pushes my creativity to new levels. And as a procrastinator, I work very well under pressure. I developed "Attacked by a Fucking Fish ... a Love Story" with the following constraints:

Genre: romantic comedy

Setting: living with parents

Object: an environmentalist.

I live the beautiful province of British Columbia, Canada, where we have an abundance of stunning mountains and rivers, and many salmon hatcheries. As I struggled to decide what to write, I thought of a dear friend who is a stream-keeper and works at a salmon hatchery. She became the inspiration for my story.

LW

Fuck literature.

Ernest Hemingway
Selected Letters 1971-1961

Wrong
Fucking
Number
JOHN SHEIRER

While in graduate school, Sally paid the bills for a year by working part-time at a weird little fast-food restaurant at the local mall. They specialized in french fries, so the place was called the "French Fry Factory." For uniforms, they wore bright yellow T-shirts and baseball caps emblazoned with the glowing orange words, "French Fry Factory." (Just for fun, the "o" in "factory" was shaped like a cog.) In the fluorescent mall lighting, that yellow and orange combination glowed almost enough to cook the fries by itself.

The restaurant had a small dining area with six tables and an open food-prep area so that anybody walking by could stare at Sally while she worked. She was often alone, taking orders and operating the cash register with her right hand while reaching back to run the fryers and the grill with her left.

The job paid a dollar over minimum wage, which helped pay her rent on a studio apartment. And Sally got one free sandwich and all the fries and drinks she wanted during each shift. All in all, it wasn't a bad deal. Each day that she worked, she skipped meals at home, and then snacked on fries and iced tea throughout the work day. When her shift ended, she would settle down for a leisurely burger and do some reading for her night classes. She hardly ever bought groceries that year, even stopping in for free fries on her occasional days off, and she actually lost fifteen pounds because the work kept her too busy to eat much.

Within a couple of weeks, Sally got a promotion to "opener." There was no extra pay, but she got to come in at 9 a.m. and open the place at 10–a much better job than "closer," which required hanging out until 10 p.m. when the only people left in the mall were semi-suspicious "lurkers." Mornings were quiet at the restaurant, and she was able to develop an organized routine for getting the grills, fryers, and registers ready for the day. She enjoyed having a couple of calm hours of light duty before the lunch rush began.

When she'd been there for about three months, Sally's morning quiet was interrupted by a phone call at precisely 9:30.

"Hello, French Fry Factory!" she sang out in her cheeriest voice.

An elderly sounding woman on the other end of the line said, "I would like to speak to Marion, please."

"I'm sorry, ma'am," Sally replied. "There's no one here by that name. I think you might have the wrong number."

The woman recited the phone number and again asked for Marion.

"That's the right number," Sally said, "but this is the French Fry Factory. We're a restaurant in the mall, not a residence."

"Marion said I should call her at this number," the woman continued, insistent and becoming frustrated.

"I'm really sorry," Sally said, "but there's no Marion here."

The woman abruptly hung up. Sally shrugged and sent the woman a silent wish that she would find her Marion, and then she got back to work blanching fries for quicker cooking later in the day.

The next morning, the phone rang again at 9:30 on the dot.

"Hello, French Fry Factory!"

"I would like to speak with Marion, please." The same voice.

"I'm sorry, but this is the French Fry Factory again."

"Marion said she'd be there." This time, Sally sensed a hint of panic.

"I'm really sorry, ma'am. Do you have a last name for Marion? Maybe I could help you look up her number."

"She said she would be there," the woman snapped and hung up.

For months, these calls continued–not every day, sometimes not even every week, but always at 9:30 in the morning. Each time, the woman seemed reluctant to believe that Marion wasn't waiting expectantly for her call. And each time, she hung up before Sally could say anything helpful.

This was back before caller-ID, so Sally eventually launched her own investigation. She asked Fred, the other "opener" (an obnoxious undergrad majoring in business) if he ever got any wrong-number calls. He said he refused to answer the phone before 10:30 when the restaurant officially opened for business. Fred eventually admitted that he may have heard the phone ring a few times in the morning, but he stuck to his philosophy that if they weren't open, he shouldn't have to answer the phone.

As the months went along, Sally tried a variety of tactic to address the telephone situation. She started answering the 9:30 calls by saying, "Hello?" in a pleasant voice, as if she were a retiree in the middle of morning coffee. That didn't help. Sometimes she picked up the phone and didn't say anything, but the woman would just hang up after a few seconds. Sally even answered a few times with, "Please don't hang up. I want to help you find Marion." But the woman would repeat, "Marion should be there," and then hang up. Once Sally even answered, "Hello, information … could I please have the last name of the party you are trying to reach?" No luck–all she heard was a click.

She was sometimes tempted to shout, "Wrong fucking number!" That might have worked to stop the calls, but that just wasn't Sally's way of doing things. Fred would have approved, which was reason enough for Sally to not to take the profane approach,

Sally didn't remember exactly when the calls stopped, but one day she realized that the woman hadn't called in a month. In the meantime, Sally had finished her master's degree and was about to start her real career, leave the French Fry Factory, and move out of the area.

During Sally's last week, the manager held a surprise going-away party. Most of her co-workers were there, and several of the handsome young guys who worked at the clothing stores in the mall stopped by for good-bye hugs. Sally had often treated them to free coffee in exchange for a few minutes of intelligent conversation. The unexpected pleasure of this party nearly brought Sally to tears as she realized how much this silly little job had meant to her for the past year.

The restaurant's owner even showed up. He was a lawyer who hardly ever came to the store. Sally heard that he operated the restaurant as a tax write-off and was upset when they actually started turning a profit. But he seemed like a nice enough guy, and Sally was glad he came to say good-bye.

Tagging along behind the owner was a very tiny woman. She had bright, happy eyes, and Sally could tell she had once been young and active. She still maintained an energetic glow that made her approachable and appealing.

"This is my grandmother, Mrs. Candelaria," the owner said after shaking Sally's hand and wishing her luck in all her future endeavors.

"Oh, Glenn, no need to be so formal," the woman scolded her grandson. Then she turned to Sally and smiled, extending her hand.

"Please, call me Marion."

AUTHOR'S NOTE

We've all worked some odd jobs. This story is based on the oddest experience I had at the oddest job in my employment history.

While I didn't receive as many strange calls as Sally did in this tale, the phone rang enough times to keep me on my toes during the early hours in a nearly abandoned mall back in the early 1980s. Today, with malls becoming modern-day ghost towns, I treasure the memories of my time flipping burgers and asking customers, that all-important question over and over again: Would you like fries with that?

JS

Cocksucker

ERIC MACHAN HOWD

He listened to big band albums on vinyl
while watching pornography and licking
stamps for the Conservative Book Club.
He never married and blew smoke rings
from cheap cigars he'd buy on Fridays.
He died sucking the fumes from an
American-made car and left piles of belongings
for the few people in his life.

The artist asks, "Why a cock?" as
needles begin their dark outlining.
During World War II sailors requested
the same ink on calf, a rooster,
to impress that their manhood
dangled this far down the leg.

I want to remember Key West and my dead
relative's ashes in the secret garden.
That white heap that refuses to be buried
in the oldest soil of an island where fowl
roam free and parrots tease tourists
with catcalls and "Wanna dance, sailor?"
He died alone in the driveway leaving
his sister to live with what he violated.

Fucked Up Young

ERIC MACHAN HOWD

Polly comes to parties uninvited, wearing her dead brother over her dress, a withering grin over her shoulder. Guests avoid her. Years ago, she ate cucumber sandwiches in a Newfield graveyard with her beau, sat their bottle of wine on top of a tomb. He asked her to marry him. "Whatever for?", she asked with a wave of her hand. They kissed and left the day in stillness. *The Rubaiyat of Omar Khayyam*, lemon squares, and a summer sanctuary. Back then, she was happy. Back then, she kept her brother's lust in a box under the bed.

Mannish Cunt

ERIC MACHAN HOWD

> *On the previous day [8 Jan 1493], when the Admiral went to*
> *the Rio del Oro [Haiti], he said he quite distinctly saw three mer-*
> *maids, which rose well out of the sea; but they are not so beautiful*
> *as they are said to be, for their faces had some masculine traits.*
> –from the *Voyages of Columbus*

The two didn't know that they could be heard from the kitchen, calling the woman who wouldn't put-out for them a cunt. They laughed at her presence, bitching about how life today is all *me too* and shit. Conversation turned back to the woman, her weakness, her stink, how ugly she became in refusing a good fuck. Their gossip grew as they continued morphing her features: prominent brow, broad shoulders, deep voice, unshaven armpits. "Fuckin' feminists," they giggled to themselves as they timed the roast between bastings. "Who needs them, right?" They stood side by side, brushed hips, and before the oven rang, patted each other on the ass. I know who they were talking about and he'll love hearing about this.

AUTHOR'S NOTE

The poems in this anthology explore issues of gender and identity. Our world is not a binary world. Ours is a world of continuums and gradients. Ours is a world full of many different flowers. I want these poems to help us question our cultural, binary, conditioning by introducing various situations where gender and/or sexual identity is unclear.

The main inspiration behind the poems in this collection comes from research on mermaids from the records and logs of sailors and travelers. At a distance, mermaids were said to be attractive and alluring, but, upon getting closer, one would find those same attractive beings less than attractive. This idea of assuming gender struck me, so I began writing some poems on these issues to explore them more. Ours is a world of continuums and gradients. We should respect that more in our lives.

EMH

The Goddamned Rug

DIANNE PEARCE

"Excuse me, ma'am. What's your name?"

I look up into the young, recently shaved face of the newest campus security recruit. Ha! I want to tell him that if he wants any kind of career, any kind of financial control over his life, he should be taking classes here, not working here. This is an old person's job, working on this campus. This is only for the has-beens and never-were. I am just trying to think of how to phrase it so that he'll believe me while his face is still young enough to have patchy facial hair.

"Excuse me, ma'am. Your students say it is professor, Professor Charles?"

"No Professor Plum, in the bookstore, with a lead pipe from the plumbing lab!" Oh, that's a good one. I am grinning like an idiot when I realize, "No wait, I was always Colonial Mustard!" My gosh, how upsetting to almost forget.

"Professor Charles, your students want to know if they can leave, and we can't allow them in the computer lab without your supervision."

"Shhh! Don't say that out loud. I tell them all the time, but they never listen. Wasn't it lucky they had seltzer in the bookstore? It's practically the same as club soda." I pour a bit on the carpet stain I am rubbing with a Wet-One. "I think it's going to move this stain; don't you?" I look to see the approval on his face, but there is concern, his lips are moving.

"Professor."

"No, hon. I am so sorry." I put the hand with the Wet-One crunkled in it on his sleeve, tug it a bit. "I didn't finish my thought. Here, sit down, on my right, not near this old stain. It's going to be leaving soon." I smile with confidence and warmth, and he does crouch down, almost sitting, his long legs folding up like those old wooden jointed rulers my father used. I liked those. Loved opening them out, folding them back up, this way, or that way, American, or Canadian measure. I imagine myself, gigantic, and folding and unfolding his long stick legs. He settles down, and I remember where I was and continue.

"You can get yourself, and myself, quite a talking-to if you throw around 'professor' like it's a simple title, like officer or madam or nurse. Oh, no no no. They will get very out of joint, the noses of the ones who have been given the title by the school. None of the rest can use it, and that takes in me as well." I shake my head ruefully and then chuckle because I think this boy doesn't probably recognize rue when he sees it, and I am thinking that I need to shake my head with another emotion, but I get distracted, so easily these days in general. Well, you know, I get distracted because the chuckle coming out of me sounds just like my dear dead grandma; I can picture her laughing that laugh, and I am in 10th grade, and she is instructing me in how to do the Charleston for some or other school project, which cannot have been worth much as I cannot remember what it was for or about now (and I am not yet breathing down the neck of my sixties even, so I should have remembered had it been even remotely relevant to life in general), though I do remember that I bought the dress I wore at Clover, of all places, like a K-Mart sort of, and long out of business, and though buying it thrilled me, because it was a flapper dress. I felt fat and awkward with it on at school, with the thigh highs rolled just below my knees and knotted, which is what Grandma had said to do, but which felt too authentic, and not nearly romantic enough. I was all nerd when I wanted to be all Gatsby.

"In any case," I say to this nice, and very young, young-man, "my grandma, in my mother's kitchen, had hiked up her dress, tucked it under her ample bosom, and then had the little ends of it, the hem, pinched just a little in her large cold bloodless fingertips, and she was all glee, switching her hands from knee-to-knee, and kicking her foot in the front, and then in the back. Oh goodness, she thought the Charleston was a fun dance. And I expect it was. Have you heard of it, the Charles…"

"Doctor Charles."

"Oh no! Don't use that. That's just as bad as professor. Lord!

Just Ms. is fine."

"Ms. Charles, your students want to know if they can leave now."

"In college, we're all adults. They can always leave if they need to."

"Well, we need to lock up the lab then, and the school closes in a half hour. It's time for you to go home ma'am."

I chuckle like Sara, like my grandma, again. She had such mischief in her laugh. "Oh now not with this stain here, honey. This rug needs me. You go on. I'll be okay with the other workers. We always stay late to get the building ship-shape. Or, in my case, the papers. Wait 'till you see, I'm always the last car in the lot."

"Ma'am, Ms. Charles, I'm going to get your things and your coat. I'll bring them to you. My supervisor says I cannot leave the lab open without you in it, so I'll get your things and lock it up. Do you feel okay, ma'am? Do you maybe need help getting up?"

"Help getting up?" The indignity of the suggestion gets me and I start to pop-up like a jack-in-the-box, or pulpit, was it pulpit? But then I see the spot again. "Georgia O'Keefe," I say to him. "I am having a breakthrough here. At first I despaired that it was gum, and me without ice or peanut butter, but it's just a really old, tight, stain. It's like a knotted shoe lace. I am an expert at knots, and I can get this one undone too. Although, they're all just glued down carpet squares, you think they'd just pry it out and pop-in a new one. But, they do combine to make the logo, and maybe they are afraid of ruining the look of the school pride. No matter, I think I'm cracking this nut."

He is starting to unfold his wooden-tape-measurement-legs. "Okay Professor Charles …"

"Zzzzt!" I wave my hand at him, like trying to swat a fly.

"Sorry, Instructor Charles. I'll be right back."

He unfolds back against the wall, and it helps him stand. He takes two strides away from me, which puts him half of the way up the hall just like that, and then, a huge surprise, he turns and says,

"Thank you for helping with the rug. I'll be right back."

Now, wasn't that sweet? I think I *will* tell him to go to college rather than working there. I think I could get through to this one.

Now that he's gone, though, I can get back to the important work, moving this stubborn stain. The weave is tight, small loops. I wonder if it is natural, or polypropinopoly, or something, made out of old pop and water bottles. I mean, I guess it's okay to talk to myself, as long as it is only silently, in my head, like I was taught in second grade, read silently. The cleaning crew is not in this hall yet, maybe not even in this wing. And, obviously, Ellen, they have long since given up on this stain. But, let's face it, they're just hired to do the work, they're not, well, not their fault maybe that it's not, what I mean is, they've not been called to clean this rug. But I am.

I don't know how I got here, sitting here, cleaning this rug, but it is delightful, and I don't want to leave, though I imagine they will make me leave. I imagine that's what my new young security guard is going to do when he gets the computer lab emptied out. I hope he remembers my laptop cord when he gathers everything up. So many papers, so many attachments, so many pieces of myself to forget at the end of the day. Fucking nuisance. Oh, Ellen, you should not curse in a professional setting. Um, a-doy yoy yoy yoy yoy, I'm talking silently, remember. God. I'm in my own head. I can fucking curse if I want to.

A class is letting out down the hall, in dribbles like a faucet with a bad washer. Dammit. I'd better get the hell out of here before I blow it. If I lose the job, I'll never get the rug clean.

I scurry up the hall after ruler-legs, and bump into him as he is coming out of my classroom. Most of the students are still in there, some from my night classes and also some from previous semesters. They often pop in on me. I never turn anyone away, though it means I end up helping with chemistry equations and sociology papers and even working on financial aid packets.

"Oh, Mrs. Charles," says the young security fellow, "you're here."

"Oh yes, where else would I be?"

"But you were in the hall, and your students…."

"I am so sorry. We ran out of staples, so I just nipped down to the school store before it closed up." I pull the box from my pocket. He looks at me like my head has just turned into a stapler. "Everybody okay here?" I say to the room.

"When are we done tonight?" one of the students asks.

"When are we supposed to be done?" I reply, crossing to look in my binder.

"An hour ago," another student replies and a few laugh.

"Ms. Charles, the school closes in 20 minutes," says Legs McRuler, the worried young security man.

"Okay guys, 10 minute warning," I say, and just like that, Legs is completely flummoxed about what he had seen before, and what he is seeing now, and, in about 12 minutes, I walk out the door, after saying a kind goodnight to Alice, the key lady, and I am safe, and no one knows about the rug.

—

But, I know about the rug. And, the following week, by the time class rolls around again, I am obsessed. And, something else happens, they change the cleaning staff around, and now, each Thursday night while I am teaching in the lab, looking out of the glass walls into the empty hall, and at the dark windows of the other, empty labs flanking it, there is a new woman who appears. She is young, thin, and she is meticulous and methodical. As I am teaching, or coaching, moving computer to computer, I see her. She pulls into view with a cart that holds a large trash receptacle and at least 3 fuzzy dusters of various lengths, plus bottles of sprays, and rags, and other delights below I cannot see from my vantage point. This young woman, she is driving me crazy.

For example, I am minding my own business, not visiting the rug, not upsetting the young guard who still looks at me askance. No, no, I am resolute in my decision to remain celibate to my desire, and, like a good little adjunct, I am resetting a test for my 30-something farmer who is trying to get into the AG program at the state college, but keeps dropping out before finishing any classes, including mine. This is our third semester together, and I am trying to help him understand part and parcel of participles, which is something, c'mon, I don't even fully understand myself, and neither of us will ever need, and I am really tapping into my altruism vein in that hopes that Caleb Ezekiel Mercy Walker will not have to repeat this class… again, when she, the new young cleaning woman, quietly moves into my view.

She parks the cart outside one of the labs, unlocks the lab door from a huge ring of keys, turns on the light, and moves inside. She's got a bottle of spray hooked into her pants pocket by the trigger, and she pulls it out and sprays the white boards, some of which,

my breath catches in my throat, still have ink on them, words, problems, notes. The ink runs, and she steps out to the cart and retrieves
a large thick pad, a wad of rags really, and returns to the boards, and
with two hands-on the thick pad, wipes up, wipes down, up, and
down. Slowly. Silently. With pressure. I see the muscles in her forearms. And Caleb or Ryan or Karyn or Taryn is asking me another
question I have answered and explained to the best of my ability as
many times as a human can do it and not have her brain rupture, but
they keep asking me to explain it again, help them, because they
don't listen, or have sniffed too many crop sprays, or no one helps
them ever and they just like being helped. And okay, okay, that's
why I got into this business, but they are distracting me from this
young woman and her thick quiet pad and methodical wiping. And
the board is getting clean over there, and shining. The full-time
teachers who have the morning classes will be blinded by the sheen.

The young cleaning woman knows what to do in a lab situation, much better than I or my students. When the boards are buffed,
she returns the thick pad to the cart, and picks up the dusters. She
knows which size is right for which surface, and she moves them
over the desks, the window and door frames, the CPUs and the key-
boards, the printer and the recycle bin. It is beautiful how silently
she makes the dusters fluff along over the surfaces like sprightly
Persian cat tails.

And sometimes …

Sometimes she drops to the floor and puts a little spray on a
rag and rubs it into a little spot on the carpet and when she does it I
put my hands behind my back or in my pockets so no one can see
the itch I have. And I try to smile at Taryn to keep my tongue from
gyrating against my molars.

I've fucking lost it.

I know I've lost it; no need to be precious or protecting of
my feelings. Elvis has left my building and been replaced by Carol
Burnett's cleaning lady.

———

I think, you know, that I could have kept it together, had I
ever been recognized as a person, instead of a ghost in the machine.
The young woman with her cart is like me. No one sees her, as she

puts her back into it on the floors and walls, as she makes the dusters dance. I wish I could be next to her in the quiet room, lonely but together, sniffing up the warm smell of ammonia and dust like cocaine.

I try to keep things in bounds, but it is not easy. I have trouble being in total possession of myself. My grip keeps loosening, and not from the arthritis. I know my husband has noticed the boxes from Amazon; I've seen him see me when I open those boxes up, when I caress the cleaning products inside. Pristine, promising, pungent, full of magic beyond what may be found even in a genie's lamp. He peeks at me from around the stairwell and, I'm sure, thinks something has gone terribly bonkers.

—

Tonight, well …
The students noticed I'm … off.
I feel like a failure.

I never meant to let them see. They, the most of them anyway, seem to think of me like a funky aunt, that sort of thing. It's okay with me. I am warm, and more permissive than Mama. But, tonight, I think I worried some of them.

I have been doing my level best to stay in the classroom, and not wander the enticingly stained hallways. The hallways are long, and they flow downhill, or up, depending on the direction, making them swift moving, or a slow contemplative climb. And so I might zip by the stain of my obsession in one direction, and on the return, it's like I'm peeking at a person through a window who cannot see me, and I can just look, and look, and look.

But no, I've been staying put and being good.

I've been keeping my back to the windows as much as possible so that I do not see the strong and beautiful cleaning woman. I have been focused. Like a freaking laser.

And then, tonight, there was a sound, like a muffled lawn mower.

It got louder.
And louder.
And I had to look.
And it was the young cleaning woman, but she was in the

air, I mean, she was taller than normal, higher up than normal, and she was moving, in a way that was not like walking she was moving, faster, higher.

It took me so by surprise that I moved to put my face against the glass, while I was talking to the students.

And then I couldn't figure it out in the dim hall light, so I went and opened the door.

She came by again, on her chariot. Standing up, muscled arms holding the handle bars.

I realized, though it took me much longer than it should have, that she was on some sort of carpet zamboni, a riding vacuum. It was cool.

"Wow," I think I said, "that's a riding vacuum. Look at that guys! That is cool; dontcha think?" I was totally casual about it, despite the beating of my heart.

They looked at me, no understanding on their faces for the magic that had just motored through our lives.

I feel crushed, defeated. My students had always seemed to enjoy me, and that made me feel freer, in the classroom, to be myself, to be who I am in a way I am not even at home. At home I have to hide the treats from Amazon, even though my husband and I are both aware of their arrivals. Here, if the students walk in on me cleaning the computer screens, they simply appreciate it. But, tonight, the beautiful riding vacuum punctured my veneer.

Then, later, another crack.

Class was over, and I was helping some students with the process of submitting papers through the plagiarism checker, when a different cleaning person, a white portly man about my age, came walking in and started erasing the notes on the white board.

The white boards wrap around the room, and today a previous teacher had not wiped them down, so there was extra just waiting for the students to leave, little messy bits of joy for me to wipe myself. And wipe, and wipe.

But this guy came in and just started spraying cleaner and wiping, and I stopped working with Marcus and said, "I got it!" And rushed to another board to start wiping off the ink.

"Oh no," he said. "It's no problem. You never have to wipe. You're the last class. We always polish them up with cleaner at the end of the night. Just leave 'em go Professor."

I stood there, eraser in my hand, frozen, no comeback, no way to stop that mugger in a Wilford Brimley suit from taking away what was rightfully mine. My only option to go back to that little bastard Marcus, who was boring as hell and never missed a goddam class, and help him with his stupid submission of his stupid summary to the stupid plagiarism software- and he knew my secret now, and so did his group mates Sade and Kennedy.

Then Marcus was all like, "Um, could we finish this, 'cause I gotta go; I'm getting picked-up."

I had to smile, smile dammit, and walk away from the board.

—

When they were all gone, I handed the key back in, and walked back to the classroom, let myself in, and took off the lock magnet so the door would close and lock behind me.

I texted my husband Joe to let him know I was going to hit the coffee shop and grade a bit and would be home after he was asleep.

I looked around at the sparkling boards and the dusted workstations and pulled out the teacher-chair and slumped into it. I went still as a slug.

About 20 minutes later, the lights went out: energy saver. If I got up and moved they would come back on. But what did it matter if I was in the dark?

If I got up and moved I would be getting up to go home, to go to sleep, to get up again the next morning and drive to one of the other two schools where I would empty my bag, smile my smile, do my duty to mankind and my paycheck, refill my bag, and drive back home to go to sleep.

I stayed a slug.

The guard went by, trying all the doors, followed by the cleaning crew, talking together. The handle on my door rattled, the small din went by, the hall lights clicked off, one, two, three, and I was alone in the school.

Finally, I felt myself take in a breath. My posture regained some self-respect.

You see, I am so comfortable in a classroom. Yes, they are

sterile environments, not in the cleanliness but in their lack of personality and quiet. So what? On a blank canvas I can be colorful. In a quiet environment I can think.

I stayed very still for a very long while, and then I stretched and walked and set the room lights back on with my motion.

I was gloriously alone, to clean, to think, to make this world whatever I wanted to make it. If, that is, an alarm didn't go off-

No alarm went off.

I stretched my arms out and spun on the ball of my foot on the low pile carpet like I was four years old. I caught sight of my reflection in the windows that were now more like mirrors. I walked to the door to the dark hall and tried it, but it would not open. In fact, the handle, that felt so corporeal one second, like another hand shaking mine, did not seem to be there anymore. I grabbed my arms with my hands, wrapping around myself. I was still fleshy and solid. The contents of the room! I ran around touching everything, everything was still solid. The windows, still there but opaque, reflective. Everything was pretty much the same except the doors. The doors had become just windows themselves, mirrored and part of the wall.

My mind, I tell you, my mind flashed to Charlotte Perkins Gilman and her yellow wallpaper. I thought, well, I thought I'd gone insane and should begin creeping about, scratching at the walls. I thought I might need to begin rocking back and forth, hugging myself. I looked to one of the mirrored windows to see if there were tears on my face. There were no tears, but as I stood there, searching the reflection of my face for signs of crazy, I noticed there was a spot, some sort of schmutz, on the glass. It looked like a greasy fingerprint. It totally ruined the shine, but I had my bottle of screen cleaner, and I could take care of it.

AUTHOR'S NOTE

Anyone who has read a few of my pieces will have figured out by now that I am an adjunct teacher, and that informs a lot of my writing because the nature of the job is to be alone on the road a lot, alone in between classes, have no colleagues or work friends to speak of, and to basically show up and perform and provide sustenance to undernourished, educationally and otherwise, students. So, in this story, the lowly adjunct is very much looking for a way to replenish herself. And she finds a very normal way to do so, which I highly recommend to other adjuncts.

DP

The three true ages of man are youth, middle age,
and how the fuck did I get old so soon?

Stephen King
Revival

Old and in the Fucking Way
ANDREW PAUL GRELL

"Wizard. Guru. Sensei. There was a reason they called us those things. It was more than code and wires. There are psychic properties of digital circuits."

That was Sean. He always had a touch of the blarney when he spoke. It didn't hurt his image, either, that he was about the size and shape of a Leprechaun. He prognosticated on.

"The ley lines are stressed like overhead power cables in a Brownsville summer, they're dropping almost to the surface. Potential node-to-nodes are becoming impossible to tabulate. No one adheres to the spells as inscribed in the RFCs; everyone is in danger of accidental high-thaumatic discharges."

"Cut the boiled potato act, you old bastard. It's us who's falling behind. They're able to get laid, go viral, fund projects, rescue kittens, and when they get tired of that, go to the Creationist websites and laugh at them or tell everyone what their political opinions have to be. We're the ones who can't find a reply to a comment we might have just put up three days ago. We're the ones who have no idea what the difference is between a wall, a timeline, and a 'story,' whatever that is, or what changing your status does. We started it all rolling. I personally slept with Linus Torvald, Ward Christianson, and Mitch Kapor at assorted conferences. Vacuum tubes! I started when computers still had vacuum tubes!" That was Charlene, perpetually jealous that she wasn't Esther Dyson and running the internet with that rhythm guitar player from the Grateful Dead.

"Settle down back there, you two! And Charlene, drop the vacuum tube thing. You know it was in the AC adapter and not the computer." That was Bernie, our bunch's self-appointed referee. You're both talking about the same thing. It's Liphschicz's Law. If someone codes a user class into a box, that box will eventually get axed and the pieces will get used for something radically different and totally unplanned. That process is what puts a drag on the system. Look at France. Minitel was supposed to be an electronic phone book but it became the world's first sexting network. True, these people are getting more trim than Nelson's Fleet, but they're boinking the people the code wants them to boink. Sometimes the decision-tree of liberty must be sprayed with the condensed air of recursive programming. Sorry, not a great analogy, it was on the fly."

Daisy, one of the few of us still in the boinking game, turned her leather club chair to face us all. Neat trick; she managed to not spill the martini balanced on the arm rest.

"Let me get this straight. Sean, you propose that the net is in danger due to abandonment of the sacred screeds, the free and meritorious Requests for Comment, which when placed into the Cannon, become the internet, fiefdoms connected by a rope of electrons, each overseen by its Lord/Root and/Root's loyal squires, pages, brevets, and free-lances."

"Sure 'n begorah, missy." Sean couldn't resist the zinger. His parents were both born in Bay Ridge.

"And Charlene. You're afraid you–we–have fallen behind the times. Is that about it?"

"That's about the size of it, sister."

Daisy had the smile of someone just about to write a 17-digit counter-example of the Goldbach Conjecture on a blackboard. "Okay, class. One of us isn't having enough fun, one says the sky is falling, and one says that those two are the head and tail of the same coin. So if we have a problem, what do we do?"

Daisy actually got some of the members to raise their hands, which quasi-statically lowered to escape embarrassment. But the entire company had the same answer: propose a hypothesis and perform an experiment.

Bernie looked around at the framed photographs of archaeological computers on the oak paneled walls of the Tabulator Club's cocktail room. ENIAC, Harvard Mark-1, Cray-1, IBM 360, Atari 800-XL. Then he looked at the people looking around; they were slowly realizing they were to have another mission. Once more into the breach. He cleared his throat. "This will be more fun than the lecture on the HP Journada, so we'll reschedule that and convene on

Thursday to pick a hypothesis. And now, why do coders always confuse Christmas and Halloween?"

Twelve throats screamed the answer: "Because October 31 equals December 25!"

Charlene and Daisy went their separate ways since they didn't want Jed to think they were double-teaming him. Because they were planning on double-teaming him. Jed always had a nightcap at Stiffy's on Columbus Avenue after Tabulator Club meetings, and the three of them wound up casually bumping into each other. Jed had been Lieutenant Senior Grade on the USS Enterprise when Rickover was nuclearizing the Navy. He was in charge of making sure that the new "black gang" didn't turn into the "glow-in-the-dark gang," a mission which he accomplished perfectly. After Viet Nam, he was seconded to the Oak Ridge Lab, just a few miles from his hometown of Clinton Tennessee. Semi-retired, Columbia traded their cold-fusion lady for Jed and gave him an associate professor sinecure. Every school wanted the inside skinny on what was going on in the Volunteer State. Charlene, of course, always called him Tennessee Jed, after the Grateful Dead song.

"Buy a lady a drink or two? Or two ladies, Tennessee Jed? You were awful quiet back at the meeting. No opinions on the shape of things to come? Ghosts of networks past?"

"Y'all know we were more than just atoms down there, doncha?"

Daisy suddenly realized that she wasn't leaking, but it was Fermi, Jed's Black and Tan coon hound, licking her ankle. Academics got relaxation of the rules from Stiffy, probably smarter than most of them even though he had to quit school in eleventh grade.

"Oh sure, I heard you repurposed the old cyclotrons to make moonshine. Neutron Bomb, I saw a bottle of it posted online."

"Almost as good as my Grandpappy's. In the gummint labs, inebriation is our profession, war is just a hobby." Jed was laying it on a little thick. Charlene moved into position; her end of the operation was cleavage distraction. It wasn't hard to distract an up-holler man.

"I'm back to full functionality, got everything checked out and tweaked, good to go. Would you like to come up after we finish our drinks? You too, Daisy, we can do a round-robin."

"Yes ma'am, Miss Charlene. I sure would love to come up."

Charlene's place was a block away, fourth floor of a walk-up. A "scientific" study demonstrated that people living in walk-ups were 2.3 pounds lighter, after controlling for all other factors, than everyone else. Daisy took the Sherpa role and helped Jed up the stairs. As soon as Charlene hit the light switch, they heard the familiar Pac-Man theme. Jed was in heaven. The console started life as the famous horizontal, two-player, sitting down video game from Plato's Retreat. It must have been pretty special if people played it when the main activity at the club was fucking other people's spouses. Charlene had replaced the static memory chips with RAM and "borrowed" the code for what had been the most popular video games of 1978. She altered the analog/digital jacks to be able to accept hand controls for any of the games. They had Break-Out, Frogger, Asteroids, Q-Bert, you name it. Once, they made the mistake of playing Strip Ms. Pac-Man; now everyone who came up generally agreed it was best to play for baseball cards or comics.

"It took me long enough, but I think I've finally got the Tetris algorithm down," Jed beamed at the ladies. Right on schedule. Daisy's tweaks to the code worked perfectly. Charlene got into position while Jed was still pleased with himself.

"So why so quiet at the meeting, Tennessee Jed? You usually have no problem telling people what to think. Lots of people can do that, but you can actually get them to listen. Something's up. Give. Don't make me have to tickle you. Enquiring minds want to know."

Daisy hit from the other side. "You know something about what Sean was talking about. What's this group for if we're not going to share information? We were both present at the creation. Remember? We started out as the FIG-Forth Special Interest Group. We optimized computer-driven telescopes from Palomar to Arecibo. We mapped the universe. Why so shy now?" Truth turned out to be a stronger motivator than the threat of tickling. Jed took an envelope out of his suit pocket.

"I got a letter this morning. It said they want me to go back to Tennessee. Oak Ridge. They need someone who still remembers hashing and x.25 packet optimizing. This definitely could be what that little Mick was going on about. Remember the immigration lottery case, Arizona, Judge Greenberg? It looks like we're now going to pay the price for courts being able to dictate to system providers. Look, I'm going to make some calls. If I have something to say, I'll say it on Thursday."

The four of them made it back down the stairs, chit-chatting while Fermi chose a spot to pee on. But what they smelled wasn't pee; it was more like a moonshine still. And then the apparition they had almost, but not quite, forgotten materialized out of the mist. Charles Melchizedek Foggler. Charlie Fogg. He walked up to Jed and punched him square in the face. Fermi leaped to Jed's defense, but Charlie Fogg landed a kick to his left flank.

"I know what you did, you bastard!" was all he said before he disappeared down the entrance to the 1 train station. A demon summoned back to Hell, they all thought.

Daisy, Charlene, and Fermi made sure Jed was okay–he was, but he'd have a nice shiner–then clamored to know what was going on. Jed blamed it on the inebriation of the down-and-out, too proud to accept help from friends. Just in case, the two women and the dog established a mobile *cordon sanitaire* around Jed and escorted him home.

The rumor spread that Jed would be speaking at the Thursday meeting; he really was a big deal, the senior coder in the Tabulator Club still working, security clearance second only to the President.

The club was standing-room-only on Thursday; people who hadn't attended in years showed up. Jed hadn't been a public nerd in a while but he did his best to look the part: Corduroy suit, pocket protector, pocket slide rule, and, since he still had a patch on his eye from when Charlie Fogg punched him he decided to bring his parrot, Ada Lovelace. He climbed the stairs to the dais and faced his fellow members, hands spread like a Cohen giving the priestly blessing to a synagogue. He was locked and loaded and had no need to clear his throat.

"Toaster. Dancing bears," he began. "It's been a fight between those two viewpoints the day Wozniak and Jobs shipped the first Apple 1. A computer that does what you want as easily as you would make a piece of toast, or would you like to see singing and dancing bears performing HMS Pinafore? It's the same today. The toaster mode, what our friend Sean champions as the sacred RFCs, interchanges the most information for the least effort and resources."

Ada Lovelace chimed in, "Least mean square, least mean square!"

Jed continued. "The proposition before us is that the formal internet does more, and does it better, cheaper, and faster than the Dancing Bears. The Bears don't care about your information flow rates. All they care about is keeping you jacked in by entertaining you. The bears are literally stealing your face right off your head."

The Parrot woke up again. "Steal your face. Steal your face!"

"I propose that we update and package Archie, Veronica, Tin, Elm, and Waffle. The only obstacle to having a viable new channel is critical user-mass, and that's now controlled by the Dancing Bears. We're going to have to all do a little heavy lifting to get this thing going. And I have some ideas about populating the new channel with help from another place. The proposition is that the old, lean internet has more utility than what we have now, and will therefore drive out the less-efficient Bears. Now we get to see if we've still got it, or if we're all just old and in the way. Today is our St. Crispin's Day. What will be your answer when your grandchildren ask you what you did this St. Crispin's day?"

Jed waited for the parrot to say "Ada wanna crispy!" and for the members to give him the best cheer they could with their aging lungs.

He laid out the battle plan. "Pat, Kyle, are you okay for beta testing?" Two thumbs up. "Larry, can you wrangle recruitment? I recommend getting every member to get ten users and have each of the ten get ten more. That's going to take a lot of incentivizing. Unless you can come up with something better and less obvious. I'm going to be recruiting my own troops. We will either demonstrate that the simplest way is the best or find out that we've been full of shit all these years and that people really prefer to be led around by the short and curlies. To quote Charlene's favorite band, 'Now is the time of returning, thought-jewels polished and gleaming. Now is the test of the boomerang, tossed in the night of redeeming.' We have our marching orders. Let's rock and roll."

Bernie formally dismissed the meeting. "Is God real?"

And the shout came back, "Not if it's defined integer!"

The beta testing rolled on, club members stayed to woo, debate, or otherwise engage the newbies. The members were able push the usership up to 3,000. It was much easier to get points across without having to debate via annotated pictures. Plenty of kitten videos and cream pie pictures were available, you just had to select alt.binaries.kittens or alt.binaries.creampie and there they were, no viruses, no click bait. Another wave of new members came in; there were millions of people who still connected via telephone modem. Using the "New-Old" system, they were now on an equal footing with everyone else on the platform. Then Jed turned on his spigot and we got an unstoppable critical mass.

The thing about getting a critical mass is that you frequently wind up with a chain reaction. And sure enough, it came after the election, on the day of the celebratory meeting for having demonstrated the value of doing things the right way. Jed was being roundly toasted and clapped on the back when Charlie Fogg came in with two U.S. Marshalls, three guys in suits with those curly things in their ears, and a Shore Patrol squad. The Shore Patrol Lieutenant cuffed Jed while the lead Marshall announced to him, and to the former revelers in the room, that he, Jedediah Alicock was under arrest for colluding with foreign agents–that would be the flood of users–to influence the results of a United States election.

I faced all of my friends in the nursing home's social room and told them that was the story of my last hurrah, the story of how I unknowingly helped get Kanye West elected president in 2024. And then I told them that often it was better to keep up with the times rather than fall behind them.

AUTHOR'S NOTE

This is a story for my generation, old computer nerds and Dead Heads. The characters are mainly people I know or have met. The debate about the whole on-line thing is still going on today, as are both the hopes and the abuses.

APG

At 70 years old, if I could give my younger self
one piece of advice, it would be to use the words
"fuck off" much more frequently.

Helen Mirren

what the fuck was i thinking? the unfortunate chest tattoo
CORTNEY COLLINS

silky collarbones on the red carpet:

the kind that remind you of a knight returning to his castle and
leaving the dragon's head at the doorstep to rest his cheek
upon the maiden's velvet skin

i once read about the origin of rouge:

at a feast sometime around the 15th century,
a glass of red wine spilled on a woman's décolletage,
leaving a stain so lovely that everyone gasped

and so it is with grapevines
dice
roses
stars

paired with crinolines and rockabilly shoes and red lipstick,
drinking Jameson and Coke next to a jukebox

that's what i was going for, but i never did have a waist
tiny enough to fit into a vintage dress and i don't drink whiskey

i once went to a wedding in Rhode Island:

the bride and groom had to shout their vows
over traffic roaring across the freeway next to the house

while everyone wobbled around the backyard drunk,
stiletto heels sinking into muddy grass

that's what i imagine this chest tattoo is like:

a bride with a swollen belly crying in the bathroom
over her shotgun wedding

i picked the design off a wall of clichés
not long after my affair with a married man—
did i really think he would leave his wife?

now i have an overgrown philodendron on either side of my sternum
and can't stop gazing at pictures of actresses at the Oscars

a ~~shitshow~~ match made in heaven

CORTNEY COLLINS

our love was written in the stars
we were stung by Scorpio's tail,
shredded by Canis Major
we were the Big Dipper with bad dip

i've done some stupid things in my life

gotten a concussion square dancing
stuck my finger in a kaleidoscope
sucked my bathrobe tie up into a vacuum hose
driven a golf cart into a creek

but the stupidest thing I've done is assume
that constellations are fated

constellations only exist because
of our imagination
we think they create stories, that
they create myths, that they create
our destinies
we ache at their beauty

but they are only estranged stars
millions of miles away from one another
separated by emptiness and the
cold blackness of space, random
configurations on a one-dimensional
horizon

our love was written in stars that
have long since died and only
appear to us as a memory of

themselves, their brilliance a mirage at
the final destination of a light year

the stupidest thing I've done is ask you
to tell me the truth

don't ever ask a question you don't
really want to know the answer to
i would have rather gazed at the wonder of
the Zodiac in the night sky than fallen into
your black hole roaming like an outlier
at the edge of the universe

AUTHOR'S NOTE

what the fuck was i thinking? the unfortunate chest tattoo: It took me a long time to admit that one of my tattoos was truly a mistake. No one wants to admit that older, wiser folks were actually right when they said tattoos might be something to regret later in life. My chest tattoo was impulsive; I had certain ideas about what it should be and, more importantly, the kind of statement it would make about me. I desperately wanted to be cool–that's about the crudest way to put it. It was so ill-conceived and hastily procured that I really didn't get what I wanted. It really is second-rate and, sadly, irreversible! Now, I find myself ogling smooth, untouched skin on women in strapless dresses and tank tops, wishing I'd never been so a.) impetuous, and b.) anxious to become something I really wasn't. I hope anyone who has had a regrettable tattoo will identify.

A ~~shitshow~~ match made in heaven: I had a very vivid dream one night in which an ex-lover came to me and said, "Honey, we were the big dipper with bad dip." For the most part, I forgot the rest of the dream, but this snippet stuck with me, and I built an entire poem around it. As brokenhearted and destroyed as I was over this love affair, I had to admit this was a bit funny, and painfully accurate. I began to toy with the idea of fated love that could actually be quite destructive and ravaging. Love that is, indeed, "written in the stars," but not in an altogether pleasant or blissful way–maybe the kind that is meant to burn us to a crisp so that we somehow emerge as better, if more complex and nuanced, versions of ourselves. In any case, I wanted to emphasize how illusory things, like constellations, can be. We create images among the stars by drawing them in our heads; similarly, we inevitably project some kind of fantasy onto those people we fall in love with. This poem is a mildly self-deprecating way of coming to terms with unavoidable disillusionment in love.

cc

I'm an artist; you give me a fucking tuba,
I'll get something out of it.

John Lennon

Shit That
Baby Out
CARRIE SZ KEANE

"Shit that baby out and I'll get you some cheese doodles," said the woman in the corner of the room. The woman was the mother-in-law. The room was a labor and delivery suite at the local hospital. The room had mauve wallpaper with teal trim. Aside from the blonde-wood rocking chair in which the mother-in-law sat, rocking, the room had plastic furniture, easy to wipe down with hospital-issue Sani-wipes. Very 80s, not updated in more than 20 years.

The patient, massively pregnant, laid in bed, wouldn't move from side to side like the nurse suggested. Kept suggesting. She just laid there. "Like a slug," said the nurse. "Her feet smell like cheese doodles," the nurse grumbled. "Ridge-runners," the nurse rolled her eyes at them.

The nurse, very seasoned, had the name Kat, kept rolling her eyes at the mother-in-law and her pregnant daughter-in-law, annoyed. Kat called people ridge-runners if they were poor. I don't know why. The hospital was in Delaware, at sea level. There are no ridges there. But, there were poor, many, many poor. The families of chicken breeders, off-shore men, fishers and crabbers and oysterers, soy and grain farmers. The farms long gone, the fish few. The families now worked at Royal Farms, or big box stores. If they worked.

The woman in the corner was fat, not too old, probably like 44, but looked like 60, a smoker. She had never lost her baby weight. "I had four," she told me, "Boys." The oldest is 22. The youngest is seven. She told me about the birth of her son, 22 years ago. She told me, in front of the laboring mom-to-be, about how she almost ripped "from my tooty to my pooty." About how the doctor almost didn't make it. How the nurse made her hold it in. Wouldn't let her push. But that, "When the canon's loaded, the bomb's gonna blow. You know, like a bullet in a barrel." She birthed in the same hospital, maybe in the same room. Now, her son was about to be a dad. He was not there. I don't know where he was. Maybe working? At Jiffy Lube. This woman, missing teeth, with frizzy, orangish, over-processed hair, with at least an inch and a half of dark roots, was my age. She sat in the rocker, eating buffalo wings, licking her fingers. The corners of her mouth gathering sauce, her lips turning orangish, to match her hair. I noticed that she didn't eat the celery that came with the wings. I was thinking that she could really stand to eat some veggies, but imagined that it was likely impossible to eat celery without any teeth. This woman, my age, was about to be a grandma.

No men were in the room.

The woman in bed was in labor. With an epidural. So, for now, she felt nothing. Just numb. She just laid there. Waiting for the forces of labor to do the work for her. This is why it's called expecting. We were all waiting. Waiting and waiting and waiting. Waiting on the next generation.

"It's like a big turd. Just poop it out," said grandma. "He wants to meet his Mom-Mom."

AUTHOR'S NOTE

Sometimes I wonder why in the world I get dropped down into other people's very personal stories, why I am the witness to the dramas of strangers. This story places me as the narrator, but is vague about my role in the scene. I am there, but almost only as an observer, like an ambulance-chaser, rubber-necker, spy, taking in details about now to record for some future time. To be present is a present. The stories are the gift.

CSK

Never Sink, Dammit
DIANNE PEARCE

Her clean blond hair is neatly pinned up and shows it—
the tattoo on the back of her neck that says *Never Sink*—
an infinity 8 entwined into an anchor.
Though the tat is old, it still looks like it is new and barbed into her
    skin.

Her hands are dirty, grease smudged over and under her trimmed
    nails, on the skin,
from repairing her radiator this morning after she delivered the
    News Journal,
after she fell asleep for one, only one second while delivering the
    News Journal
and hit the decorative boulder of the development
into which she was driving to deliver the News Journal.

And if she was going to fall asleep for only one second
couldn't the one second have been a second where her car went
    straight?
Maybe the stacks of News Journals had shifted in the back, pulled
    her into the rock.
Maybe it was inevitable.

Her arms are scratched and cut up, red
from reaching into the hot car to fix the radiator and put in the new
    hose,
which was a tight squeeze,
which was something she had to do so she could drive to college
    this morning
after cracking up on the paper route.
Paper route- Ha! What a name we give it.

I'm not talking smiling-1950s-ten-year-old-boy-with-a-perfect-
    bike-and-a-clean-and-neat-satchel paper route.
C'mon.
I am talking beat-up Chevy Malibu paper route
named Betsy just like my mother's broke-down Malibu was,
and this student squeezed her pink, white, strong, tight-fleshed
    capable forearms in there
and fixed the dang thing herself
with skills she learned over time watching YouTube videos
because she got tired-a-paying for fixing.

My student's fingers are covered with little dark spots that look
    like scabs,
which she rubs and tells me are probably chiggers,
and are probably on her back too,
and are probably from laying under the car in the sandy dirt next to
    the house in the early dawn,
after she got home from delivering the News Journal
because she had to fix that radiator quick,
quick as that one small dammed second she fell asleep driving.

Everything has to be quick quick
because she had to get the kids up and dressed and fed and washed
    and ready and off to school
so that she could go to school herself,
so that she could come to my class,
35 minutes late,
because she is so happy to be going back to school,
though she is embarrassed about her hands,
but I tell her the hands are okay.
I give her some oatmeal hand cream and a bag for her books,
stay 45 minutes late so she can finish an assignment from the next
    unit forward
because she craves the quiet before she goes to work at Walmart,
and she wants to be ahead in class assignments just in case. Just in
    case. She knows how it goes.
When she finishes next week's work and hits submit, I tell her the
    truth,
which is that she is doing great in class.

And when she packs up my old book bag and rushes out the door
    to Walmart
her smile is a big as a smile can be
on a sinewy single mom who has spent the last 8 hours delivering
    the News Journal in the dark,
crashing her car,
fixing her radiator in the pre-dawn light on her back in a bed of
    sandy chiggers,
then getting her kids off to school with them looking like some-
    body cares and with hot food in them.
To rush to come and see me with a light in her eyes the tired
    cannot yet extinguish.
To rush to come and spend two hours and 45 earnest minutes
pecking away on a one-paragraph summary of an essay
that analyzes zombie movies.
It was written by a privileged Hollywood son, that essay.
The school picked it for the classes to summarize
because it is "culturally significant"
because "the students can relate."

My student leaves me that day, a week ahead on her assignments,
    smiling, stepping lightly.

I never see her again.

I guess this is the moment where people who believe pray,
but I have had too many of her sisters to believe in magic, though I
    look for her every day.
And every day morning slips away from me into afternoon, and I
    leave the classroom to head to my own second job,
second of three,
so, I know, when it comes down to it,
there is nothing to do but put the rubber on the road and burn it up
    as long as there is rubber to burn.

Fill up the bags with books and computer and work and supplies.

Sling 'em over the droopy shoulder.

WHAT SORT OF FUCKERY IS THIS?

Raise the empty travel coffee mug to all those seen and never seen
  again

Suck out that last little drop of wet air.

Vow to never sink, dammit.

AUTHOR'S NOTE

When I began my "career" in higher education I was still pursuing my second masters, and I truly felt that higher education was the key to a better life. In this poem, I have come to see that, in todays' America, whether a working mother works unskilled jobs or skilled jobs to keep hot food in her kids, if she is working more than one, she is working against the waves. One slip at the wrong time, and it all goes south, no matter how hard your effort has been. Life, then, is a fuckery, and those of us who make it into the second half, dammit, we have something to be proud of, something to raise our glasses to. Thank you for supporting all the writers in this book, and may you never sink!

DP

HELLUVA
LOT OF TALENT
[AUTHOR BIOS]

NOEL ALCOBA

The son of a diplomat, Noel Alcoba grew up on three continents. This exposure to diverse landscapes, accents, and cultures forged his eclectic world view. It also made him an equal-opportunity heckler, which is reflected in most of his writing. Professionally, he wears a uniform and works in the local sheriff's office evidence unit. When not sorting through guns, drugs, counterfeit cash (or the occasional samurai sword), he writes short and long fiction. Alcoba is currently completing two novels that have nothing to do with police work, but do involve genetic editing, bright yellow spandex, and mechanical butterflies. Alcoba resides in the Pacific Northwest with his lovely wife, Alison, and their twenty-pound Maine coon, Gritty Malone. Find him on Facebook and Twitter.

ALBERTO AMBARD

Alberto Ambard (Venezuela, 1970) divides his time between writing and practicing maxillofacial prosthodontics. He coauthored the novel *High Treason* in 2012. His forthcoming novel, *Dogma, A Red Door, and A Birthday* is scheduled for publication in 2020. His short stories have also appeared in the *Pennsylvania Literary Journal* and *Adelaide Magazine*. Like H. Murakami, Ambard's love of music is often exposed in his writing. Likewise, his work is a reflection of his diverse background. A descendant of French, Spanish, and Venezuelan families, he has lived or spent significant time in the remote Afro-Caribbean coastal town Caracas, the Amazon, Tokyo, Chicago, and Birmingham, Alabama. Ambard currently resides in Portland, Oregon, with his wife and children.
albertoambard.com

BILL AYRES

Bill Ayres is the son of a United Methodist minister. He teaches a kindergarten Sunday school class. His poems have recently appeared in *Commonweal*, *The Windhover*, and *The Anglican Theological Review*.
Stop laughing.

HOWARD BROWN

Howard Brown resides in Lookout Mountain, Tennessee. His poetry has appeared in *Tuck Magazine*, *Burningword Literary Journal*,

Blue Collar Review, The Beautiful Space, Pure Slush Magazine, Poetry Super Highway, Old Hickory Review, and *Lone Stars Magazine and Printed Words.* In 2012, he published a collection of poems entitled *The Gossamer Nature of Random Things.* Brown's poem, "Pariah," placed first in the poetry division of the 2015 William Faulkner Literary Competition sponsored by the Union County Mississippi Heritage Museum and Tallahatchie Riverfest. He has published short fiction in *Louisiana Literature, F**k Fiction, Crack the Spine, Pulpwood Fiction, Extract(s),* and *Gloom Cupboard.*

V.L. BRUNSKILL

V.L. Brunskill is the award-winning author of the Savannah novel, and the forthcoming memoir, <u>*The Killing Closet*</u>. She is a blogger at <u>adoptionfind,</u> where she shares lessons learned from her (pre-internet) adoption search, and her journey toward spiritual healing. In addition to her personal blog, Brunskill blogs about business management for C4CM's *The Human Blog* and *Law Practice Management Advisor Blog.* Long before penning her first novel, Brunskill was putting pen to paper as a freelance music journalist at *Metronome Magazine, North Shore Magazine, CREEM, SPIN,* and the *Boston Phoenix.* From rock stars to rocking ions, she went on to become senior editor of an IT magazine, and a technical writer in the ion implantation field. Having found her birth family in 1991, Brunskill's reunion journey entailed a daunting seven-year-search for her birth mother, and another five-year search for her birth father. She moved South to be closer to both.

WILLIAM BUTLER

Author William Butler is "Southern born, with all the influences that encompasses." He resides in Memphis, home of the blues, birthplace of rockabilly and rock'n roll. He has been a writer since 1957 and has "just been watching the River flow."

LUANNE CASTLE

Luanne Castle's *Kin Types* (Finishing Line Press), a chapbook of poetry and flash nonfiction, was a finalist for the 2018 Eric Hoffer Award. Her first poetry collection, *Doll God,* winner of the 2015 New Mexico-Arizona Book Award, was published by Aldrich Press. A Pushcart nominee, Castle studied at the University of California,

Riverside (PhD); Western Michigan University (MFA); and Stanford University. Her writing has appeared in *Copper Nickel, TAB, The American Journal of Poetry, Glass: A Journal of Poetry, Verse Daily, Broad Street, Lunch Ticket, Grist, River Teeth*, and other journals.

TERRI CLIFTON

Terri Clifton is a writer, photographer, and Delaware coast native who was awarded a fellowship in 2013 for Emerging Artist in literature by the Delaware Division of Arts. Her short stories and poetry have been published in several anthologies and journals and she has recently completed two novels. Her nonfiction book, *A Random Soldier*, was published in 2007. Passionate about nature, art, and dance, Clifton resides with her husband, a wildlife artist, on a historic farm along the Delaware Bay.
facebook.com/TerriCliftonAuthor

CAROLYN COLBURN

Carolyn Colburn writes creative nonfiction, fiction, and poetry. She holds an MFA in Writing from Goddard College and has been awarded a Loft-McKnight Fellowship and a Minnesota State Arts Board Grant. Colburn has worked as a musician, teacher, typesetter, and contract writer. Her writing has appeared in the anthologies *Amethyst and Agate, One Minute of Knowing, Onion River Review" Screed*, and occasionally makes the short/long list elsewhere. Colburn's novel, *Minimum Maintenance*, was published in 2010. Colburn divides her time between a one hundred-year-old house in Duluth, Minnesota, and a cabin on Lake Superior near the Canadian border.

CORTNEY COLLINS

Cortney Collins holds a BA in Religious Studies and a law degree, both from the University of Arizona in Tucson. Her poems have been published by South Broadway Ghost Society and the Naropa Vagina Monologues Zine. She was a March 2019 Tupelo Press 30/30 volunteer poet, and cofacilitates a weekly poetry workshop for persons on probation in conjunction with Speakout! at Colorado State University. A Nebraska native, Collins resides in Northern Colorado with her beloved cat, Pablo. She loves the sight of Orion hanging low in the night sky in the winter, and Rocky Mountain thunderstorms in the summer.

WILLIAM F. CRANDELL

Fighting a dirty war as a rifle platoon leader and then marching for peace afterward gave William F. Crandell a bone-deep understanding of why honor and integrity are life-and-death concerns. Crandell returned home from Vietnam with a zest for adventure, a skeptic's eye, and a hundred thousand stories. He quickly acquired both an FBI file of his own and a doctorate in American history, but oddly enough, it was the years of spiritual retreat in the mountains that set his infantryman's feet back on solid ground. The writing came naturally–he'd been a foreign correspondent for an Ohio newspaper before college, and wrote fiction to stay awake in some of the jobs he held. Still, the years on Capitol Hill and in Federal law enforcement agencies gave him a player's knowledge of how crime and power operate, along with an appreciation of the dedication and the slime beneath the skin of America's capital. Awarded a Maryland State Arts Council Individual Artist Award for his private detective novel, *Let's Say Jack Kennedy Killed the Girl*, Crandell has published short stories, book reviews, scholarly articles, journalism, state and federal reports, political analyses, and congressional testimony that he presented in Washington hearings. An Ohio native, Crandell received all his degrees at Ohio State University, completing his doctorate in American History with a study of the interaction of McCarthyism and Republican politics. After "The Faith-Based Diet" won PRIZM's Mark Twain Award for Humor/Social Commentary in 2012, Crandell and his writer wife, Judith Speizer Crandell, relocated to Delaware so they could write at the ocean's edge. His work can be found in anthologies such as *Equinox* and *Suspicious Activity*.

ANTHONY CRUTCHER

A native of Chattanooga, Tennessee, Anthony Crutcher is the husband of one wife and the father of two children. He discovered poetry as a form of self-expression while in high school. Following a career as an economist, Crutcher now concentrates his efforts on writing poetry and teaching yoga. In addition to writing, he is part of the Southern Lit Alliance in Chattanooga. His latest concentration is on creating his first book of poetry for publication.

DAVID W. DUTTON

David W. Dutton is a semi-retired residential designer who was born and raised in Milton, Delaware. He has written two novels, several short stories, and eleven plays. His musical comedy, *oh! Maggie*, in collaboration with Martin Dusbiber, was produced by the Possum Point Players and the Lake Forest Drama Club. He wrote two musical reviews for the Possum Point Players: *An Evening With Cole Porter* (in collaboration with Marcia Faulkner) and *With a Song in My Heart*. He also wrote the one-act play, *Why the Chicken Crossed the Road*, commissioned and produced by the Delmarva Chicken Festival. In 1997, Dutton was awarded a fellowship as an established writer by the Delaware Arts Council. In 1998, he received a first-place award for his creative nonfiction by the Delaware Literary Connection. His piece, "Who is Nahnu Dugeye?" was subsequently published in the literary anthology, *Terrains*. More recently, Dutton's work has appeared in the anthologies, *Halloween Party 2017*, *Solstice*, *Equinox*, and *Aurora*. In fall 2018, Dutton's third novel, *One of the Madding Crowd*, was published by Devil's Party Press. In 2019, it was awarded best original novel by the Delaware Press Association. Dutton, his wife, Marilyn, and their Rottweiler, Molly, currently reside in Milton.

LISA FOX

Lisa Fox is a pharmaceutical market research consultant by day and fiction writer by night. Her short story, "The Fruit Stand," appears in the Devil's Party Press anthology *Suspicious Activity*. Other works have appeared in *Theme of Absence*, *Unlikely Stories Mark V*, *Credo Espoir*, *Ellipsis Zine*, *Foliate Oak Literary Magazine*, and at ubiquitousbooks.com. Fox placed third in the NYC Midnight 2018 Flash Fiction Challenge, from a field of over 3,000 writers worldwide. She resides in northern New Jersey with her husband, two sons, and their oversized dog, and relishes the chaos of everyday suburban life.

ANDREA GOYAN

Andrea Goyan is a writer, actress, and master Pilates teacher. Her short stories have appeared in several anthologies and online magazines including the *Newfound Journal*. She is also a playwright with over a dozen works produced. One of Goyan's new short plays will be read at the Little Black Dress INK's 2019 Female Playwrights

Onstage Festival, and a few more short stories will be released later in 2019. She resides in Los Angeles with her husband, a dog, and two cats.
andreagoyan.com

ANDREW PAUL GRELL

Andrew Paul Grell resides in a park in Manhattan with Melody, his wife of 30 years, and their Malti-poo puppy, Cyrus King of Persia. At fifty-nine, he is an "emerging writer," having been anthologized in *American Writers Review* and *Surprised by Joy* as well as the online journals *Writers Newsletter* and *Ugly Writers*. He is the author of recently released science fiction novel *SCAPEGOATS: The Goat Protocols* (Golden Fleece Press). By day, Grell uses mathematical models to ferret out fraud, and he gets around by bicycle.

DESIREE HARVEY

Desiree Harvey holds an MA in English and currently teaches academic writing in the greater Philadelphia region. She and her beloved husband reside in Wilmington, Delaware.

PHILIPPA HAWLEY

Philippa Hawley loves to write about relationships and families, in all their strange and varied forms. Much of her inspiration comes from working for over 30 years as a medical doctor, specializing in family medicine and women's health. She often weaves health issues into her writing. Philippa resides with her husband in Wivenhoe, a beautiful, if somewhat quirky, English riverside town, where she is a member of two local writing groups. Now retired, Hawley enjoys travelling and travel writing, as well as short stories. In 2011 Hawley completed the Open University course Start Writing Fiction as a confidence builder before joining local writing classes. She has since self-published three novels of contemporary romance fiction, the most recent of which is *Lawn House Blues* (2018).
philippahawley.com

MARK HEIN

Author Mark Hein started writing poetry on his dad's portable Underwood 60 years ago, in a study overlooking a grove of eucalyptus on the southern edge of San Francisco. Today, the grove and typewriter are gone. But the poems now number more than a thousand.

However, except for a couple of years in grad school, Hein notes that he never sought to publish any of them. "I was busy growing a family, being a journalist, and then a psychotherapist, and working in theatre. Now all that changes."

ERIC MACHAN HOWD

Eric Machan Howd of Ithaca, New York, is a poet and musician who supports his arts as an assistant professor of professional and technical writing at Ithaca College. His poems have appeared in *Nimrod*, *River City*, *Yankee Magazine*, and *The Healing Muse*. His poem, "Mycology," won the 2018 Switchback Poetry Award from the University of San Francisco's *Switchback Journal*. In 2019, Howd was invited to the University of Ljubljana (Slovenia) as a guest poet and lecturer at a conference on Slovenian and American poetry. Howd recently returned to graduate school to receive his second graduate degree, an MFA in creative writing (poetry) from the Vermont College of Fine Arts.

MARK KODAMA

Mark Kodama is a trial attorney and former newspaper reporter who resides in Washington, DC. His short stories and poems have been published in *Commuter Lit*, *Dastaan World Magazine*, *Dissident Voice Magazine*, *Literary Yard*, *Mercurial Stories*, *Spillwords*, *Tuck Magazine*, and *World of Myth Magazine*.

SARAH LEAMY

Sarah Leamy is a writer, cartoonist, and auto-journalist based in New Mexico. Born in England, she has spent most of her life in the Southwestern United States after exploring Europe in her early twenties and the States in her thirties. Two of her novels have won Best Gay Fiction in the NM/AZ Book Awards. *Van Life*, Leamy's travelogue, was named Grand Winner in the Northwest Book Contest of 2017. She is the founder, CEO and managing editor of Wanderlust Journal (wanderlust-journal.com), an online sharing platform for travel writing from across the globe.

Leamy's work (a mix shorts, book reviews, and poems) has been recently published in *Hunger Mountain*, *Santa Fe Project Quarterly*, *National Book Review Circle*, and *Bunbury Magazine*, and was a finalist and honorable mention with *Glimmer Train* twice in 2018.

sarahleamy.com

CLAIRE McCABE

Claire McCabe divides her time between homes in Delaware and Maryland, living with three cats, two dogs, and a life partner. She teaches writing at the University of Delaware and writes poetry with both online and local writing groups, "loving every minute of it." McCabe holds an MFA in poetry from the Solstice program at Pine Manor College.

JAN McGUIRE

After a career in law enforcement, Jan McGuire returned to school late in life and now teaches English at an alternative high school in the Omaha area. Forever a late bloomer, she completed her Master's in English at the University of Nebraska-Omaha in 2018. McGuire was a finalist for the John J. McKenna Graduate Fellowship Award in Creative Nonfiction in 2017 and 2018. She returned to writing when her teenage daughters felt she needed a hobby. In 2017, McGuire's "I'm Not Hovering, I'm Writing" was published in *Brevity Magazine's Nonfiction Blog*. In 2018, "The Dancer" was published in River Teeth's online publication, *Beautiful Things*.

MAUREEN McVEIGH

Maureen McVeigh's essays and short stories recently appeared in *Cold Noon, Mothers Always Write, Flash Fiction Magazine*, and *Calyx*. She was a runner-up in the *Philadelphia City Paper* fiction writing contest. McVeigh teaches creative writing at West Chester University and has taught for the University of New Orleans MFA program in Cork, Ireland. She holds an MFA from Rosemont College. McVeigh resides in the Philadelphia area with her husband, son, and daughter.

PAUL MILENSKI

Paul Milenski works on assignment as a Care and Protection Investigator for the Massachusetts Trial Court and writes fiction and poetry full time. In addition to the United States, Milenski's work has been published in the Commonwealth Countries, China, Singapore, Chile, Germany, Denmark, Russia, Turkey, Iran, South Africa, and Poland. Milenski resides with his wife, B-Mile (a local television celebrity), in Dalton, Berkshire County, Massachusetts.

JANNA MILLER

Janna Miller has worked in libraries since she was sixteen. "I find that this setting often makes its way into my stories, being the nexus of stories themselves." Miller writes mostly lyrical fantasy, science-fiction, and dark fairy-tales. She is currently writing a book of eco science fiction and interconnectivity "with some other various drips and drops." Miller loves to be with her family, explore unusual crafts, and read.
millersminusculemystories.wordpress.com

ALICE MORRIS

Alice Morris holds an MS in counseling from Johns Hopkins. She comes to writing with a background in art–published in *The New York Art Review,* and a West Virginia textbook. Her poetry appears in such places as *The White Space-Selected Poems, Delaware Beach Life, The Broadkill Review, Silver Birch Press*, *Rat's Ass Review*, and in several anthologies, most recently, *Sanctuary,* endorsed by Pulitzer Prize winner Jonathan Freedman. In 2018 she placed fifth in a Clutch-themed fiction contest, received the Florence C. Colt-man Award for Creative Writing, was nominated twice for the Pushcart Prize–then nominated by the Pushcart Board of Contrib-uting Editors to be considered for the Pushcart Prize. In 2019 a sin-gle poem and a single short story won second and third places, re-spectively, in the Delaware Press Association's Communications Contest. Her poem, "Watercress," is presently a finalist in the Art of Stewardship contest. Work is forthcoming in *Backbone Mountain Review, Paterson Literary Review*, *Gargoyle*, and several antholo-gies. Morris, a member of both the Rehoboth Beach Writer's Guild and Coastal Writers, is presently completing her first full-length po-etry collection.

LAURA NELSON

By day, Laura Nelson works as a labor and employment specialist for the State of Colorado. In the evenings and on weekends, she works on her writing career. Nelson's work has appeared various publications including *Paranormal Underground, Birdy Magazine, A Tall Ship, A Star, and Plunder*, and *Potter's Field 6.*
Nelson also writes nonfiction articles about pirates, and she has pub-lished a book featuring several of them called *The Whydah Pirates Speak*. She is currently completing a second volume. When not

working or working at writing, Nelson enjoys reading, playing with her cats, and attending Tai Chi class.

DIANNE PEARCE

Dianne Pearce founded The Milton Workshop in 2015, and Devil's Party Press in 2017. She is a graduate of both the West Chester University and Vermont College writing programs, earning an MA and an MFA. Pearce has taught writing in Delaware, California, Pennsylvania, and Maryland. She sometimes takes on editing projects for other writers, and has done both writing and advocacy for causes close to her heart, among them adoption, developmental disabilities, and animals. Pearce is an adoptive parent of a wonderful daughter, Sophie, and is married to her best friend, David Yurkovich. dpearcewrites.com

FELIX PIRE

Felix Pire is a character actor who has appeared in the films *12 Monkeys, Phat Girlz, Dear God*, and *It's My Party*. Television credits include *Prison Break* (FOX) and *NYPD Blue* (ABC). Onstage he received the 1997 New York Outer Critic's Circle Award for Outstanding Solo Performance for the *Men on the Verge of a His-Panic Breakdown*, an off-Broadway play by Guillermo Reyes, which also won Best Play in a Smaller Theatre at 1995 Los Angeles Ovation Awards. *The Origins of Happiness in Latin*, a solo play Pire wrote at the Mark Taper Forum's Latino Theatre Initiative, won the California Community Foundation's Brody Arts Grant and the Arizona Theatre Company's 2001 National Latino Playwriting Award. In 2003, Pire was awarded the ABC Entertainment Television Development Group's "Certificate in Recognition of Creative Excellence" for the screenplay, *Hurricane Nena*. Pire taught solo performance and improvisation at the American Academy of Dramatic Arts for over a decade, and has taught film acting, improvisation, acting, and solo performance at UCLA and UCLA Extension. He is the creator/producer of the webisode series *LosTiteresTV* on YouTube, Facebook, Twitter, and Instagram. felixpire.com

RÉMI SAVARD

Rémi Savard grew up in what is probably the francophonest part of Quebec, Canada. In his early twenties, Savard moved to Ottawa to teach French. He notes that "because language has its way around barriers, I ended up learning more than I taught."

KRYSTINA SCHULER
Whether it was getting lost in a book as a child, writing a term paper in college, or editing a legal brief as a paralegal, Schuler has always loved the written word. A few years ago, she tried her hand at fiction and hasn't been able to stop tapping at the keys since. She self-published her first romance novel, *The Girl in the Gallery*, in 2015, and is currently working on a second novel. In 2018, her short story, "Afternoon Showers," appeared in the anthology, *Beach Fun*. She is the facilitator for the Write Touch Writers Group and served as a juror for the 2018 Scholastic Art and Writing Awards for the Delaware District. A New England native, Schuler grew up in Connecticut and is now a Mid-Atlantic transplant where she lives with her husband and son. When not writing, she can often be found teaching herself to play piano and ukulele, or listening to a range of eclectic music. She also enjoys long bike rides with her family and enjoys dying her hair purple. She cannot whistle, and she don't like the taste of honey
krystinaschuler.com
facebook.com/krystinaschuler.author

JOHN SHEIRER
John Sheirer lives in Northampton, Massachusetts, with his wonderful wife, Betsy, and happy dog, Libby. He has taught writing and communications for 26 years at Asnuntuck Community College in Enfield, Connecticut, where he also serves as editor and faculty advisor for the *Freshwater Literary Journal*. Sheirer writes a monthly column on current events for his hometown newspaper, the *Daily Hampshire Gazette*. His books include memoir, fiction, poetry, essays, political satire, and photography.
JohnSheirer.com

JUDITH SPEIZER CRANDELL
Having resided on both coasts and in between, Judith Speizer Crandell has happily landed in Milton, Delaware. Solitary walks along the Atlantic beaches soothe her soul. Shared beach walks with her husband, Bill, a fellow writer, and their rescue dog, Windsor, enliven her soul. Proximity to the ocean fuels her creativity. An award-

winning writer and teacher of fiction and nonfiction, she's received residencies at Yaddo, A Room of One's Own (AROHO), as well as selection as a semi-finalist in the Tucson Festival of Books Literary Awards Competition. She attended writers' conferences at San Miguel Allende, the Joiner Center/University of Massachusetts, Mendocino and Byrdcliffe. The Maryland State Arts Council granted her their Individual Artist Fellowship for her novel, *The Resurrection of Hundreds Feldman*. Most recently, her new home state chose her to attend the Delaware Division of the Arts and the Delaware Arts Council 2018 Seashore Writers Retreat. Her fiction has appeared in publications including *Cleveland* magazine, the *Hudson Review*, the *Sun* and *Gamut* and most recently in the anthologies *Halloween Party 2017*, *Solstice*, *Equinox*, and *Suspicious Activities*. Her general background includes print journalism and speechwriting. *The Woman Puzzle*, one of her novels, is scheduled for 2019 publication. judithsca.wordpress.com

LOLA STEEL

Lola Steel is a storyteller at heart. She is happiest when crafting homes for the words that find their way out of her mind. With a penchant for exploring what makes us tick, her poems, short stories, and novellas are as varied, and often as dark as her imagination. A believer in the adage that we all live many lives in this one, her path of being a writer has been the one constant throughout her own journey, and she enjoys creating escapes in which others can indulge. Steel's dreams of living on an island with goats someday has been partly achieved as she writes from her home on Vancouver Island on the west coast of British Columbia, Canada. Steel has been published in the *DASH Literary Journal* and online at Writing in A Woman's Voice. Her debut novel, *Trip the Road Fantastic*, is due for publication in 2019.

DAVID STURM

David Sturm, a Baltimore native, was a retired newspaper reporter who resided in Silver Spring, Maryland. His first novel, *Welcome to Breezewood*, was published in June 2019 by Devil's Party Press. Mr. Sturm died on July 3, 2019.

CARRIE Sz KEANE

Carrie Sz Keane studied journalism and English at the University of

Maryland. She later apprenticed as a midwife in rural Appalachia in Kentucky before studying nurse-midwifery at Yale University. While at Yale, Keane was awarded a humanities honor in creative writing for a piece entitled "Modern Nurse Nancy," the story about working night shifts as a new nurse on a postpartum unit, which was later published in a Canadian nursing textbook. Upon graduating in 2004, Keane began journaling and writing the stories of her work as a midwife. She is actively writing a journalistic memoir of her career. Keane works at an active obstetrics and gynecology practice in Delaware as a sexual health clinician, providing prenatal care, contraception, annual examinations, STD screenings, and birth support for females. Her stories and essays, which have been published in *Solstice* and other anthologies, focus on maternal health in America and her role as a witness on the frontlines of female healthcare.

PAULENE TURNER

Paulene Turner is an Australian writer of novels, short stories, and short plays. A former Sydney journalist, she wrote her first novel as a National Novel Writing Month exercise. Since then, she has drafted three more books with the same characters and is now planning the fifth, and final, instalment in her young adult series. Her love of writing began with screenplays. *Space Cadet*, Turner's animation feature, was nominated by the Australian Writers Guild as best unproduced feature nationally. But as the film industry is tough to crack, Turner eventually crossed over to the "dark side" of narrative fiction. Her writing style still features dialogue and cinematic-influenced visual scenes. Her short stories have appeared in anthologies in the US and Australia. Turner also writes ten-minute theatre plays, many of which she has directed for Short and Sweet, Sydney–the biggest little play festival in the world.
pauleneturnerwrites.com

K.T. VANDERLAAG

Author K.T. Vanderlaag is a self-described "displaced North Easterner residing in south Florida with my incredibly supportive husband, three dogs, a hateful parrot, and two of my three grown sons." Vanderlaag began writing poetry in her teens but only began submitting her work for publication in 2019. She writes freestyle and particularly enjoys writing in structured poems stating that she "likes the challenge of the constraints." Vanderlaag is a history freak and a textile artist. "I live in a very messy house as I have some kind of project going on everywhere and little time for much else."

LESLIE WIBBERLEY

Leslie Wibberley is a slightly maddened mother to two outstanding young women and one slightly insane Cocker Spaniel, and wife to a loving and extremely tolerant husband. She holds a BSc in physiotherapy with a minor in psychology, but states that writing has always been her passion. Wibberley's short stories and narrative nonfiction pieces can be found online and in print literary journals, magazines, and anthologies, including *Chicken Soup for the Soul* where three of her works appear. Wibberley's work has placed five times in four years in the Annual Writer's Digest Competition, including a first place award in the genre category in 2018. She's also placed first in several flash fiction contests.

LILIANA WIDOCKS

Liliana Widocks is a Romanian living in the United Kingdom. She describes herself as "a writer when that doesn't bother anyone, and a blogger when I feel suddenly opinionated." The majority of Widocks' work is published in Romanian, on her blogs and website. Her work has also appeared on two popular Romanians online platforms/sites (Republica.ro and catchy.ro). She recently started two blogs in English, "one with just a handful of poems and some short stories, tiny baby steps; the other, more recent, inviting everyone to write and publish a little story about themselves, a kind of soul stamp of our unique adventures." A book of Widocks' poetry was released in summer 2018, in her hometown of Suceava, in Romania, with the help of the local cultural authority. "I am somebody exactly like you," Widocks notes. "When today is too lazy to come up with a story, I sit down and write one of my own."
lilianawidocks.com
Iveturnedmyselfintoastory.com

LES ZIG

Les Zig is the author of *The Shadow in the Wind* (Pinion Press), *August Falling* and *Just Another Week in Suburbia* (Pantera Press), and *Pride* (Busybird Publishing). He's had three screenplays optioned, and stories and articles published in various print and digital journals. Zig blogs, often yelling at clouds.
leszig.com

"Fuck it, Dude. Let's go bowling."

Walter Sobchak
The Big Lebowski

DEVIL'S PARTY PRESS PRESENTS

HALLOWEEN PARTY
2 0 1 9

COME FOR THE MAYHEM. STAY FOR THE MURDER.

FALL 2019

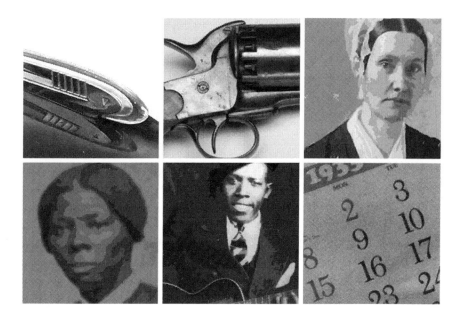

Devil's Party Press proudly presents an original novel by **Mark Alan Polo**

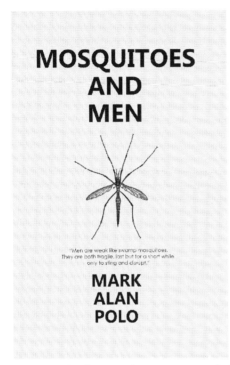

AFTER A TWENTY-FIVE-YEAR ABSENCE, Faustus Madigan returns home to Greyhaven, a formerly illustrious 18th-century plantation in Peaceable, South Carolina, for a most unanticipated family reunion.

Titus, father to The Madigans, is dead.

Nothing can prepare Faustus for the changes that have occurred in his family members following his departure from Peaceable, so many years earlier.

Nor can he foresee the monumental shift in the family dynamic that has occurred because of Titus' death. During his brief visit, old acquaintances are rekindled, new bonds are formed, and long-buried family secrets are unearthed.

There is always a price to pay for survival.

Available now on AMAZON and at finer bookstores worldwide.

SUBSCRIBE ... FOR LOVE

NOTHING SCREAMS
"I LOVE YOU, DAMMIT!"
LIKE AN ANNUAL
DEVIL'S PARTY PRESS SUBSCRIPTION.

EACH YEAR YOU'LL RECEIVE
FIVE ORIGINAL DPP TITLES
(INCLUDING NOVELS AND ANTHOLOGIES)
DELIVERED DIRECT TO YOUR DOOR.

AND AS YOU PROBABLY ALREADY KNOW,
A DPP SUBSCRIPTION MAKES
AN AWESOME FUCKING GIFT.

complete details at **devilspartypress.com**

68015275R00219

Made in the USA
Columbia, SC
05 August 2019